character and crisis:
a contemporary reader

PHILIP LEVINE
FRESNO STATE COLLEGE

HENRI COULETTE
CALIFORNIA STATE COLLEGE AT LOS ANGELES

---

character and crisis: a contemporary reader

McGRAW-HILL BOOK COMPANY
NEW YORK ST. LOUIS SAN FRANCISCO TORONTO

CHARACTER AND CRISIS: A Contemporary Reader

Library of Congress Catalog Card Number: 65-28820

4567891011 VB 1098

JAMES BALDWIN, *"Equal in Paris," from* Notes of a Native Son *by James Baldwin. Copyright © 1955, 1954, 1953, 1951, 1950, 1949 by James Baldwin. Reprinted by permission of the publishers, The Beacon Press, Inc.*

DANIEL BELL, *"The Racket-ridden Longshoremen," from* The End of Ideology *by Daniel Bell. Copyright © 1960 by The Free Press of Glencoe. Reprinted by permission of The Free Press of Glencoe.*

SAUL BELLOW, *"The Wrecker," from* New World Writing. *Copyright 1954 by New American Library of World Literature, Inc. Reprinted by permission of Russell & Volkening, Inc., Literary Agents.*

The Wrecker Copyright 1954 by SAUL BELLOW. *All rights reserved, including the right of reproduction in whole or in part in any form. Caution: Professionals and amateurs are hereby warned that this play, being fully protected under the copyright laws of the United States, the British Empire including the Dominion of Canada, and all the other countries of the Copyright Union, is subject to royalty. All rights, including professional, amateur, motion-picture, recitation, public reading, radio and television broadcasting, and the rights of translation into foreign languages, are strictly reserved. Permission for any use of the play must be obtained in writing from the author.*

WILLIAM BLAKE, *"London," from* Selected Poems *(The Laurel Poetry Series: Blake), Richard Wilbur and Ruthven Todd, eds., Dell Publishing Co., Inc., 1960.*

ALBERT CAMUS, *"Letters to a German Friend," from* Resistance, Rebellion, and Death *by Albert Camus, trans. by Justin O'Brien. Copyright 1960 by Alfred A. Knopf, Inc. Reprinted by permission of the publisher.*

HENRI COULETTE, *"Hermit's Return," from* North American Review, *vol. 1, no. 1. Reprinted by permission. "Evening in the Park," from* The Paris Review, *no.* 22. *Reprinted by permission.*

DEMETRIOS CAPETANAKIS, *"Abel," from* The Shores of Darkness *by Demetrios Capetanakis, published and copyrighted 1949 by The Devin-Adair Co., New York. Reprinted by permission of the publishers.*

HART CRANE, *"National Winter Garden," from* The Collected Poems of Hart Crane. *Copyright © 1961 by Liveright Publishing Corporation. Reprinted by permission of Liveright Publishing Corporation, New York.*

LOREN EISELEY, *"The Judgment of the Birds," from* The Immense Journey *by Loren Eiseley. Copyright © 1956 by Loren Eiseley. Reprinted by permission of Random House, Inc.*

S. S. GARDONS, *"The Mouse," "Fourth of July," and "The Survivors," from* The Hudson Review, *vol. XII, no. 4 (Winter, 1959–1960). Copyright © 1960 by The Hudson Review, Inc. Reprinted by permission.*

PIERRE GASCAR, *"The Season of the Dead," from* Beasts and Men *by Pierre Gascar, trans. by Jean Stewart. Copyright © 1956 by Little, Brown and Company. Reprinted by permission of Little, Brown and Company–Atlantic Monthly Press, Methuen & Co., Ltd., London, and Editions Gallimard, Paris.*

ALLEN GINSBERG, *"America," from* Howl *(Pocket Poets Series #4) by Allen Ginsberg. Copyright © 1956 by Allen Ginsberg. Reprinted by permission of City Lights Books.*

PAUL GOODMAN, *"Youth in the Organized Society," Chapters 1 and 2 from* Growing Up Absurd *by Paul Goodman. Copyright © 1960 by Paul Goodman. Reprinted by permission of Random House, Inc.*

THOM GUNN, *"Innocence," from* My Sad Captains *by Thom Gunn, The University of Chicago Press, 1961. Reprinted by permission of The University of Chicago Press and the author.*

WELDON KEES, *"Robinson," "Robinson at Home," "Relating to Robinson," and "Aspects of Robinson," from* Collected Poems of Weldon Kees. *Copyright 1960 by Stonewall Press. Reprinted by permission of University of Nebraska Press.*

PHILIP LARKIN, *"Church Going," from* The Less Deceived *by Philip Larkin. Copyright 1956 by The Marvell Press. Reprinted by permission of The Marvell Press, Hessle, Yorkshire, England.*

D. H. LAWRENCE, *"Reflections on the Death of a Porcupine," from* The Later D. H. Lawrence, *Alfred A. Knopf, Inc., 1952. Originally published in* Reflections on the Death of a Porcupine and Other Essays *by Centaur Press of Philadelphia, 1925. Reprinted by permission.*

ROBERT LOWELL, *"Memories of West Street and Lepke," from* Life Studies *by Robert Lowell. Copyright © 1958 by Robert Lowell. Reprinted by permission of Farrar, Straus & Giroux, Inc.*

MARY MCCARTHY, *"Artists in Uniform" and "Settling the Colonel's Hash," from* On the Contrary *by Mary McCarthy. Copyright © 1953, 1961 by Mary McCarthy. Reprinted by permission of Farrar, Straus & Giroux, Inc.*

DWIGHT MACDONALD, *"The Responsibility of Peoples," from* Memoirs of a Revolutionist *by Dwight Macdonald. Copyright © 1957 by Dwight Macdonald. Reprinted by permission of Farrar, Straus & Company, Inc.*

NORMAN MAILER, *"The Third Presidential Paper—The Existential Hero," from* The Presidential Papers of Norman Mailer. *Copyright © 1960, 1963 by Norman Mailer, from* Esquire Magazine. *Reprinted by permission of the author and the author's agents, Scott Meredith Literary Agency, Inc.*

JAMES MICHIE, *"Dooley Is a Traitor," from* Possible Laughter *by James Michie. Copyright © 1959 by The Macmillan Company. Reprinted by permission of Rupert Hart-Davis Limited, London.*

HENRY MILLER, *"Of Art and the Future," from* Sunday after the War *by Henry Miller. Copyright 1944 by Henry Miller. Reprinted by permission of New Directions, Publishers.*

GEORGE ORWELL, *"A Hanging" and "Politics and the English Language," from* Shooting an Elephant and Other Essays *by George Orwell. Copyright 1945, 1946, 1949, 1950 by Sonia Brownell Orwell. Reprinted in the United States by permission of Harcourt, Brace & World, Inc., and in Canada by permission of Martin Secker & Warburg, Ltd.*

PREFACE

Our purpose in editing this text was at once simple and ambitious: we wanted to assemble a collection of eminently readable, teachable selections—selections that might be more profitably read and taught because brought together.

Initially we chose pieces that shocked us into awareness. Sometimes that awareness was of ourselves, for example, the awareness *into* the unfulfilled adolescent within us that Paul Goodman's essay gave us; at other times the awareness was of a world we had never known, the world of Eiseley's "Judgment of the Birds" or Gascar's "Season of the Dead." A few pieces, such as Orwell's essay on a hanging, present material which is itself shocking, and others, such as the poems by Blake and Lowell, startled us because they defied our limited conceptions of the range of human experience available to a particular literary genre. We looked for selections that would illuminate the contemporary American scene, and if it turned out that some were of another place or another time we did not exclude them. The major divisions of the book suggested themselves; that is to say, certain pieces, Goodman's for example, came first and suggested companions which were complementary, supplementary, or contradictory.

As teachers our function was commonly mediator between author and student, and so we thought it might be valuable to extend that function into this book and include our own responses to the writing and to the experiences with which the writing deals. These "Afterwords" were essays we enjoyed writing or felt compelled to write, and they were written in what might be called our *own* voices, the voices of our poems, class discussions, and conversations, and the chances are good that they are stronger writing and more interesting reading than the perfunctory introductions we did not write.

So in order to reach a state of awareness we begin with shock. And why not? We had learned, or felt we had learned, that our primary obligation in beginning English courses was not as simple as it had first seemed. Perhaps one was hired to teach a few graces in English composition and gradually and tenderly expose the students to respectable examples of writing in English. And it was hoped that the students might emerge from the course as better thinkers. But how did one do this? How did one reach students gradually and tenderly? We had found that we tended to reach the students suddenly or not at all, and that they learned when they were excited, they learned when they were offended, they learned when they were kept interested and awake. And we as teachers were more effective when we took a less passive attitude toward what they wrote, and what they read, and what they thought about. Through the years of teaching we had both come to feel that if we could help their minds and imaginations to waken from the long slumber of adolescence and our own from the longer torpor of middle age, then both they and we might become better, more interesting people.

PHILIP LEVINE
HENRI COULETTE

CONTENTS

1

of crime and punishment

DWIGHT MACDONALD

the responsibility of peoples

We talk of the Turks and abhor the cannibals; but may not some of them go to heaven before some of us? We may have civilized bodies and yet barbarous souls. We are blind to the real sights of this world; deaf to its voice; and dead to its death.

HERMAN MELVILLE

Germans have thought in politics what other peoples have done. . . .

Although Germany has only accompanied the development of nations with the abstract activity of thought, without taking an active part in the real struggles incident to this development, she has, on the other hand, shared in the suffering caused by national development without sharing in its enjoyments, or their partial satisfaction. Abstract activity on the one side corresponds to abstract suffering on the other side.

Consequently, one fine day Germany will find herself at the level of European decay before she has ever stood at the level of European emancipation. The phenomenon might be likened to a fetish-worshipper who succumbs to the diseases of Christianity. . . .

The only liberation of Germany that is practical or possible is a liberation motivated by the theory that declares man to be the Supreme Being of mankind. . . . In Germany, no brand of serfdom can be extirpated without extirpating every kind of serfdom. . . . The emancipation of Germans is the emancipation of mankind.

KARL MARX *1844*

Now I must say goodbye. Tomorrow mother goes into the gas chamber, and I will be thrown into the well.

FROM A LETTER WRITTEN BY A CHILD
IN A POLISH "DEATH CAMP"

"We were a little nervous when she was taken," the girl's mother said afterwards. "You never know what will happen when they start to use the electric needle. But we should not have worried. She never gave the Germans a single name or address and no one was arrested."

The girl was a member of the French underground; she was

caught by the Gestapo; she was tortured, while her mother was held in a nearby cell so she could hear her daughter's screams; and she died. This was Europe under the Nazis: the matter-of-fact reference to torture; the technological modernity of the instrument; the mother's politicalized attitude—"we should not have worried," since "she never gave a single name." Something has happened to the Germans—to some of them, at least; something has happened to Europe—to some of it, at least. What is it? Who or what is responsible? What does it mean about our civilization, our whole system of values? This is the great moral question of our times, and on what our hearts as well as our heads answer to it depends largely our answer to the great practical questions.

In this article, I want to consider this question as an aspect of the general problem of what my friend, Nicola Chiaromonte, calls "the responsibility of peoples."

In the last war, we believed many "atrocity stories" which later turned out to have been propaganda. Compared to the German atrocities which are reported by the press in this war, those of 1917, however revolting in detail, were (1) quantitatively negligible (rarely involving more than a score or so of alleged victims), and (2) deeds done in hot blood by individual soldiers using bayonets or guns rather than the systematic tortures and massacres with specially designed instruments that are now reported. So tender was the civilian mood of those days that the British were able to arouse great indignation over the execution of Edith Cavell, who, as a spy, by all the rules of warfare "deserved" her fate. Today we are more tough-minded—we have to be, or go crazy, so severe are the shocks administered to our moral sensibilities, indeed to our very nervous systems, by each morning's newspaper. Yet even so, one's heart fails at some of the reports.

The French War Crimes Commission recently estimated that between 200,000 and 250,000 French civilians had been killed by the Germans during their occupation of France. The Commission has also assembled a museum of torture devices: branding irons, pincers for pulling out fingernails, an "electrical shoe," a steel helmet studded with screws that can slowly be tightened. . . . Not since the Spanish Inquisition has such an array been seen. Who would have dared predict, in the 19th century, that one of the most advanced nations in Europe would employ such instruments? Marx himself might well have shrunk from the supposition. His epigram of 1844 must now be reversed: the Germans have *done* in politics what other peoples have up to now dared only to *think*.

In the last war, all this could have been dismissed as propaganda. But the great difference between the "atrocity stories" of World War I and those of World War II is that the latter are as convincingly authenticated as the former were not. To disbelieve the accounts of today, one would have to assume that almost every war correspondent is a liar on a Munchausen scale, that various neutral observers are liars, that certain internationally known religious and charitable institutions have fabricated detailed reports. We know, also, from the Nazis' own theories and from what they did in Germany itself that such horrors are not improbable.

Let us not only accept these horrors; let us insist on them. Let us not turn aside even from the greatest of all: the execution of half the Jewish population of Europe, some four million men, women, and children, in Silesian and Polish "death factories." * In the last war, the farthest our propagandists ventured was to fabricate the tale of the German "corpse factories," in which the bodies of dead soldiers were alleged to have been boiled down for their fat and chemicals. Not only was this untrue, but it would never have occurred to any one in 1917 even to *invent* a story about abattoirs in which human beings took the place of cattle. And yet we know, from irrefutable evidence, that *these things have been done*. They are part of our world and we must try to come to some kind of terms with them.

Detailed reports about the "death camps" have only come out within the past year. The chief ones I have seen are the descriptions of the camps at Auschwitz and Birkenau in Upper Silesia which appeared in the N. Y. *Times* of July 2 and 5, 1944, sent in from Switzerland; the stories in the *Times* (Aug. 27) and *Time* (Sept.

* *This essay appears here as published in* Politics, *March, 1945. The following footnote was added in 1953:* Later estimates put it at six million. By an ironical twist of history, the victims have now become oppressors in their turn. Since 1948, some 800,000 Arab refugees, who fled from Palestine during the fighting, have been living wretchedly in camps around the country's borders maintained by UN charity. The Israeli government—opposed by no important Jewish group that I know of—refuses to let them back and has given their homes, farms, and villages to new Jewish settlers. This is rationalized by the usual "collective responsibility" nonsense. This expropriation cannot, of course, be put on the same plane as the infinitely greater crime of the Nazis. But neither should it be passed over in silence.

11) based on a Russian-conducted tour of the former death camp at Maidanek; and the report, based on stories by three eyewitnesses who were able to escape, of the Auschwitz and Birkenau camps that was released by the War Refugees Board, a Government agency, on Nov. 26, 1944. The first report is the most impressive, because it was put out by the well-known Swiss relief organization, the Fluchtlingshilfe of Zurich, whose head is the Rev. Paul Vought. It is also sponsored by the Ecumenical Refugee Committee of the World Council of Churches. But in all the reports, the atmosphere is the same: rationality and system gone mad; the discoveries of science, the refinements of modern mass organization applied to the murder of noncombatants on a scale unknown since Genghis Khan.

These camps, which the Nazis called "model extermination camps" and which were operated by specially trained *Judenvernichtung* (Jew-killing) experts, were literally "death factories," often with railroad sidings running into them for the transport of their raw materials. These "materials" were processed in an orderly fashion: shaved, bathed, deloused, each given a slip of paper with his or her number typed on it, then routed into another room where this number was tattooed on the body—on the breasts of the women. (So in Kafka's "The Penal Colony," the mechanism executes the criminal by tatooing the record of his crime on his body—one of too many modern instances in which reality has now caught up with Kafka's imagination.) The cooperation of the victims was necessary to save time (and make production records possible). By experiment, it was found that death came quicker when the body was warm, washed and wet. The execution buildings were therefore sometimes given the appearance of bathing establishments, the illusion being methodically carried out by having two attendants in white jackets give each victim a towel and a piece of soap. There were even simulated shower-entries in the death chamber itself: a concrete room into which as many naked persons were packed as possible. "When everybody is inside, the heavy doors are closed. Then there is a short pause, presumably to allow the room temperature to rise to a certain level, after which SS men with gas masks climb the roof, open the traps in the ceiling, and shake down a preparation in powder form labeled 'Cyklon,' for use against vermin, which is manufactured by a Hamburg concern. It is presumed that this is a cyanide mixture of some sort which turns into a gas at a certain temperature. After three minutes, every one in the chamber is dead." The bodies were then taken into the crematorium (which at Maidanek looked like "a big bake shop or a very small blast furnace") where they were cut up by butchers, loaded onto iron stretchers and slid on rollers into the coke-fed ovens. With such methods, death was produced on a mass scale: at Birkenau alone, over a million and a half persons are estimated to have perished from April, 1942, to April, 1944.

As in the Chicago stockyards, no by-products were wasted. The clothes and shoes were shipped into Germany to relieve the shortage of consumption goods: "We came to a large warehouse. It was full of shoes. A sea of shoes. . . . They were piled like coal in a bin halfway up the walls. Boots. Rubbers. Leggings. Slippers. Children's shoes, soldiers' shoes, old shoes, new shoes. . . . In one corner, there was a stock of artificial limbs." Also: "Near the ovens were the remains of a room with a big stone table. Here gold fillings were extracted from the teeth. No corpse could be burned without a stamp on the chest: 'INSPECTED FOR GOLD FILLINGS.' " The ashes and bones of the burned bodies were used to fertilize cabbage fields around the camps. Nor did the Germans, devotees of science, lose the chance to advance human knowledge. All identical twins that passed through Birkenau were removed for "biological examination" at a German scientific institute. In the Vosges section of France, a "laboratory camp" was recently discovered, where thousands of persons were experimented on, always with fatal results. Some were vivisected, some were given leprosy and plague, some were blinded (to see if their sight could be restored), many were put to death by gas while observers watched their reactions through a window. Perhaps the most humanly appalling details of all were certain juxtapositions which one would be tempted to say showed a typical Germanic tastelessness, were it not for our own "war-theme" advertisements. Thus at a Dutch camp, there were found certain cells so constructed as to cause death by slow suffocation—and a nursery for prisoners' children whose walls were decorated with scenes from fairy tales. And at Maidanek, the camp loudspeaker blared out all day over the countryside . . . Viennese waltzes.

But enough! We may say that those who planned and carried out such things were insane. This may have often been true, in a medical sense. But once granted the ends, the means were rational enough—all too rational. The Nazis learned much from mass production, from modern business organization. It all reads like a sinister parody of Victorian illusions about scientific method and the desirability *in itself* of man's learning to control his environment. The environment was controlled at Maidanek. It was the human beings who ran amok.

1. *the German war crimes are unique*

A considerable portion of the atrocious acts of the Germans in this war are chargeable rather to war in general than to any special inhumanity of the Germans.

There was much moral indignation, for example, about the robot bombs. But the effects of "saturation bombing," which the British and American air forces have brought to a high degree of perfection, are just as indiscriminate and much more murderous. "The Allied air chiefs," states this morning's paper, "have made the long-awaited decision to adopt deliberate terror bombing of German population centers. . . . The Allied view is that bombardment of large German cities creates immediate need for relief. This is moved into the bombed areas both by rail and road, and not only creates a traffic problem but draws transport away from the battle front. Evacuation of the homeless has the same result." The only mistake in the above is to say the decision has just been adopted; actually, the Allies have used "terror bombing" for several years. We might also recall the indignation we felt, in 1940, at the strafing of refugees by the Luftwaffe. "How typically Nazi!" we exclaimed—but we were more tender-minded in those days. The first contracts have already been let for the manufacture of our own robot bombs, and no one at all conversant with modern warfare doubts that the robot bomb will be a key weapon in World War III.*

The ruthless economic exploitation, accompanied by mass starvation, to which the Nazis subjected Europe when they held it was deplorable. But our own press for many months now has

* Six months after this was written, "we" humane and democratic Americans dropped atomic bombs on Hiroshima and Nagasaki, destroying in the twinkling of an eye some 90,000 civilians—men, women and children. This was the climax of the Anglo-American policy of massacring civilian populations from the air, a policy which later evidence shows to have been morally indefensible, politically disastrous, and militarily of dubious value. See Appendix A. *(Footnote added in 1953)*

carried articles about the failure of the Allies to provide any more food to the "liberated" (and hungry) Europeans than the Germans did (and often, as in Italy and Belgium, not as much). "Military necessity" apparently rules "us" as absolutely as it ruled "them," and with the same terrible results for the peoples of Europe.

Some of the most horrible brutalities chargeable to the Nazis have been committed in their attempts to deal with the maquis. Throughout military history, franc-tireurs have always been dealt with severely; the Hague rules of warfare even authorize the shooting of civilian hostages in reprisal for franc-tireur attacks on the invading soldiery. One should not forget that the Germans occupied almost all of Europe for four years, and that our own armies are only just beginning to occupy enemy territory. If a German resistance movement materializes that is anything like as determined as the one the Nazis had to deal with, we shall probably see our own armies climbing down a bit from their present pinnacle of moral superiority.*

Even the extermination of large numbers of helpless people is not so unknown in modern times as our own propagandists would have us think. Great numbers of the colored races have been wiped out since 1800 by the whites: the "rubber atrocities" of the Amazon and the Belgian Congo (cf. Conrad's *Heart of Darkness*); the large scale executions that followed the Boxer Rebellion in China; the slaughter of the bulk of the Australian Black-fellows and the American Indians; not to mention dozens of lesser "episodes" throughout Asia and Africa. In England itself, furthermore, in the first half of the last century, millions of men, women and children of the working class were starved and worked to death in conditions which were often almost as brutal and degrading as those of Maidanek and which had the disadvantage of prolonging the victims' suffering much longer (cf. the Parliamentary "Blue Books" of the period, Engels' *Condition of the English Working Class* in 1844, or J. L.

* The resistance did not materialize, and, on the whole, the conduct of the American and British armies in Germany was no worse than that of most conquerers—a modest enough standard. The Red Army, however, sank far below even this standard. The first few weeks of the Russian occupation of Eastern Germany, Austria, and Hungary were an orgy of unrestrained and wholesale raping and killing on a scale unknown in the West for many centuries. See the four terrible first-hand reports by survivors I printed in *Politics* (January 1946, pp. 4–8; October 1946, pp. 315–319). *(1953)*

and Barbara Hammond's *Lord Shaftesbury*). And in Soviet Russia in the last fifteen years, millions of peasants and political prisoners have been starved to death in State-created famines or worked to death on forced-labor projects.

After the acids of sophisticated inquiry have done their worst, however, a considerable residue remains. It is this residue which makes the German atrocities in this war a phenomenon unique at least in modern history.

It is partly a question of the intimate individual cruelty shown in much of the Germans' behavior. That the Allied forces will execute hostages and burn down towns if "necessary" I have no doubt; but I should be surprised if they do it on the scale the Germans did (50 lives for one was the lowest "rate of exchange") or with the brutality and sadism shown in the extermination of whole villages and the common use of the most revolting tortures.

But it is mostly what might be called the "gratuitous" character of the worst atrocities. What has been done by other peoples as an unpleasant by-product of the attainment of certain ends has been done by the Germans at Maidanek and Auschwitz as an end in itself. What has been done elsewhere in violation of the doer's code of ethics, and hence in a shamefaced way draped over with hypocritical apologies, has been done here in conformance with the avowed Nazi moral code, and thus done as publicly and proclaimed as exultantly as the winning of a great battle.* The Allied bombing of German

* Untrue, indeed the reverse of the truth. "Why I wrote so false a statement, I don't know," I wrote later. "There was no evidence for it: the intoxication of rhetoric must be my only feeble excuse." Another excuse was that I failed to make a crucial distinction (that others also fail to make) between the *death* camps (as: Maidanek, Auschwitz, Oswiecim) and the *concentration camps* (as: Buchenwald, Dachau, Sachsenhausen). The latter existed through the Hitler regime; the death rate in them was very high, but their aim was to terrorize, torture, and demoralize the prisoners, and also, during the war, to exploit their labor, rather than just to kill them. Their existence was no secret—the Nazis indeed took care to let the Germans know about them—in general, not in revolting detail—as a means of intimidating opposition. They could not have been kept secret anyway, since they were all in Germany itself and since, up to 1940, their prisoners were all Germans. But the death camps were mostly in Poland, and they "processed" only Jews, most of them Polish, and other non-Germans. So they could be kept secret, and they were. Only Germans with very good connections with the high army staff ever learned of their existence. For their aim

cities killed many innocent civilians (though not as many as a single one of the German death camps), but there was at least this much humane rationality about it; that it was thought necessary to the winning of the war, which in turn was thought necessary to the self-preservation of the Allied nations. Furthermore, some kind of an argument could be made that it *was* necessary. But the extermination of the Jews of Europe was not a means to any end one can accept as even plausibly rational. The Jews constituted no threat to their executioners; no military purpose was served by their extermination; the "racial theory" behind it is scientifically groundless and humanly abhorrent and can only be termed, in the strictest sense of the term, neurotic. The Jews of Europe were murdered to gratify a paranoiac hatred (as the robot bomb was christened "V" for "Vengeance") but for no reason of policy or advantage that I can see.*

was simply to kill all the Jews, male and female, adults and children, for no alleged political or criminal offenses, but just because they were Jews. And this aim would have disgusted and shocked everybody, in Germany or out of it, except fanatical Nazis.

The blueprints for "mobile gas chambers" (closed trucks specially equipped to asphyxiate people) were approved by Hitler in the fall of 1941, and the first units began operating in occupied Russian territory in the spring of 1942. The first death camps were opened in the fall of 1942 and operated to the fall of 1944, when Himmler closed them down, without telling Hitler, as part of his preparations to open negotiations with the Anglo-Americans, behind Hitler's back, for a truce. Rumors began circulating about the mobile gas chambers and later the death camps in 1942, and the British Foreign Office almost certainly was informed by Moscow about the camps early in 1943. *The Black Book of Polish Jewry* appeared that year, with sensational reports of the camps. But precisely because the whole thing *was* so sensational, so beyond all Western experience—indeed beyond good and evil, as the acts of an insane person are juridically recognized to be—these reports for some time were simply not believed. There are even many stories of Jews who were warned but refused to believe it, and dutifully reported for shipment to Maidanek. It was not till the summer of 1944 that the nonGerman world began to believe it, and if some Germans then heard about the death camps from Allied broadcasts, what wonder if they discounted it as enemy "atrocity stuff"? But most were not even that much informed. (Best source on the death camps is Leon Poliakov's *Breviare de la Haine,* Paris, 1951.) *(1953)*

* This statement provoked much dissent at the time, but I have become more and more convinced of its truth, especially after reading Hannah Arendt's brilliant and profound *The Origins of Totalitarianism* (Harcourt Brace, 1951). *(1953)*

Or consider the Stalin regime's massacres, the only other ones of our day which have been on the Nazi scale. In Russia today there is much less respect for human life and less ideological resistance to acts of violence on a mass scale than there is in the bourgeois democracies. Yet even here, there is at least the justification for, say, the State-induced famine of 1932 that it represented the carrying out, by brutal and abhorrent means (which of course corrupted the ends—but that is another story) an agricultural policy whose aim was to increase productivity. This may not be a good end in itself, but it is certainly not a bad one. It is, in any case, rational. And the kulaks were starved incident to this aim, not because there was any desire to exterminate them in themselves. It may be said, justly, that it makes little difference to the dead kulak or to the dead Jew what the motives of his executioners were. But it makes a great deal of difference of the executioners, and to our evaluation of their act.*

To put it briefly: the English mill-owners in the last century and the Russian bureaucrats in this one showed a disregard for human life which was shocking enough. But the Nazis have not *disregarded* human life. They have, on the contrary, paid close attention to it. They have taken it for the pure, disinterested pleasure of taking it. There was no ulterior motive behind Maidanek, no possible advantage to its creators beyond the gratification of neurotic racial hatreds. What has previously been done only by individual psychopathic killers has now been done by the rulers and servants of a great modern State. This *is* something new.

We now come to the question: who is responsible for these horrors?

2. *German anti-Semitism is not a "people's action"*

If we can conceive of a modern people as collectively responsible in a moral sense at all, then it must be held accountable only for actions which it takes spontaneously and as a whole, actions which are approved by the popular *mores*. It cannot be indicted for things done by sharply differentiated sub-groups.

*** I now think I overestimated the rationality of Stalin's policy. At first it was more rational than Hitler's but the dynamic of totalitarianism seems to lead towards irrationality, and by 1945 there was less to choose between the two horrors, in this respect, than I then thought. *(1953)***

How does this apply to the Germans and the Jews? It is true there was and is widespread anti-Semitism in Germany, as in this country. But anti-Semitism is one thing and violent persecution of Jews is another. If the German people as a whole had approved of the Nazis' Jewish policy, one would expect that between 1933 and the present, a period in which the Nazis used the State power to place the Jews outside the pale of legality and indeed of humanity itself, there would have been many mob attacks on Jewish institutions and individuals. Actually, as far as I can recall, the American press reported none. And I remember distinctly that in 1938 when the Nazis took advantage of the assassination, by a Jew, of their Parisian diplomatic agent, Vom Rath, to intensify the anti-Jewish terror in Germany, the press reports stressed that there was very little hostility shown by the street crowds against the Jews. The controlled German press was filled with incitements to anti-Jewish violence. Storm troopers and SS men arrested thousands of Jews with great publicity, wrecked Jewish stores, burned synagogues; but the crowds that watched these organized atrocities were silent and withdrawn when they did not venture to express their disapproval. There were many more cases reported of Germans who dared to help Jews than of those who helped the Nazi pogromists—and this, too, in papers like the N. Y. *Times* which were not at all friendly to Nazi Germany.

In contrast, the constant and widespread acts of violence against Negroes throughout the South, culminating in lynching, may be considered real "people's actions," for which the Southern whites bear collective responsibility. As Dollard showed in *Caste and Class in a Southern Town,* the brutality with which Negroes are treated is not the work of a differentiated minority or of individual sadists but is participated in, actively or with passive sympathy, by the entire white community. "White aggression against Negroes and the social patterns which permit it are forms of social control. They are instrumentalities for keeping the Negro in his place and maintaining the supraordinate position of the white caste. . . . It must not be supposed that the major or perhaps even the most significant part of white aggression against Negroes consists of the few dramatic acts of lynching featured in the newspapers. *Massive and continuous pressures of other types are far more important in achieving social stability.*" (My italics.)

So too with the 1943 Detroit race riot, in which hundreds of

Negroes were killed or horribly beaten up by large mobs of whites, in the very heart of the city. This kind of behavior has the general support of the Southern white people, and has enough popular support even in a Northern city like Detroit to allow it to be carried out without interference from the police. This latter point suggests that whereas anti-Negro violence in America is a real "folk" activity, carried on *against* the State and its police (which, of course, wink at it), in Germany it is the reverse: pogroms are carried out by the State and the forces of "law and order" *against* the folkways.*

But *someone* killed the Jews of Europe? And those who did were Germans. True. But a particular kind of Germans, specialists in torture and murder, whom it would be as erroneous to confuse with the general run of Germans as it would be to confuse the brutality-specialists who form so conspicuous a part of our own local police forces (and who occasionally burst out in such sensational horrors as the Chicago Memorial Day massacre) with the average run of Americans. It is of capital significance that the death camps for Jews and the mass killings of Russian prisoners of war have apparently not been entrusted to regular German Army units but rather to specially selected and trained SS squads. The Swedish journalist, Avid Fredborg, for example, has this interesting description in his book, *Behind the Steel Wall*:

* This is, I think, one of my shrewdest points. But I must add that the Negroes have made remarkable gains since 1945: Jim Crow segregation in the armed forces has been largely abolished; the Supreme Court for the first time has begun to enforce the 14th and 15th Amendments and even the Civil Rights Acts of 1866, 1870, and 1875, so that the whole structure of "white supremacy" in the South is cracking, and Negroes are *beginning* to vote in large numbers, to be admitted to hitherto all-white Southern universities, and to travel unsegregated on interstate trains. Lynchings have become very rare (sometimes a whole year goes by without one, as against the old days when several hundred Negroes died annually "*pour encourager les autres*"), and several cases have arisen in which white men have actually been punished for murdering Negroes. These post-1945 advances toward racial equality have come about because a more determined assertion of their rights by Negroes has coincided with a less determined denial of those rights by the whites, who now show a (belated) bad conscience that may be somewhat connected with the necessity for a united nation to face the Nazi and now the Soviet threat. There is still plenty of "folk activity" against Negroes, as the recent episode in Cicero, Ill., showed, but on the government level there has been a notable improvement since 1945. *(1953)*

SS soldiers forming the execution squads in the East are carefully chosen. They are recruited from the most brutal elements and are gradually trained to become harder and more ruthless. At first they may only have to take Jews out for street cleaning and snow shoveling. After a time they are assigned to perform single executions. Only after this training is completed are they ordered to do mass executions.

Many have refused to take part in these and have been shot. . . . Others have had nervous breakdowns and have been sent to asylums. Even the most hardened have at times caved in. Time and again, physicians have been called to attend soldiers on leave who have had severe attacks of hysteria or prolonged insomnia or delirium tremens (soldiers in the firing squads often get intoxicated before executions, and many stay so continually). . . .

The chief instrument for these ghastly practices is the SS. Sometimes it seems that the SS is driving the policy beyond the intention of the Party leaders. In any case, it is certain the German public has little real knowledge of what is going on.

Bruno Bettelheim's article on Nazi concentration camp life in the August, 1944 issue shows in detail how *given complete control over the individual,* it is possible to condition even anti-Nazis to accept Nazi values. Major Applegate's little treatise, *Kill—or Be Killed,* indicates that it is not only the Nazis who are consciously trying to break down the civilized individual's inhibitions against taking life.

But if the Nazis can thus condition their SS men and their concentration camp prisoners, cannot they—and have they not in fact—so conditioned the German people as a whole? To some extent, of course they can and have, especially in the case of the youth. Hitler said in 1937:

We still have among us old-fashioned people who are not fit for anything. They get in our way like cats and dogs. But this does not worry us. We will take away their children. *We will not permit them to lapse into the old way of thinking. We will take them away when they are ten years old and bring them up in the spirit of nationalism until they are eighteen. They shall not escape us. They will join the Party, the SA, the SS and other formations. Later on they will do two years of military service. Who shall dare say that such a training will not produce a nation?*

But we must remember that the great majority of present-day Germans were adults when Hitler came to power, and that even what the Nazis called their "conquest of youth" (a revealing phrase, by the way) is not complete, judging from reports of executions of university students. More important, it would seem probable that the kind of extreme *behavior* required of mass-executioners and torturers can only be psychologically conditioned by extreme *situations*, as Bettelheim calls them, involving either complete physical control of the individual in a prison camp or else his willing cooperation in a lengthy and rigorous training process. Neither of these conditions is possible in the case of the average German: eighty million people, or even ten or five million can neither be subjected to concentration-camp control nor can they be put through any elaborate training course (even if they consented to be). Propaganda and force are not adequate substitutes for the more intimate types of conditioning; their effect is weakened and even negated constantly by the family and working life of the individual, which goes on still along the traditional lines of Western civilization.*

Nazi Germany is often called "one big concentration camp," but one should not forget that this is a metaphor and not a literal description. Misled by the metaphor, some *Politics* readers have drawn from Bettelheim's article, for instance—the unwarranted conclusion that the whole German population—and even that of the occupied Europe of 1940–1943, which journalists also have called "one big concentration camp"—was being conditioned by the Nazis as effectively as the prisoners Bettelheim writes about. The fallacy in the case of Europe is apparent at a glance: as "Gallicus" showed in the January, 1945 issue, the Nazis failed to make much impression even on the youth, and soon found themselves confronted by an overwhelmingly hostile population—and, worse, corrupted by it. In Germany itself, the Nazis obviously could make more progress, since the German people were offered superior material rewards and since national hatred of a foreign conqueror was not involved. But even

* Stalin's regime has gone much further toward subjecting the whole population to "extreme situations" by "concentration-camp control" and "the more intimate types of conditioning" than Hitler's did. Morally, this makes the Russian people no more "responsible" than the German people were, but practically it does present a problem that, however painful, must be faced up to by pacifists and other men of good will. *(1953)*

there it seems unlikely that propaganda and terrorism applied to a population still working and living in comparative (by concentration-camp standards) freedom have been sufficient to effectively Nazify a people the majority of whom were definitely anti-Nazi when Hitler assumed power in 1933. The very fact that concentration camps have continued to exist on a large scale is one proof of a continued popular opposition to Nazism, as are the scores of executions for "treason" which are still announced daily.*

3. *things happen* to *people*

All this is not to deny that Nazism has had a great effect on the German people. It is simply to deny that this effect has as yet changed the average German's attitudes enough to cause him to commit pogroms or to approve of them when his Nazi rulers commit them; and to indicate the limitations on Nazi indoctrination outside the concentration camp and the special training schools. The Germans have been changed by Nazism, but it has been a slower process and has gone less far than concentration-camp analogies would

* A wrong inference, I now believe. Perplexing though it is, the fact seems to be that, as Hannah Arendt writes in *The Origins of Totalitarianism* (p. 379): "Terror increased both in Soviet Russia and Nazi Germany in inverse ratio to the existence of internal political opposition, so that it looks as though political opposition had not been the pretext of terror (as liberal accusers of the regimes were wont to assert) but rather the last impediment to its full fury." Viz.: the Nazis killed six million Jews not when they were fighting to consolidate their power in 1933–36 but in 1942–44, when they had long since destroyed effective opposition, when the Jews offered no threat to them at all, and when the German people were forced to back them in the war as a matter of national survival. And viz.: Lenin's "Red Terror" of 1918–20, when internal opposition was still strong and the Red Army was fighting defensively on Russian soil against a half dozen invading armies, was minuscule compared to the terror Stalin unleashed in 1937–39, years after forced-collectivization had crushed the peasants into shape, the first Five Year Plan the workers, and Stalin's intra-party tactics the Old Bolsheviks (the Moscow Trials were merely the juridical ratification of a *fait* long ago *accompli*). In more normal or at least familiar kinds of societies, even dictatorships like Peron's or Mussolini's, repression is used to overcome resistance. In the irrational world of totalitarianism, it is sometimes so used (executions soared after the 1944 attempt on Hitler's life), but in general it increases as the opposition weakens, since the rulers are chiefly concerned not with just keeping their power but with a laboratory experiment in changing men into bundles of conditioned reflexes. *(1953)*

suggest, and certainly less far from our town Teutonophobes claim.*

It is a process, furthermore, which is also going on in our own society, in England, and in Russia—in the last-named perhaps† even faster and farther than in Germany itself. Modern society has become so tightly organized, so rationalized and routinized that it has the character of a mechanism which grinds on without human consciousness or control. The individual, be he "leader" or mass-man, is reduced to powerlessness vis-à-vis the mechanism. More and more, things happen TO people.

Some examples, mostly drawn from the "democratic" side in this war, may suggest what I mean:

A. The *New Yorker* of Aug. 12, 1944 ran a profile of a 22-year-old lieutenant in the Army Air Force who had just completed thirty bombing missions in the European theater. He seemed to be of superior intelligence, not politically radical; his main personal interest was in jazz music. "Whatever I tell you," he said to the interviewer, "boils down to this: I'm a cog in one hell of a big machine. The more I think about it, and I've thought about it a lot lately, the more it looks as if I'd been a cog in one thing after another since the day I was born. Whenever I get set to do what I want to do, something a whole lot bigger than me comes along and shoves me back into place. It's not especially pleasant, but there it is." The lieutenant's personal aspirations would seem modest and attainable enough: to live with his wife, to have a home, to play and hear good jazz. Our society has been unable to give him these satisfactions. Instead, it puts him in the plexiglass nose

* The more virulent of them, like Vansittart and Rex Stout, have concocted a theory of German "responsibility" which is just the reverse of the one discussed here: that the German people, far from having been conditioned to Nazi attitudes by external pressure (which of course implies they were decent people *before* Hitler) have been warlike barbarians throughout European history. This is such an obvious inversion of Nazi racial theory, and is so wide open to the same scientific refutations that it does not seem worth wasting any more space on here. Combating it is a task for the propagandist, not for the analyst: like the Nazis' ideas on the Jewish people, it is as easy to refute on the scientific plane as it is difficult to combat on the psychological level. It seems more fruitful here to discuss a more sophisticated and tenable theory of German collective responsibility.

† I would now delete this word. *(1953)*

of a bomber and sends him out to kill his fellow men and destroy their homes, at the most terrible psychological cost to himself, as the profile makes clear. Society is not ungrateful, however: the lieutenant wears the Purple Heart, the Distinguished Flying Cross, and the Air Medal with three oak-leaf clusters.

B. At the Mare Island, California, naval base last summer two munitions ships blew up while they were being loaded. In a twinkling, the blast leveled everything for miles around and killed some three hundred sailors. The next day, the admiral in charge issued an Order of the Day in which he paid tribute to the "heroism" and "self-sacrifice" of the dead.

Now obviously the men who were killed were killed because they happened to be around when the explosives went off, and not because of any decision or action of their own. (So, too, civilians die in air raids; and so, too, nine out of ten soldiers die in a modern battle because they happen to be around when a bomb or shell lands.) The dead had no choice but to be "heroic," in the admiral's concept of heroism: TNT offers no surrender terms. These particular sailors had not even a choice about being around so dangerous a neighborhood: they were mostly Negroes, and they were assigned to this dirty and dangerous work because of their race (about which they had had no choice either). Indeed, they most definitely did not want the job. The fifty Negro sailors who were recently convicted and sentenced to long prison terms for mutiny were all employed at Mare Island unloading munitions and most of them were survivors of last summer's blast. They felt so strong a disinclination, after the tragedy, towards sharing their dead comrades' "heroic" fate that they risked a possible death penalty for mutiny.

The admiral's Order of the Day was thus a fantastic distortion of reality. Yet the administrative reflex which prompted him to issue it was sound. Instinctively, he felt it necessary to give to something which was non-purposive and impersonal a *human* meaning, to maintain the fiction that men who die in modern war do so not as chance victims but as active "patriots," who heroically *choose* to sacrifice their lives for their countries. It was his misfortune that the Mare Island explosion did not even superficially lend itself to this purpose. It is the good fortune of our war correspondents that battle deaths can be given at least a superficial plausibility along these lines.

C. The people of London are constantly being applauded for their "heroism" by war propagandists, and doubtless many individual Londoners did show heroic qualities during the bombing raids. But others doubtless also showed mean and cowardly traits. Insofar as the concept of heroism can be applied, it must be used on an individual not a collective basis. But when journalists salute the "heroism" of the Londoners or of the Russian people—they really mean a kind of collective heroism which can never exist actually, since as a collectivity the people of London had no alternative except to endure the bombings. As a Cockney retorted to a war correspondent: "Everyone's sticking it? And just what the bloody hell do you think anyone can do? You'd think we had some bloody choice in the matter!"

D. Perhaps the most heavily bombed community in this war is the strategic British-held island of Malta, which in a 28-month period had 2,315 air-raid alerts, or an average of three a day. One in 200 of the civilian population died during these raids. Some time ago the British Government awarded a collective Victoria Cross to the people of Malta for their "heroism"—which, once more, consisted in simply enduring what they had to endure, since their British masters would not have allowed them to leave the island anyway. And only the other day the same Government issued a booklet on the "siege of Malta" full of the usual nonsense, on which the N. Y. *Times* commented with the usual idiocy: "The island remained unconquered, a light and a symbol."

An incident reported in *Time* of Aug. 7, 1944 illuminates the myth of Malta. It seems that on July 14, 1943, a British army captain caught a Maltese citizen looting his parked car. He took him to the Maltese police, who promptly freed the thief and put the captain in jail—for false arrest. When it appeared that the Maltese authorities planned to keep the captain in jail indefinitely, his commanding officer appealed to the British Governor (without result) and finally direct to London. The British Government replied that "in view of the present tense relations with the Maltese population and urgent military necessities, it is impossible to intervene." The captain remained in solitary confinement for nine months, until April, 1944, when his case came up in a Maltese civil court. He was then sentenced to thirteen *additional* months imprisonment at hard labor. Lord Gort, the British Military Governor, ventured to reduce the sentence, on appeal, to three months.

"We talk on tiptoe in Malta," explained an English officer.

"We dare not cross a Maltese citizen in any way. Military experience demands appeasement of the pro-Fascist population." Whether the Maltese are pro-Fascist or anti-British or both is not the present point. The thing is that the collectively decorated people of "heroic Malta" detest their British "allies." We may be sure that the British don't allow their army officers to be treated this way by "natives" unless there are compelling reasons.

E. With their customary thoroughness, the Germans have carried what might be called "collective irresponsibility" to its logical extreme. To cope with the Anglo-American armies poured into France after D-Day, they impressed great numbers of Poles, Russians, Frenchmen, Italians, Czechs, Georgians, Mongolians—most of them war prisoners given a choice between starvation and service in the Reichswehr. In some German regiments, the colonel needed an interpreter to make his commands understood. Even crack SS divisions were filled out with these foreign conscripts, all of whom, even the Mongolians, were officially listed as "Volksdeutsche." The Allies in France found themselves confronted by a veritable International in Reichswehr uniforms. Many of these "Volksdeutsche" shot their officers and came over to the Allied side at the first chance, giving our High Command a typical modern problem. Were they allies? (But they wore the German uniform.) Or were they prisoners? (But they hated the uniform they wore.) All that could be said with certainty is that they were fought on the German side. The passive verb is intentional: the modern soldier does not "fight"; he "is fought," like a battleship or other inanimate mechanism.*

* The Communist soldier also "is fought." At this writing, the Korean truce negotiations have been hung up for a year on the issue of whether prisoners shall be forcibly repatriated. The Communists insist they shall be; the UN that they be allowed to choose whether to go back or not. The firmness of the UN position may be partly due to memories of the shameful forced repatriation of Russian prisoners by the West in 1945–46. This was one of the dirty deals at Yalta between Stalin and Roosevelt, and it was dishonorably honored by the West until the political break with Russia in the fall of 1946. British and American MP's (who "were fought" also by their commanders) performed the noble work of herding and dragging Russian prisoners—some of whom cut their throats rather than return—into trains to be shipped back to the land of socialism, where they were punished because (a) they had been taken prisoner, and (b) they were assumed to be "unreliable elements," since they had lived beyond the Iron Curtain and so had a standard of comparison with conditions in Soviet Russia. *(1953)*

The following story was related by George Orwell in his column in the Oct. 13, 1944 London *Tribune*:

> *Among the German prisoners captured in France there are a certain number of Russians. Some time back two were captured who did not speak Russian or any other language that was known either to their captors or their fellow-prisoners. They could, in fact, only converse with one another. A professor of Slavonic languages, brought down from Oxford, could make nothing of what they were saying. Then it happened that a sergeant who had served on the frontiers of India overheard them talking and recognized their language, which he was able to speak a little. It was Tibetan! After some questioning he managed to get their story out of them.*
>
> *Some years earlier they had strayed over the frontier into the Soviet Union and been conscripted into a labour battalion, afterwards being sent to western Russia when the war with Germany broke out. They were taken prisoner by the Germans and sent to North Africa; later they were sent to France, then exchanged into a fighting unit when the Second Front opened, and taken prisoner by the British. All this time they had been able to speak to nobody but one another, and had no notion of what was happening or who was fighting whom.*
>
> *It would round the story off neatly if they were now conscripted into the British Army and sent to fight the Japanese, ending up somewhere in Central Asia, quite close to their native village, but still very much puzzled as to what it is all about.*

4. *political animism—the theory of the "organic state"*

The above instances suggest that the difference between "civilized" and "primitive" social organization is growing less. The great circle is slowly closing, and a contemporary Soviet or German citizen would feel more in common with an Australian bushman in many ways than with, let us say, a French *philosophe* of 1780 or a Jeffersonian democrat of 1810. In place of the rigid, unexamined customs which determine the individual's behavior in primitive communities, there is substituted today a complex politico-economic organization which is equally "given" and not-to-be-criticized in its ultimate aims and assumptions, and which overrides with equal finality the individual's power of choice.

The parallel goes farther. As primitive man endowed natural forces with human animus, so modern man attributes to a nation or a people qualities of will and choice that belong in reality only to individuals. The reasons are the same in both cases: to reduce mysterious and uncontrollable forces to a level where they may be dealt with. The cave dweller feels much more comfortable about a thunderstorm if he can explain it as the rage of someone like himself only bigger, and the urban cave dwellers of our time feel much better about war if they can think of the enemy nation as a person like themselves only bigger, which can be collectively punched in the nose for the evil actions it collectively chooses to do. If the German people are not "responsible" for "their" nation's war crimes, the world becomes a complicated and terrifying place, in which un-understood social forces move men puppetlike to perform terrible acts, and in which guilt is at once universal and meaningless. Unhappily, the world is in fact such a place.

One of the reasons anthropology is so interesting to the politically-minded today is because its method of observation, already used successfully on primitive societies, can be applied very usefully to contemporary society, and is already being so applied by Dollard, Benedict, the Lynds and others. May we not, indeed, expect some future historian to write of us as one scholar has written of the ancient Hebrews:

> *They explained nearly all phenomena by the direct action of superhuman and invisible persons and powers, resembling the human spirit. Like the 'primitives,' they recognized no essential difference between the spiritual and the material. Like them, too, they conceived of a solidarity, or more accurately, a practical identity, between many beings, events and things which we regard as absolutely distinct.*

This animistic confusion marks the common man's thinking (with plenty of help from his political rulers) not only on relations between nations but also on the relation between the State and the individual citizen. Precisely because in this sphere the individual is most powerless in reality, do his rulers make their greatest efforts to present the State not only as an instrument for *his* purposes but as an extension of *his* personality. They have to try to do this because of the emphasis on the free individual which the bourgeois revolution has made part of our political assumptions (for how long?).

Hegel, who developed an anti-individualist theory of Statism while the cannons of the Napoleonic wars were still echoing, saw the problem clearly and tried to meet it in such terms as these:

> *In the State, everything depends upon the unity of the universal and the particular. In the ancient States, the subjective purpose was absolutely one with the will of the State. In modern times, on the contrary, we demand an individual opinion, an individual will and conscience. The ancients had none of these in the modern sense; the final thing for them was the will of the State.* While in Asiatic despotisms, the individual had no inner self and no self-justification, in the modern world man demands to be honored for the sake of his subjective individuality.*
>
> *The union of duty and right has the twofold aspect that what the State demands as duty should directly be the right of the individual, since the State is nothing but the organization of the concept of freedom. The determinations of the individual will are given by the State objectivity, and it is through the State alone that they attain truth and realization. . . .*
>
> *To the complete State belongs, essentially, consciousness and thought. The State knows thus what it wills, and it knows it under the form of thought. . . . The State must be regarded as a great architectonic edifice, a hieroglyph of reason, manifesting itself in reality. . . . That the State is the self-determining and the completely sovereign will, the final decision being necessarily referred to it—that is easy to comprehend.*
>
> (HEGEL, THE PHILOSOPHY OF LAW)

We may be sure, at any rate, that Stalin—or Roosevelt—would find these animistic formulations of the great philosopher of modern reaction "easy to comprehend." Nor would they be at all fazed by another passage in the same essay:

---

* Hegel fails to mention the great and shining exception: the Greeks, who, to Plato's disgust, were individualistic and democratic to what today would be considered an insane degree. They found the State sometimes boring, sometimes absurd, and sometimes hateful, but never worthy of a man's respect. For an informative, learned, witty, and fascinating account of these curious folk, to whom we are still indebted for most of the few decent and agreeable aspects our culture still retains, see H. D. F. Kitto's *The Greeks* (Penguin Books). There were only a few hundred thousand of them, and their society lasted only a century or so, but never in history have so many owed so much to so few. *(1953)*

> *The people without its monarch and without that whole organization necessarily and directly connected with him is a formless mass, which is no longer a State. In a people, not conceived in a lawless and unorganized condition, but as a self-developed and truly organic totality—in such a people, sovereignty is the personality of the whole, and this is represented in reality by the person of the monarch.*

Will, consciousness, conscience, thought, personality—these are the attributes of the Hegelian State, the whole theory culminating in the "person of the monarch" as the symbol and expression of the "organic totality." The "responsibility of peoples" is direct and all-embracing, according to such a theory.

"Lives of nations," said Roosevelt in his 1940 Inaugural Address, "are determined not by the count of years, but by the lifetime of the human spirit. The life of a man is three-score years and ten. . . . The life of a nation is the fulness of the measure of its will to live. . . . A nation, like a person, has a body. A nation, like a person, has a mind. . . . A nation, like a person, has something deeper, something more permanent. . . . It is that something which matters most to its future, which calls for the most sacred guarding of its present."

5. *if everyone is guilty, no one is guilty*

From the "Organic State" conception, it follows that no individual citizen or group of citizens may think or act otherwise than in accordance with the policies laid down by those in control of the State apparatus. When cells in a biological organism cut loose from their organic function, the result is cancer. Similar behavior by the citizen-cells of the Organic State is political cancer. The old Roman fable of the belly and the members by which the patricians defended their position against the plebs, this is still the basic argument of the "organicists."

In an organism, obviously no line can be drawn between the whole (the nation, or the people) and the parts (the individual citizens, the specific classes and interest-groups). The hands that strangle are no more guilty than the belly which nourishes them; the specialized "Jew-killing experts" are no more guilty than the peasants who raise the food they eat or the metalworkers who forge their instruments.

Thus the theory is convenient for those in power on two scores: internally, it preserves the ladder of hierarchy, making rebellious behavior treason not only to those in authority but also to the alleged common interests of everybody, to what is reverently termed "national unity" these days; in time of war, it makes it possible to treat the enemy population as a homogeneous single block, all of them equally wicked and detestable. This second use is what concerns us here: it is the theoretical underpinning of the concept that the German people are responsible for the horrors of Nazism.

But if everyone is guilty, then no one is guilty. The dialectics of this are wonderfully illustrated in an anecdote quoted by Hannah Arendt ("Organized Guilt and Universal Responsibility," *Jewish Frontier*, January, 1945) from *PM* of Nov. 12, 1944. An American correspondent interviews an official of a "death camp" who had fallen into the hands of the Russians:

> *Q. Did you kill people in the camp?* A. *Yes.*
>
> *Q. Did you poison them with gas?* A. *Yes.*
>
> *Q. Did you bury them alive?* A. *It sometimes happened.*
>
> *Q. Did you personally help to kill people?* A. *Absolutely not. I was only paymaster in the camp.*
>
> *Q. What did you think of what was going on?* A. *It was bad at first, but we got used to it.*
>
> *Q. Do you know the Russians will hang you?* A. *(bursting into tears) Why should they? What have I done?*

What have I done? These words ring true. One feels that the worthy paymaster—imagine the civilization that has produced the job of paymaster in a death camp!—is sincerely outraged by the proposal to hang him for his part in killing several million human beings. What had he done indeed? Simply obeyed orders and kept his mouth shut. It was what he had *not* done that shocks our moral sensibilities. But from the standpoint of the Organic State he is no more and no less guilty than every other person in Germany and deserves hanging no more and no less. Soldiers must obey their officers, just as citizens must obey the law. Stalin and Roosevelt would certainly not permit their own soldiers to discriminate, on the frivolous grounds of personal conscience, between one military order and another. Harold Denny in the N. Y. *Times* of Feb. 17, 1945 tells about a captured noncom who had witnessed the execution of forty Jewish men, women and children in Brest-Litovsk. "The only thoughts I had about it," he said, "were that it was ordered from above and that those who ordered it must have had their important reasons. By now we have been educated in such a manner that we no longer discuss given orders but agree to them without question." Asked whether he himself would be capable of carrying out such an order, he replied, after reflection, that he thought he would be, adding: "I cannot say I would have had fun doing it—not the least little bit. It could only be under the compulsion of an order. To volunteer for it, that I could not do."

It is not the law-breaker we must fear today so much as he who obeys the law. The Germans have long been noted for their deep respect for law and order. This foible, which one could smile at as an amiable weakness in the past, has assumed a sinister aspect under the Nazis. One of the most hopeful auguries for the future of this country, with the Permanent War Economy taking shape, is that we Americans have a long and honorable tradition of lawlessness and disrespect for authority.

Only those who are willing to resist authority themselves when it conflicts too intolerably with their personal moral code, only they have the right to condemn the death-camp paymaster. Certainly those who preach, or practice, the Organic State have no such right. (For all that, the Russian authorities, untroubled by such nice points, have probably long since hung the fellow—while we agonize over the rights and wrongs of the case.) Yet can even *we* really condemn the paymaster? For the Organic State is by no means only an ideological slogan devised by those in authority; it also corresponds to the real arrangement of things in the modern world. The principles on which our mass-industry economy is built—centralization of authority, division of labor (or specialization of function), rigid organization from the top down into which each worker fits at his appointed hierarchical level—these have been carried over into the political sphere. The result is that, as we have seen above, the individual has little choice about his behavior, and can be made to function, by the pressure and terror wielded by the masters of the Organic State, in ways quite opposed to any he would voluntarily choose. I have been told that the Nazis created a Jewish section of the Gestapo and that these creatures were much more feared by their fellow Jews than were the regular Gestapo men, since they would never dare take a bribe or show the slightest good nature. There were also Jewish policemen in the Warsaw ghetto, working loyally with the Nazis. We may imagine the pressure against these individuals, and their families, which produced this behavior. And doubtless some Jews refused to play the role, and took the consequences. But probably not very many, for such Jews were heroes, and there are not many heroes among the Jews or among any other peoples today (except primitive folk like the Greeks and the Poles). Our paymaster was not a hero, and the Russians hung him for not being one—as they would have hung him for being one in *their* State.*

With their usual unerring cynicism, the Nazis exploit this moral weakness in the German people—that they are not heroes. The official SS organ recently editorialized:

> *There are no innocents in Germany. We have not yet met a single German who for political reasons had refused marriage, children, family support, reductions of taxes or paid vacations only because National Socialism had made them possible. On the contrary, they grew fat and stout under the prosperity of National Socialism. They felt no pangs of conscience at the "Aryanization" of Jewish businesses. They had their full share in the prosperity. And they shouted "Hurrah" to our victories. . . . There were, it is true, lamblike innocents who did not want to declare war upon any country and who did for the German war effort only as much as they had to. But even these did not object to making money from the war or from National Socialism. They liked to ride in their new cars on our new highways and to travel on our "Strength through Joy" excursions. Nobody, after all, has preferred a democratic death to a National Socialist life.*
>
> EDITORIAL IN *Das Schwarze Korps*, QUOTED IN THE *Neue Volkszeitung*, NEW YORK CITY, FOR FEB. 10, 1945

* Since the war ended, we have had much experience, most of it depressing, in trying to access criminal responsibility for political crimes. The de-Nazification program and the Nuremberg Trials got all snarled up in the Responsibility of Peoples. That bewildering concept also transmuted the whole population of Berlin in three years from Nazi beasts to democratic heroes. See "The Germans—Three Years Later." *(1953)*

The *Schwarze Korps,* of course, exaggerates: as we shall presently see, scores of Germans every day "prefer" (at least get—which I admit is not necessarily quite the same thing) a "democratic death" to a "National Socialist life." But, from the Organic standpoint, it is quite true that "no one is innocent." With their customary political logic, the Nazis of late have deliberately tried to involve the whole German people in the moral responsibility for their crimes. In her brilliant article in the *Jewish Frontier,* Hannah Arendt describes this process and its political consequences.

> *The terror-organizations, which were at first strictly separated from the mass of the people, admitting only persons who could show a criminal past or prove their preparedness to become criminals, have since been continually expanded. . . . Whereas those crimes which have always been a part of the daily routine of concentration camps since the beginning of the Nazi regime were at first a jealously guarded monopoly of the SS and Gestapo, today members of the Wehrmacht are assigned at will to the duties of mass murder. These crimes were at first kept secret by every possible means and any publication of such reports was made punishable as atrocity propaganda. Later, however, such reports were spread by Nazi-organized whispering campaigns and today these crimes are openly proclaimed under the title of "measures of liquidation" in order to force "Volksgenossen" whom difficulties of organization made it impossible to induct into the "Volksgemeinschaft" of crime at least to bear the onus of complicity and awareness of what was going on. These tactics resulted in a victory for the Nazis, and the Allies abandoned the distinction between Germans and Nazis. . . .*
>
> *National Socialism's chances of organizing an underground movement in the future depends on there being no visible signs of distinction any longer, and above all on the victorious powers' being convinced that there really are no differences between Germans.*

6. *we, too, are guilty*

If "they," the German people, are responsible for the atrocious policies and actions of "their" (in the possessive and possessing sense, again) government, then "we," the peoples of Russia, England and America, must also take on a big load of responsibility.

We forced defeated Germany, after World War I, into a blind alley from which the only escape was another blind alley, Nazism; this we did by throwing our weight against socialist revolution. After Hitler took power, more or less with our blessing as a lesser evil to revolution, we allowed him to rearm Germany in the hopes we could turn him against Russia, and we used "non-intervention" to aid him and Mussolini to overthrow the Spanish Republic in the "dress rehearsal" for World War II.

In the present war, we have carried the saturation bombing of German cities to a point where "military objectives" are secondary to the incineration or suffocation of great numbers of civilians; we have betrayed the Polish underground fighters in Warsaw into the hands of the Nazis, have deported hundreds of thousands of Poles to slow-death camps in Siberia, and have taken by force a third of Poland's territory; we have conducted a civil war against another ally, Greece, in order to restore a reactionary and unpopular monarch; we have starved those parts of Europe our armies have "liberated" almost as badly as the Nazis did, and if we explain that the shipping was needed for our armies, they can retort that the food was needed for *their* armies; we have followed Nazi racist theories in segregating Negro soldiers in our military forces and in deporting from their homes on the West Coast to concentration camps in the interior tens of thousands of citizens who happened to be of Japanese ancestry; we have made ourselves the accomplice of the Maidanek butchers by refusing to permit more than a tiny trickle of the Jews of Europe to take refuge inside our borders; we have ruled India brutally, imprisoning the people's leaders, denying the most elementary civil liberties, causing a famine last year in which hundreds of thousands perished; we have—

But this is monstrous, you say? We, the people, didn't do these things. They were done by a few political leaders, and the majority of Americans, Englishmen and (perhaps—who knows?) Russians deplore them and favor quite different policies. Or if they don't, then it is because they have not had a chance to become aware of the real issues and to act on them. In any case, *I* can accept no responsibility for such horrors. I and most of the people I know are vigorously opposed to such policies and have made our disapproval constantly felt in the pages of the *Nation* and on the speaker's platforms of the Union for Democratic Action.

Precisely. And the Germans could say the same thing. And if

you say, but why didn't you get rid of Hitler if you didn't like his policies, they can say: But you people (in America and England, at least) merely had to vote against your Government to overthrow it, while we risked our necks if we even talked against ours. Yet you Britishers have tolerated Churchill for five years, and you Americans have thrice reelected Roosevelt by huge majorities.

It is a terrible fact, but it is a fact, that few people have the imagination or the moral sensitivity to get very excited about actions which they don't participate in themselves (and hence about which they feel no personal responsibility). The scale and complexity of modern Governmental organization, and the concentration of political power at the top, are such that the vast majority of people are excluded from this participation. How many votes did Roosevelt's refugee policy cost him? What political damage was done the Churchill-Labor government by its treatment of India, or by last year's Bombay famine? What percentage of the American electorate is deeply concerned about the mass starvation of the Italians under the Allied occupation? As the French say, to ask such questions is to answer them.

7. *the political meaning of collective war guilt*

The theory of the German people's collective responsibility for Nazi policies not only (1) ignores the deep cleavages between the Nazis and the people, but also (2) cements these cracks up again.

(1) If the theory were correct, one would expect to find the German people following the Nazis' war leadership with docility if not with enthusiasm. Actually, according to official German figures (N. Y. *Times*, Dec. 20, 1944), "People's Courts" executions (mostly involving treason and other offenses against the State) rose 5,000% in the first four years of the war: from 99 in 1939 to 1,292 in 1941 to 5,336 in 1943. These figures don't include the death sentences passed in the regular courts, nor the thousands of Germans executed annually without trial by the Gestapo, the Elite Guard, etc. The 1944 figures are unavailable but are probably much higher than 1943: estimates of the executions after last summer's attempt on Hitler's life run into the tens of thousands. "After the proclamation of total mobilization as a link in 'the holy war of the entire people,'" writes a neutral correspondent just back from Germany (N. Y. *Times Magazine*, Sept. 24, 1944), "Nazi leaders ordered all Nazis to report

immediately to the Gestapo any defeatist utterances. . . . Well above a hundred of my worker friends and their acquaintances have recently disappeared, 'spurlos versenkt.'" Facts like these, even if we grant there is little organized opposition to the Nazis inside Germany, suggests the fuel is ready from which might spring the flames of an anti-Nazi revolution, if the right spark were provided. But it would be difficult to say which dreads such a spark the most, the Nazis or the Big Three.

(2) It is likely that not since 1934 have the Nazis commanded the popular support they have today. Goebbels and Roosevelt are agreed on one thing at least: that the German people's destiny is identical with that of the Nazis. On the one hand, we have the Nazis organizing a popular *maquis* to carry on the struggle against the Allies for years after the war, pointing to the Morgenthau Plan as conclusive evidence of the Jewish plot against Germany, and telling the German people—with the novel advantage that the propaganda is true—that there is no alternative except a fight to the bitter end under Hitler's leadership. On the other hand, we have the Big Three insisting on "unconditional surrender" (a formula, let us note, which was evolved not by the totalitarian Stalin nor the Tory Churchill but by the common man's friend, Roosevelt), proposing to enslave millions of German males, to reduce Germany to a semi-agricultural status, etc. Thus from both sides of the battle-lines, the German people are told that the Nazis' survival is their only hope of survival, that the Nazis *are Germany* (a claim the Nazis have long made but up to now have been unable to get generally accepted).

For one curious result of the "all-are-guilty" line, which is put forward by those who profess the utmost detestation of Nazism, is that it makes Nazism (or its equivalent called by some other name) the logical *postwar* form of regime for defeated Germany. This comes out nakedly if one considers the most fully developed "organic" theory on Germany—that, fittingly enough, propounded by the Nazis' fellow totalitarian regime in Russia. One finds Moscow promoting hatred of Germans as Germans (not only as Nazis) and proposing the most Draconic treatment of Germany after the war, and at the same time encouraging German military nationalism through the Von Seidlitz officers' committee. A contradiction? Only superficially. The "organic" theory leads precisely to the retention of the Nazis and *junkers* as the German people's rulers. The logic: all are guilty;

therefore no one is more guilty than another; therefore, the Nazis and the *junkers* are no more guilty than their opponents; therefore, if it is convenient—and it *is* convenient—it is permissible to keep the Nazis and *junkers* (except a few that are hung for demonstration purposes) in power. Thus we have Stalin using the generals and Eisenhower using the SS and the Nazi police. "In Germany there will be no fraternization," proclaimed Eisenhower's Order of the Day of Oct. 12, 1944. "We go in as conquerors." * The logical result of this Order was reported in the London *Tribune* of Nov. 24, 1944: "Front-line correspondents report that posters have been put up everywhere in the British and American zones announcing that 52 different Nazi organizations are to be disbanded. This figure does not, however, include all Nazi organizations. Some of these have been ordered to their stations and barracks, to await further orders. Among them are the Hitler Youth, the Nazi Police, and the SS." Some all-are-guilty enthusiasts even insist that the German people

* Eisenhower's Order of the Day resulted in such edifying scenes as the following, reported by a private in the occupation forces in the Sept. 1945 *Politics*: "We had finished eating and there was a large amount left over. Children of between six and ten were standing around hoping to catch a morsel. We then proceeded to dig a hole and bury the food." For, according to the purest form of the Responsibility of Peoples doctrine, no moral distinction is made between children and grown-ups. "Would not the punishment of all Germans inflict needless hardship on millions of German children who can in no way be held responsible for the crimes of their elders?" a man in the audience asked Major Erwin Lessner during a 1945 Town-Meeting-of-the-Air debate between the major and Dorothy Thompson. "Of course it would," admitted, or rather insisted, the major. "These innocent German children are the potential soldiers of World War III, just as the innocent German children who had been fed after 1918 later served in Hitler's army and did remarkably well." Today, General Eisenhower (and doubtless the major too) thinks highly of the German people, since he needs them desperately in his NATO army, and it is a plus and not a minus for German kids that they are "potential soldiers of World War III." In seven years, the German people have risen from beasts to defenders of democracy, and the Russian people have changed as radically in the reverse direction.

Personally, I find the attitude of Louis XIV more congenial. France was at war with England when the second Eddystone Lighthouse was being built, early in the eighteenth century. A French privateer carried off the builders to France, where they were imprisoned. Louis XIV learned of this action when the French captain applied to him for a reward. *Le Roi Soleil* was indignant. "I am at war with England, not with mankind," he declared, in the grand manner. And he sent the Eddystone builders back to England with rich presents, thoughtfully filling their prison cells with the French captain and crew. *(1953)*

are so despicable that they *deserve* to be ruled forever by the Nazis! Thus the most extreme anti-Nazism turns into its dialectical opposite.

So much for the effect on the German people of the collective responsibility theory. It is equally disastrous for the Allied peoples. Last summer everyone thought the war in Europe would be over by the fall. The Anglo-Americans had broken out of Normandy and were racing across France in pursuit of the disorganized German armies; the Russians were advancing on all their fronts; an attempt on Hitler's life was almost successful; the popular mood inside Germany was one of panic and loss of confidence in Hitler's leadership. At that moment, it would not have taken much political pressure to pry loose the people from the Nazis and to bring the whole structure down. Instead of applying this pressure, the Allies reiterated the "unconditional surrender" line, embellished with such grace notes as the Morgenthau Plan. They succeeded in convincing the German people, as Hitler's most frenetic orations could not have convinced them, that their only hope was to stand firm behind the Nazis. To make sure the Germans didn't miss the point, the American High Command staged a special demonstration at Aachen, the first sizable German city our troops reached. Aachen was defended by a single second-rate division, reinforced by one SS unit and a few fortress troops. The defenders cooperated splendidly with the attackers: for one week, the city, ringed with American divisions and artillery units, was bombed and shelled. It was finally taken "the hard way," by an all-out infantry assault backed up by tanks and God knows what else. Militarily, not exactly brilliant. But politically sound enough, for the city was reduced to rubble, thousands of its inhabitants were killed (and a good many American soldiers, too), and notice was served on all Germany (and on the Americans) of what was in store for it (and them).

It is not worth wasting printer's ink to prove that, militarily, the "Aachen policy" is inferior to a policy which would split the German people from the Nazis, and that such a policy would save an enormous number of American, British and Russian lives. But when have military considerations been allowed to interfere with the more serious business of politics (except, of course, when bestarred generals urge strikers not to interfere with the "war effort")? The Big Three want things to be done in an orderly way, with the masses' properly constituted rulers remaining on top; they don't want any unauthorized popular movements behind their own lines and they don't want them behind the enemy lines either. Only a liberal editor would seriously point out to them that military victory could be had more rapidly by encouraging the internal break-up of Germany. They are well aware of that fact, but, as responsible ruling-class leaders, they are unwilling to abandon their principles for the sake of military expediency.*

"Modern war," wrote Simone Weil, "appears as a struggle led by all the State apparatuses and their general staffs against all men old enough to bear arms. . . . The great error of nearly all studies of war . . . has been to consider war as an episode in foreign policies, when it is especially an act of interior politics, and the most atrocious act of all." (*Politics*, February, 1945.)

The common peoples of the world are coming to have less and less control over the policies of "their" governments, while at the same time they are being more and more closely identified with those governments. Or to state it in slightly different terms: as the common man's *moral* responsibility diminishes (assuming agreement that the degree of moral responsibility is in direct proportion to the degree of freedom of choice), his *practical* responsibility increases. Not for many centuries have individuals been at once so powerless to influence what is done by the national collectivities to which they belong, and at the same time so generally held responsible for what is done by those collectivities.

Where can the common peoples look for relief from this intolerable agonizing contradiction? Not to their traditional defender, the labor movement. This no longer exists in Russia, and in the

---

* No! No! Marxistical baby-talk! Not a question of "the masses' properly constituted rulers remaining on top" at all; goes much deeper than these antiquated class-war concepts, profound a century ago but now superficial and misleading. The only serious threat to Nazi rule from within Germany during the war came not from the masses, but from the upper class: the conspiracy of generals and Junker aristocrats, plus a couple of liberal politicians, which culminated in the near-assassination of Hitler in August, 1944. The conspirators wanted to overthrow the Nazis and make peace simply because they were (correctly) convinced that Hitler was leading Germany to ruin. They envisaged a capitalist democracy not very different from our own (or from the present Bonn Government, for that matter), and certainly no revolutionary upheaval. Yet the concept of the Responsibility of Peoples, as expressed in Roosevelt's "unconditional surrender" line, was so strong that they got no encouragement or support from the Allies in their effort to destroy Hitler's rule from within. *(1953)*

two great bourgeois democracies, it has quite lost touch with the humane and democratic ideals it once believed in. Last fall, the British Trade Union Congress endorsed, 5 to 1, a statement that the German people are responsible for the crimes of Nazism; and a few weeks later the CIO convention over here resolved: "The German people must . . . atone for the crimes and horrors which they have visited on the earth." Such international working-class solidarity as once existed has vanished, and the workers of the world, including and especially those of the Soviet Union, are as brutally and rabidly nationalistic—*in their capacity as organized workers*—as their own ruling classes are.

We must look both more widely and more deeply for relief from the dilemma of increasing political impotence accompanied by increasing political responsibility. To our essential humanity and to a more sensitive and passionate respect for our own and other people's humanity.

Harold Denny in the N. Y. *Times* of Feb. 18, 1945, tells the story of a captured SS private. He was a young Ukrainian farmer who was impressed into the SS when the Germans retreated from Russia last summer. Fed up, apathetic, without interest even in tracing his family, he "appears to have no hatreds, no likes and little resentment. . . . To all questions he replies, 'I cannot know anything about that. Everything's so mixed up.' He looks and acts like a man in a profound state of shock." But the Ukrainian-farmer-SS-man had learned one thing, and he gave it as his only value-judgment:

"We are all human beings. If we had peace, if people would work together, they'd perhaps be comrades. But now—."

GEORGE ORWELL

a hanging

It was in Burma, a sodden morning of the rains. A sickly light, like yellow tinfoil, was slanting over the high walls into the jail yard. We were waiting outside the condemned cells, a row of sheds fronted with double bars, like small animal cages. Each cell measured about ten feet by ten and was quite bare within except for a plank bed and a pot for drinking water. In some of them brown silent men were squatting at the inner bars, with their blankets draped round them. These were the condemned men, due to be hanged within the next week or two.

One prisoner had been brought out of his cell. He was a Hindu, a puny wisp of a man, with a shaven head and vague liquid eyes. He had a thick, sprouting moustache, absurdly too big for his body, rather like the moustache of a comic man on the films. Six tall Indian warders were guarding him and getting him ready for the gallows. Two of them stood by with rifles and fixed bayonets, while the others handcuffed him, passed a chain through his handcuffs and fixed it to their belts, and lashed his arms tight to his sides. They crowded very close about him, with their hands always on him in a careful, caressing grip, as though all the while feeling him to make sure he was there. It was like men handling a fish which is still alive and may jump back into the water. But he stood quite unresisting, yielding his arms limply to the ropes, as though he hardly noticed what was happening.

Eight o'clock struck and a bugle call, desolately thin in the wet air, floated from the distant barracks. The superintendent of the jail, who was standing apart from the rest of us, moodily prodding the gravel with his stick, raised his head at the sound. He was an army doctor, with a grey toothbrush moustache and a gruff voice. "For God's sake hurry up, Francis," he said irritably. "The man ought to have been dead by this time. Aren't you ready yet?"

Francis, the head jailer, a fat Dravidian in a white drill suit and gold spectacles, waved his black hand. "Yes sir, yes sir," he bubbled. "All iss satisfactorily prepared. The hangman iss waiting. We shall proceed."

"Well, quick march, then. The prisoners can't get their breakfast till this job's over."

We set out for the gallows. Two warders marched on either

side of the prisoner, with their rifles at the slope; two others marched close against him, gripping him by arm and shoulder, as though at once pushing and supporting him. The rest of us, magistrates and the like, followed behind. Suddenly, when we had gone ten yards, the procession stopped short without any order or warning. A dreadful thing had happened—a dog, come goodness knows whence, had appeared in the yard. It came bounding among us with a loud volley of barks, and leapt round us wagging its whole body, wild with glee at finding so many human beings together. It was a large woolly dog, half Airedale, half pariah. For a moment it pranced round us, and then, before anyone could stop it, it had made a dash for the prisoner and, jumping up, tried to lick his face. Everyone stood aghast, too taken aback even to grab at the dog.

"Who let that bloody brute in here?" said the superintendent angrily. "Catch it, someone!"

A warder, detached from the escort, charged clumsily after the dog, but it danced and gambolled just out of his reach, taking everything as part of the game. A young Eurasian jailer picked up a handful of gravel and tried to stone the dog away, but it dodged the stones and came after us again. Its yaps echoed from the jail walls. The prisoner, in the grasp of the two warders, looked on incuriously, as though this was another formality of the hanging. It was several minutes before someone managed to catch the dog. Then we put my handkerchief through its collar and moved off once more, with the dog still straining and whimpering.

It was about forty yards to the gallows. I watched the bare brown back of the prisoner marching in front of me. He walked clumsily with his bound arms, but quite steadily, with that bobbing gait of the Indian who never straightens his knees. At each step his muscles slid neatly into place, the lock of hair on his scalp danced up and down, his feet printed themselves on the wet gravel. And once, in spite of the men who gripped him by each shoulder, he stepped slightly aside to avoid a puddle on the path.

It is curious, but till that moment I had never realized what it means to destroy a healthy, conscious man. When I saw the prisoner step aside to avoid the puddle I saw the mystery, the unspeakable wrongness, of cutting a life short when it is in full tide. This man was not dying, he was alive just as we are alive. All the organs of his body were working—bowels digesting food, skin renewing itself, nails growing, tissues forming—all toiling away in solemn foolery. His nails would still be growing when he stood on the drop, when he was falling through the air with a tenth-of-a-second to live. His eyes saw the yellow gravel and the grey walls, and his brain still remembered, foresaw, reasoned—reasoned even about puddles. He and we were a party of men walking together, seeing, hearing, feeling, understanding the same world; and in two minutes, with a sudden snap, one of us would be gone—one mind less, one world less.

The gallows stood in a small yard, separate from the main grounds of the prison, and overgrown with tall prickly weeds. It was a brick erection like three sides of a shed, with planking on top, and above that two beams and a crossbar with the rope dangling. The hangman, a grey-haired convict in the white uniform of the prison, was waiting beside his machine. He greeted us with a servile crouch as we entered. At a word from Francis the two warders, gripping the prisoner more closely than ever, half led half pushed him to the gallows and helped him clumsily up the ladder. Then the hangman climbed up and fixed the rope round the prisoner's neck.

We stood waiting, five yards away. The warders had formed in a rough circle round the gallows. And then, when the noose was fixed, the prisoner began crying out to his god. It was a high, reiterated cry of "Ram! Ram! Ram! Ram!" not urgent and fearful like a prayer or cry for help, but steady, rhythmical, almost like the tolling of a bell. The dog answered the sound with a whine. The hangman, still standing on the gallows, produced a small cotton bag like a flour bag and drew it down over the prisoner's face. But the sound, muffled by the cloth, still persisted, over and over again: "Ram! Ram! Ram! Ram! Ram!"

The hangman climbed down and stood ready, holding the lever. Minutes seemed to pass. The steady, muffled crying from the prisoner went on and on, "Ram! Ram! Ram!" never faltering for an instant. The superintendent, his head on his chest, was slowly poking the ground with his stick; perhaps he was counting the cries, allowing the prisoner a fixed number—fifty, perhaps, or a hundred. Everyone had changed color. The Indians had gone grey like bad coffee, and one or two of the bayonets were wavering. We looked at the lashed, hooded man on the drop, and listened to his cries—each cry another second of life; the same thought was in all our minds: oh, kill him quickly, get it over, stop that abominable noise!

Suddenly the superintendent made up his mind. Throwing up his head he made a swift motion with his stick. "Chalo!" he shouted almost fiercely.

There was a clanking noise, and then dead silence. The prisoner had vanished, and the rope was twisting on itself. I let go of the dog, and it galloped immediately to the back of the gallows; but when it got there it stopped short, barked, and then retreated into a corner of the yard, where it stood among the weeds, looking timorously out at us. We went round the gallows to inspect the prisoner's body. He was dangling with his toes pointed straight downwards, very slowly revolving, as dead as a stone.

The superintendent reached out with his stick and poked the bare brown body; it oscillated slightly. "*He's* all right," said the superintendent. He backed out from under the gallows, and blew out a deep breath. The moody look had gone out of his face quite suddenly. He glanced at his wrist-watch. "Eight minutes past eight. Well, that's all for this morning, thank God."

The warders unfixed bayonets and marched away. The dog, sobered and conscious of having misbehaved itself, slipped after them. We walked out of the gallows yard, past the condemned cells with their waiting prisoners, into the big central yard of the prison. The convicts, under the command of warders armed with lathis, were already receiving their breakfast. They squatted in long rows, each man holding a tin panikin, while two warders with buckets marched round ladling out rice; it seemed quite a homely, jolly scene, after the hanging. An enormous relief had come upon us now that the job was done. One felt an impulse to sing, to break into a run, to snigger. All at once everyone began chattering gaily.

The Eurasian boy walking beside me nodded towards the way we had come, with a knowing smile: "Do you know, sir, our friend [he meant the dead man] when he heard his appeal had been dismissed, he pissed on the floor of his cell. From fright. Kindly take one of my cigarettes, sir. Do you not admire my new silver case, sir? From the boxwalah, two rupees eight annas. Classy European style."

Several people laughed—at what, nobody seemed certain.

Francis was walking by the superintendent, talking garrulously: "Well, sir, all hass passed off with the utmost satisfactoriness. It was all finished—flick! like that. It iss not always so—oah, no! I have known cases where the doctor wass obliged to go beneath the gallows and pull the prissoner's legs to ensure decease. Most disagreeable!"

"Wriggling about, eh? That's bad," said the superintendent.

"Ach, sir, it iss worse when they become refractory! One man, I recall, clung to the bars of hiss cage when we went to take him out. You will scarcely credit, sir, that it took six warders to dislodge him, three pulling at each leg. We reasoned with him. 'My dear fellow,' we said, 'think of all the pain and trouble you are causing to us!' But no, he would not listen! Ach, he wass very troublesome!"

I found that I was laughing quite loudly. Everyone was laughing. Even the superintendent grinned in a tolerant way. "You'd better all come out and have a drink," he said quite genially. "I've got a bottle of whisky in the car. We could do with it."

We went through the big double gates of the prison into the road. "Pulling at his legs!" exclaimed a Burmese magistrate suddenly, and burst into a loud chuckling. We all began laughing again. At that moment Francis' anecdote seemed extraordinarily funny. We all had a drink together, native and European alike, quite amicably. The dead man was a hundred yards away.

JAMES MICHIE

dooley is a traitor

"So then you won't fight?"
"Yes, your Honour," I said, "that's right."
"Now is it that you simply aren't willing,
Or have you a fundamental moral objection to killing?"
Says the judge, blowing his nose
And making his words stand to attention in long rows.
I stand to attention too, but with half a grin
(In my time I've done a good many in).
"No objection at all, sir," I said.
"There's a deal of the world I'd rather see dead—

Such as Johnny Stubbs or Fred Settle or my last land-lord,
  Mr. Syme.
Give me a gun and your blessing, your Honour, and I'll
  be killing them all the time.
But my conscience says a clear no
To killing a crowd of gentlemen I don't know.
Why, I'd as soon think of killing a worshipful judge,
High-court, like yourself (against whom, God knows, I've
  got no grudge—
So far), as murder a heap of foreign folk.
If you've got no grudge, you've got no joke
To laugh at after."
                    Now the words never come flowing
Proper for me till I get the old pipe going.
And just as I was poking
Down baccy, the judge looks up sharp with "No smoking,
Mr. Dooley. We're not fighting this war for fun.
And we want a clearer reason why you refuse to carry a
  gun.
This war is not a personal feud, it's a fight
Against wrong ideas on behalf of the Right.
Mr. Dooley, won't you help to destroy evil ideas?"
"Ah, your Honour, here's
The tragedy," I said. "I'm not a man of the mind.
I couldn't find it in my heart to be unkind
To an idea. I wouldn't know one if I saw one. I haven't one
  of my own.
So I'd best be leaving other people's alone."
"Indeed," he sneers at me, "this defence is
Curious for someone with convictions in two senses.
A criminal invokes conscience to his aid
To support an individual withdrawal from a communal
  crusade
Sanctioned by God, led by the Church, against a godless,
  churchless nation!"
I asked his Honour for a translation.
"You talk of conscience," he said. "What do you know of
  the Christian creed?"
"Nothing, sir, except what I can read,

That's the most you can hope for from us jail-birds.
I just open the Book here and there and look at the words.
And I find when the Lord himself misliked an evil notion
He turned it into a pig and drove it squealing over a cliff into the ocean,
And the loony ran away
And lived to think another day.
There was a clean job done and no blood shed!
Everybody happy and forty wicked thoughts drowned dead.
A neat and Christian murder. None of your mad slaughter
Throwing away the brains with the blood and the baby with the bathwater.
Now I look at the war as a sportsman. It's a matter of choosing
The decentest way of losing.
Heads or tails, losers or winners,
We all lose, we're all damned sinners.
And I'd rather be with the poor cold people at the wall that's shot
Than the bloody guilty devils in the firing-line, in Hell and keeping hot."
"But what right, Dooley, what right," he cried,
"Have you to say the Lord is on your side?"
"That's a dirty crooked question," back I roared.
"I said not the Lord was on my side, but I was on the side of the Lord."
Then he was up at me and shouting,
But by and by he calms: "Now we're not doubting
Your sincerity, Dooley, only your arguments,
Which don't make sense."
('Hullo,' I thought, 'that's the wrong way round.
I may be skylarking a bit, but my brainpan's sound.')
Then biting his nail and sugaring his words sweet:
"Keep your head, Mr. Dooley. Religion is clearly not up your street.
But let me ask you as a plain patriotic fellow
Whether you'd stand there so smug and yellow
If the foe were attacking your own dear sister."
"I'd knock their brains out, mister,

On the floor," I said. "There," he says kindly, "I knew you were no pacifist.
It's your straight duty as a man to enlist.
The enemy is at the door." You could have downed
Me with a feather. "Where?" I gasp, looking round.
"Not this door," he says angered. "Don't play the clown.
But they're two thousand miles away planning to do us down.
Why, the news is full of the deeds of those murderers and rapers."
"Your Eminence," I said, "my father told me never to believe the papers
But to go by my eyes,
And at two thousand miles the poor things can't tell truth from lies."
His fearful spectacles glittered like the moon: "For the last time what right
Has a man like you to refuse to fight?"
"More right," I said, "than you.
You've never murdered a man, so you don't know what it is I won't do.
I've done it in good hot blood, so haven't I the right to make bold
To declare that I shan't do it in cold?"
Then the judge rises in a great rage
And writes DOOLEY IS A TRAITOR in black upon a page
And tells me I must die.
"What, me?" says I.
"If you still won't fight."
"Well, yes, your Honour," I said, "that's right."

letters to a german friend

The *Letters to a German Friend** were published in France after the Liberation in a limited edition and have never been reprinted. I have always been opposed to their circulation abroad for the reasons that I shall give.

This is the first time they have appeared outside of France and I should not have made up my mind to this had it not been for my long-standing desire to contribute, insofar as I can, to removing the stupid frontiers separating our two territories.

But I cannot let these pages be reprinted without saying what they are. They were written and published clandestinely during the Occupation. They had a purpose, which was to throw some light on the blind battle we were then waging and thereby to make our battle more effective. They are topical writings and hence they may appear unjust. Indeed, if one were to write about defeated Germany, a rather different tone would be called for. But I should simply like to forestall a misunderstanding. When the author of these letters says "you," he means not "you Germans" but "you Nazis." When he says "we," this signifies not always "we Frenchmen" but sometimes "we free Europeans." I am contrasting two attitudes, not two nations, even if, at a certain moment in history, these two nations personified two enemy attitudes. To repeat a remark that is not mine, I love my country too much to be a nationalist. And I know that neither France nor Italy would lose anything—quite the contrary—if they both had broader horizons. But we are still wide of the mark, and Europe is still torn. This is why I should be ashamed today if I implied that a French writer could be the enemy of a single nation. I loathe none but executioners. Any reader who reads the *Letters to a German Friend* in this perspective—in other words, as a document emerging from the struggle against violence—will see how I can say that I don't disown a single word I have written here.

---

* The first of these letters appeared in the second issue of the *Revue Libre* in 1943; the second, in No. 3 of the *Cahiers de Libération* in the beginning of 1944. The two others, written for the *Revue Libre,* remained unpublished.

first letter

You said to me: "The greatness of my country is beyond price. Anything is good that contributes to its greatness. And in a world where everything has lost its meaning, those who, like us young Germans, are lucky enough to find a meaning in the destiny of our nation must sacrifice everything else." I loved you then, but at that point we diverged. "No," I told you, "I cannot believe that everything must be subordinated to a single end. There are means that cannot be excused. And I should like to be able to love my country and still love justice. I don't want just any greatness for it, particularly a greatness born of blood and falsehood. I want to keep it alive by keeping justice alive." You retorted: "Well, you don't love your country."

That was five years ago; we have been separated since then and I can say that not a single day has passed during those long years (so brief, so dazzlingly swift for you!) without my remembering your remark. "You don't love your country!" When I think of your words today, I feel a choking sensation. No, I didn't love my country, if pointing out what is unjust in what we love amounts to not loving, if insisting that what we love should measure up to the finest image we have of her amounts to not loving. That was five years ago, and many men in France thought as I did. Some of them, however, have already been stood up against the wall facing the twelve little black eyes of German destiny. And those men, who in your opinion did not love their country, did more for it than you will ever do for yours, even if it were possible for you to give your life a hundred times. For their heroism was that they had to conquer themselves first. But I am speaking here of two kinds of greatness and of a contradiction about which I must enlighten you.

We shall meet soon again—if possible. But our friendship will be over. You will be full of your defeat. You will not be ashamed of your former victory. Rather, you will longingly remember it with all your crushed might. Today I am still close to you in spirit—your enemy, to be sure, but still a little your friend because I am withholding nothing from you here. Tomorrow all will be over. What your victory could not penetrate, your defeat will bring to an end. But at least, before we become indifferent to each other, I want to leave you a clear idea of what neither peace nor war has taught you to see in the destiny of my country.

I want to tell you at once what sort of greatness keeps us going. But this amounts to telling you what kind of courage we applaud, which is not your kind. For it is not much to be able to do violence when you have been simply preparing for it for years and when violence is more natural to you than thinking. It is a great deal, on the other hand, to face torture and death when you know for a fact that hatred and violence are empty things in themselves. It is a great deal to fight while despising war, to accept losing everything while still preferring happiness, to face destruction while cherishing the idea of a higher civilization. That is how we do more than you because we have to draw on ourselves. You had nothing to conquer in your heart or in your intelligence. We had two enemies, and a military victory was not enough for us, as it was for you who had nothing to overcome.

We had much to overcome—and, first of all, the constant temptation to emulate you. For there is always something in us that yields to instinct, to contempt for intelligence, to the cult of efficiency. Our great virtues eventually become tiresome to us. We become ashamed of our intelligence, and sometimes we imagine some barbarous state where truth would be effortless. But the cure for this is easy; you are there to show us what such imagining would lead to, and we mend our ways. If I believed in some fatalism in history, I should suppose that you are placed beside us, helots of the intelligence, as our living reproof. Then we reawaken to the mind and we are more at ease.

But we also had to overcome the suspicion we had of heroism. I know, you think that heroism is alien to us. You are wrong. It's just that we profess heroism and we distrust it at the same time. We profess it because ten centuries of history have given us knowledge of all that is noble. We distrust it because ten centuries of intelligence have taught us the art and blessings of being natural. In order to face up to you, we had first to be at death's door. And this is why we fell behind all of Europe, which wallowed in falsehood the moment it was necessary, while we were concerned with seeking truth. This is why we were defeated in the beginning: because we were so concerned, while you were falling upon us, to determine in our hearts whether right was on our side.

We had to overcome our weakness for mankind, the image we had formed of a peaceful destiny, that deep-rooted conviction of ours that no victory ever pays, whereas any mutilation of mankind is irrevocable. We had to give up all at once our knowledge and our hope, the reasons we had for loving and the loathing we had for all war. To put it in a word that I suppose you will understand when it comes from me whom you counted as a friend, we had to stifle our passion for friendship.

Now we have done that. We had to make a long detour, and we are far behind. It is a detour that regard for truth imposes on intelligence, that regard for friendship imposes on the heart. It is a detour that safeguarded justice and put truth on the side of those who questioned themselves. And, without a doubt, we paid very dearly for it. We paid for it with humiliations and silences, with bitter experiences, with prison sentences, with executions at dawn, with desertions and separations, with daily pangs of hunger, with emaciated children, and, above all, with humiliation of our human dignity. But that was natural. It took us all that time to find out if we had the right to kill men, if we were allowed to add to the frightful misery of this world. And because of that time lost and recaptured, our defeat accepted and surmounted, those scruples paid for with blood, we French have the right to think today that we entered this war with hands clean—clean as victims and the condemned are—and that we are going to come out of it with hands clean—but clean this time with a great victory won against injustice and against ourselves.

For we shall be victorious, you may be sure. But we shall be victorious thanks to that very defeat, to that long, slow progress during which we found our justification, to that suffering which, in all its injustice, taught us a lesson. It taught us the secret of any victory, and if we don't lose the secret, we shall know final victory. It taught us that, contrary to what we sometimes used to think, the spirit is of no avail against the sword, but that the spirit together with the sword will always win out over the sword alone. That is why we have now accepted the sword, after making sure that the spirit was on our side. We had first to see people die and to run the risk of dying ourselves. We had to see a French workman walking toward the guillotine at dawn down the prison corridors and exhorting his comrades from cell to cell to show their courage.

Finally, to possess ourselves of the spirit, we had to endure torture of our flesh. One really possesses only what one has paid for. We have paid dearly, and we have not finished paying. But we have our certainties, our justifications, our justice; your defeat is inevitable.

I have never believed in the power of truth in itself. But it is at least worth knowing that when expressed forcefully truth wins out over falsehood. This is the difficult equilibrium we have reached. This is the distinction that gives us strength as we fight today. And I am tempted to tell you that it so happens that we are fighting for fine distinctions, but the kind of distinctions that are as important as man himself. We are fighting for the distinction between sacrifice and mysticism, between energy and violence, between strength and cruelty, for that even finer distinction between the true and the false, between the man of the future and the cowardly gods you revere.

This is what I wanted to tell you, not above the fray but in the thick of the fray. This is what I wanted to answer to your remark, "You don't love your country," which is still haunting me. But I want to be clear with you. I believe that France lost her power and her sway for a long time to come and that for a long time she will need a desperate patience, a vigilant revolt to recover the element of prestige necessary for any culture. But I believe she has lost all that for reasons that are pure. And this is why I have not lost hope. This is the whole meaning of my letter. The man whom you pitied five years ago for being so reticent about his country is the same man who wants to say to you today, and to all those of our age in Europe and throughout the world: "I belong to an admirable and persevering nation which, admitting her errors and weaknesses, has not lost the idea that constitutes her whole greatness. Her people are always trying and her leaders are sometimes trying to express that idea even more clearly. I belong to a nation which for the past four years has begun to relive the course of her entire history and which is calmly and surely preparing out of the ruins to make another history and to take her chance in a game where she holds no trumps. This country is worthy of the difficult and demanding love that is mine. And I believe she is decidedly worth fighting for since she is worthy of a higher love. And I say that your nation, on the other hand, has received from its sons only the love it deserved, which was blind. A nation is not justified by such love. That will be your undoing. And you who were already conquered in your greatest victories, what will you be in the approaching defeat?"

July 1943

second letter

I have already written you once and I did so with a tone of certainty. After five years of separation, I told you why we were the stronger—because of the detour that took us out of our way to seek our justification, because of the delay occasioned by worry about our rights, because of the crazy insistence of ours on reconciling everything that we loved. But it is worth repeating. As I have already told you, we paid dearly for that detour. Rather than running the risk of injustice we preferred disorder. But at the same time that very detour constitutes our strength today, and as a result we are within sight of victory.

Yes, I have already told you all that and in a tone of certainty, as fast as I could write and without erasing a word. But I have had time to think about it. Night is a time for meditation. For three years you have brought night to our towns and to our hearts. For three years we have been developing in the dark the thought which now emerges fully armed to face you. Now I can speak to you of the intelligence. For the certainty we now feel is the certainty in which we see clearly and everything stands out sharp and clear, in which the intelligence gives its blessing to courage. And you who used to speak flippantly of the intelligence are greatly surprised, I suppose, to see it return from the shadow of death and suddenly decide to play its role in history. This is where I want to turn back toward you.

As I shall tell you later on, the mere fact that the heart is certain does not make us any the more cheerful. This alone gives a meaning to everything I am writing you. But first I want to square everything again with you, with your memory and our friendship. While I still can do so, I want to do for our friendship the only thing one can do for a friendship about to end—I want to make it explicit. I have already answered the remark, "You don't love your country," that you used to hurl at me and that I still remember vividly. Today I merely want to answer your impatient smile whenever you heard the word "intelligence." "In all her intelligences," you told me, "France repudiates herself. Some of your intellectuals prefer despair to their country—others, the pursuit of an improbable truth. We put Germany before truth and beyond despair." Apparently that was true. But, as I have already told you, if at times we seemed to prefer justice to our country, this is because we simply wanted to love our country in justice, as we wanted to love her in truth and in hope.

This is what separated us from you; we made demands. You were satisfied to serve the power of your nation and we dreamed of giving ours her truth. It was enough for you to serve the politics of reality whereas, in our wildest aberrations, we still had a vague conception of the politics of honor, which we recognize today. When I say "we," I am not speaking of our rulers. But a ruler hardly matters.

At this point I see you smile as of old. You always distrusted words. So did I, but I used to distrust myself even more. You used to try to urge me along the path you yourself had taken, where intelligence is ashamed of intelligence. Even then I couldn't follow you. But today my answers would be more assured. What is truth, you used to ask? To be sure, but at least we know what falsehood is; that is just what you have taught us. What is spirit? We know its contrary, which is murder. What is man? There I stop you, for we know. Man is that force which ultimately cancels all tyrants and gods. He is the force of evidence. Human evidence is what we must preserve, and our certainty at present comes from the fact that its fate and our country's fate are linked together. If nothing had any meaning, you would be right. But there is something that still has a meaning.

It would be impossible for me to repeat to you too often that this is where we part company. We had formed an idea of our country that put her in her proper place, amid other great concepts —friendship, mankind, happiness, our desire for justice. This led us to be severe with her. But, in the long run, we were the ones who were right. We didn't bring her any slaves, and we debased nothing for her sake. We waited patiently until we saw clearly, and, in poverty and suffering, we had the joy of fighting at the same time for all we loved. You, on the other hand, are fighting against everything in man that does not belong to the mother country. Your sacrifices are inconsequential because your hierarchy is not the right one and because your values have no place. The heart is not all you betray. The intelligence takes its revenge. You have not paid the price it asks, not made the heavy contribution intelligence must pay to lucidity. From the depths of defeat, I can tell you that that is your downfall.

Let me tell you this story. Before dawn, from a prison I know, somewhere in France, a truck driven by armed soldiers is taking eleven Frenchmen to the cemetery where you are to shoot them. Out of the eleven, five or six have really done something: a tract, a few meetings, something that showed their refusal to submit. The five or six, sitting motionless inside the truck, are filled with fear, but, if I may say so, it is an ordinary fear, the kind that grips every man facing the unknown, a fear that is not incompatible with courage. The others have done nothing. This hour is harder for them because they are dying by mistake or as victims of a kind of indifference. Among them is a child of sixteen. You know the faces of our adolescents; I don't want to talk about them. The boy is dominated by fear; he gives in to it shamelessly. Don't smile scornfully; his teeth are chattering. But you have placed beside him a chaplain, whose task is to alleviate somewhat the agonizing hour of waiting. I believe I can say that for men who are about to be killed a conversation about a future life is of no avail. It is too hard to believe that the lime-pit is not the end of all. The prisoners in the truck are silent. The chaplain turns toward the child huddled in his corner. He will understand better. The child answers, clings to the chaplain's voice, and hope returns. In the mutest of horrors sometimes it is enough for a man to speak; perhaps he is going to fix everything. "I haven't done anything," says the child. "Yes," says the chaplain, "but that's not the question now. You must get ready to die properly." "It can't be possible that no one understands me." "I am your friend and perhaps I understand you. But it is late. I shall be with you and the Good Lord will be too. You'll see how easy it is." The child turns his head away. The chaplain speaks of God. Does the child believe him? Yes, he believes. Hence he knows that nothing is as important as the peace awaiting him. But that very peace is what frightens the child. "I am your friend," the chaplain repeats.

The others are silent. He must think of *them.* The chaplain leans toward the silent group, turning his back on the child for a moment. The truck is advancing slowly with a sucking sound over the road, which is damp with dew. Imagine the gray hour, the early-morning smell of men, the invisible countryside suggested by sounds of teams being harnessed or the cry of a bird. The child leans against the canvas covering, which gives a little. He notices a narrow space between it and the truck body. He could jump if he wanted. The chaplain has his back turned and, up front, the soldiers are intent on finding their way in the dark. The boy doesn't stop to think; he tears the canvas loose, slips into the opening, and jumps. His fall is hardly heard, the sound of running on the road, then nothing more. He is in the fields, where his steps can't be heard. But the flapping of the canvas, the sharp, damp morning air penetrating the truck make the chaplain and the prisoners turn around. For a second the priest stares at those men looking at him in silence. A second in which the man of God must decide whether he is on the side of the executioners or on the side of the martyrs in keeping with his vocation. But he has already knocked on the partition separating him from his comrades. "*Achtung!*" The alarm is given. Two soldiers leap into the truck and point their guns at the prisoners. Two others leap to the ground and start running across the fields. The chaplain, a few paces from the truck, standing on the asphalt, tries to see them through the fog. In the truck the men can only listen to the sounds of the chase, the muffled exclamations, a shot, silence, then the sound of voices again coming nearer, finally a hollow stamping of feet. The child is brought back. He wasn't hit, but he stopped surrounded in that enemy fog, suddenly without courage, forsaken by himself. He is carried rather than led by his guards. He has been beaten somewhat, but not much. The most important lies ahead. He doesn't look at the chaplain or anyone else. The priest has climbed up beside the driver. An armed soldier has taken his place in the truck. Thrown into one of the corners, the child doesn't cry. Between the canvas and the floor he watches the road slip away again and sees in its surface a reflection of the dawn.

I am sure you can very well imagine the rest. But it is important for you to know who told me this story. It was a French priest. He said to me: "I am ashamed for that man, and I am pleased to think that no French priest would have been willing to make his God abet murder." That was true. The chaplain simply felt as you do. It seemed natural to him to make even his faith serve his country. Even the gods are mobilized in your country. They are on your side, as you say, but only as a result of coercion. You no longer distinguish anything; you are nothing but a single impulse. And now you are fighting with the resources of blind anger, with your mind on weapons and feats of arms rather than on ideas, stubbornly confusing every issue and following your obsession. We, on the other hand, started from the intelligence and its hesitations. We were powerless against wrath. But now our detour is finished. It took only a dead child for us to add wrath to intelligence, and now we are two against one. I want to speak to you of wrath.

Remember, when I expressed amazement at the outburst of one of your superiors, you said to me: "That too is good. But you don't understand. There is a virtue the French lack—anger." No, that's not it, but the French are difficult on the subject of virtues. And they don't assume them unless they have to. This gives their wrath the silence and strength you are just beginning to feel. And it is with that sort of wrath, the only kind I recognize in myself, that I am going to end this letter.

For, as I told you, certainty is not gaiety of heart. We know what we lost on that long detour; we know the price we are paying for the bitter joy of fighting in agreement with ourselves. And because we have a keen sense of the irreparable, there is as much bitterness as confidence in our struggle. The war didn't satisfy us. We had not yet assembled our reasons for fighting. It is civil war, the obstinate, collective struggle, the unrecorded sacrifice that our people chose. This war is the one they chose for themselves instead of accepting it from idiotic or cowardly governments, a war in which they recognize themselves and are fighting for a certain idea they have formed of themselves. But this luxury they permitted themselves costs them a dreadful price. In this regard, too, my people deserve more credit than yours. For the best of their sons are the ones who are falling; that is my cruelest thought. In the derision of war there is the benefit of derision. Death strikes everywhere and at random. In the war we are fighting, courage steps up and volunteers, and every day you are shooting down our purest spirits. For your ingenuousness is not without foresight. You have never known what to select, but you know what to destroy. And we, who call ourselves defenders of the spirit, know nevertheless that the spirit can die when the force crushing it is great enough. But we have faith in another force. In raining bullets on those silent faces, already turned away from this world, you think you are disfiguring the face of our truth. But you are forgetting the obstinacy that makes France fight against time. That hopeless hope is what sustains us in difficult moments; our comrades will be more patient than the executioners and more numerous than the bullets. As you see, the French are capable of wrath.

December 1943

third letter

Until now I have been talking to you of my country and you must have thought in the beginning that my tone had changed. In reality, this was not so. It is merely that we didn't give the same meaning to the same words; we no longer speak the same language.

Words always take on the color of the deeds or the sacrifices they evoke. And in your country the word "fatherland" assumes blind and bloody overtones that make it forever alien to me, whereas we have put into the same word the flame of an intelligence that makes courage more difficult and gives man complete fulfillment. You have finally understood that my tone has really never changed. The one I used with you before 1939 is the one I am using today.

You will probably be more convinced by the confession I am going to make to you. During all the time when we were obstinately and silently serving our country, we never lost sight of an idea and a hope, forever present in us—the idea and the hope of Europe. To be sure, we haven't mentioned Europe for five years. But this is because you talked too much of it. And there too we were not speaking the same language; our Europe is not yours.

But before telling you what ours is, I want to insist that among the reasons we have for fighting you (they are the same we have for defeating you) there is perhaps none more fundamental than our awareness of having been, not only mutilated in our country, wounded in our very flesh, but also divested of our most beautiful images, for you gave the world a hateful and ridiculous version of them. The most painful thing to bear is seeing a mockery made of what one loves. And that idea of Europe that you took from the best among us and distorted has consequently become hard for us to keep alive in all its original force. Hence there is an adjective we have given up writing since you called the army of slavery "European," but this is only to preserve jealously the pure meaning it still has for us, which I want to tell you.

You speak of Europe, but the difference is that for you Europe is a property, whereas we feel that we belong to it. You never spoke this way until you lost Africa. That is not the right kind of love. This land on which so many centuries have left their mark is merely an obligatory retreat for you, whereas it has always been our dearest hope. Your too sudden passion is made up of spite and necessity. Such a feeling honors no one, and you can see why no European worthy of the name would accept it.

You say "Europe," but you think in terms of potential soldiers, granaries, industries brought to heel, intelligence under control. Am I going too far? But at least I know that when you say "Europe," even in your best moments, when you let yourselves be carried away by your own lies, you cannot keep yourselves from thinking of a cohort of docile nations led by a lordly Germany toward a fabulous and bloody future. I should like you to be fully aware of this difference. For you Europe is an expanse encircled by seas and mountains, dotted with dams, gutted with mines, covered with harvests, where Germany is playing a game in which her own fate alone is at stake. But for us Europe is a home of the spirit where for the last twenty centuries the most amazing adventure of the human spirit has been going on. It is the privileged arena in which Western man's struggle against the world, against the gods, against himself is today reaching its climax. As you see, there is no common denominator.

Don't worry that I shall use against you the themes of an age-old propaganda; I shall not fall back on the Christian tradition. That is another problem. You have talked too much of it too, and, posing as defenders of Rome, you were not afraid to give Christ the kind of publicity he began to be accustomed to the day he received the kiss that marked him for torture. But, after all, the Christian tradition is only one of the traditions that made this Europe, and I am not qualified to defend it against you. To do so would require the instinct and inclination of a heart given over to God. You know this is not the case with me. But when I allow myself to think that my country speaks in the name of Europe and that when we defend one we are defending both, then I too have my tradition. It is the tradition both of a few great individuals and of an inexhaustible mass. My tradition has two aristocracies, that of the intelligence and that of courage; it has its intellectual leaders and its innumerable mass. Now tell me whether this Europe, whose frontiers are the genius of a few and the heart of all its inhabitants, differs from the colored spot you have annexed on temporary maps.

Remember, you said to me, one day when you were making fun of my outbursts: "Don Quixote is powerless if Faust feels like attacking him." I told you then that neither Faust nor Don Quixote was intended to attack the other and that art was not invented to bring evil into the world. You used to like exaggerated images and you continued your argument. According to you, there was a choice between Hamlet and Siegfried. At that time I didn't want to choose and, above all, it didn't seem to me that the West could exist except in the equilibrium between strength and knowledge. But you scorned knowledge and spoke only of strength. Today I know better what I mean and I know that even Faust will be of no use to you. For we have in fact accepted the idea that in certain cases choice is necessary. But our choice would be no more important than yours if we had not been aware that any choice was inhuman and that spiritual values could not be separated. Later on we shall be able to bring them together again, and this is something you have never been able to do. You see, it is still the same idea; we have seen death face to face. But we have paid dear enough for that idea to be justified in clinging to it. This urges me to say that your Europe is not the right one. There is nothing there to unite or inspire. Ours is a joint adventure that we shall continue to pursue, despite you, with the inspiration of intelligence.

I shan't go much further. Sometimes on a street corner, in the brief intervals of the long struggle that involves us all, I happen to think of all those places in Europe I know well. It is a magnificent land molded by suffering and history. I relive those pilgrimages I once made with all the men of the West: the roses in the cloisters of Florence, the gilded bulbous domes of Krakow, the Hradschin and its dead palaces, the contorted statues of the Charles Bridge over the Ultava, the delicate gardens of Salzburg. All those flowers and stones, those hills and those landscapes where men's time and the world's time have mingled old trees and monuments! My memory has fused together such superimposed images to make a single face, which is the face of my true native land. And then I feel a pang when I think that, for years now, your shadow has been cast over that vital, tortured face. Yet some of those places are ones that you and I saw together. It never occurred to me then that someday we should have to liberate them from you. And even now, at certain moments of rage and despair, I am occasionally sorry that the roses continue to grow in the cloister of San Marco and the pigeons drop in clusters from the Cathedral of Salzburg, and the red geraniums grow tirelessly in the little cemeteries of Silesia.

But at other moments, and they are the only ones that count, I delight in this. For all those landscapes, those flowers and those plowed fields, the oldest of lands, show you every spring that there are things you cannot choke in blood. That is the image on which I can close. It would not be enough for me to think that all the great shades of the West and that thirty nations were on our side; I could not do without the soil. And so I know that everything in Europe, both landscape and spirit, calmly negates you without feeling any rash hatred, but with the calm strength of victory. The weapons the European spirit can use against you are the same as reside in this soil constantly reawakening in blossoms and harvests. The battle we are waging is sure of victory because it is as obstinate as spring.

And, finally, I know that all will not be over when you are crushed. Europe will still have to be established. It always has to be established. But at least it will still be Europe—in other words, what I have just written you. Nothing will be lost. Just imagine what we are now, sure of our reasons, in love with our country, carried along by all Europe, and neatly balanced between sacrifice and our longing for happiness, between the sword and the spirit. I tell you once more because I must tell you, I tell you because it is the truth and because it will show you the progress my country and I have made since the time of our friendship: henceforth we have a superiority that will destroy you.

April 1944

fourth letter

> *Man is mortal. That may be; but let us die resisting; and if our lot is complete annihilation, let us not behave in such a way that it seems justice!*
>
> OBERMANN, LETTER 90

Now the moment of your defeat is approaching. I am writing you from a city known throughout the world which is now preparing against you a celebration of freedom. Our city knows this is not easy and that first it will have to live through an even darker night than the one that began, four years ago, with your coming. I am writing you from a city deprived of everything, devoid of light and devoid of heat, starved, and still not crushed. Soon something you can't even imagine will inflame the city. If we were lucky, you and I should then stand face to face. Then we could fight each other knowing what is at stake. I have a fair idea of your motivations and you can imagine mine.

These July nights are both light and heavy. Light along the Seine and in the trees, but heavy in the hearts of those who are awaiting the only dawn they now long for. I am waiting and I think of you; I still have one more thing to tell you—and it will be the last. I want to tell you how it is possible that, though so similar, we should be enemies today, how I might have stood beside you and why all is over between us now.

For a long time we both thought that this world had no ultimate meaning and that consequently we were cheated. I still think so in a way. But I came to different conclusions from the ones you used to talk about, which, for so many years now, you have been trying to introduce into history. I tell myself now that if I had really followed your reasoning, I ought to approve what you are doing. And this is so serious that I must stop and consider it, during this summer night so full of promises for us and of threats for you.

You never believed in the meaning of this world, and you therefore deduced the idea that everything was equivalent and that good and evil could be defined according to one's wishes. You supposed that in the absence of any human or divine code the only values were those of the animal world—in other words, violence and cunning. Hence you concluded that man was negligible and that his soul could be killed, that in the maddest of histories the only pursuit for the individual was the adventure of power and his only morality, the realism of conquests. And, to tell the truth, I, believing I thought as you did, saw no valid argument to answer you except a fierce love of justice which, after all, seemed to me as unreasonable as the most sudden passion.

Where lay the difference? Simply that you readily accepted despair and I never yielded to it. Simply that you saw the injustice of our condition to the point of being willing to add to it, whereas it seemed to me that man must exalt justice in order to fight against eternal injustice, create happiness in order to protest against the universe of unhappiness. Because you turned your despair into intoxication, because you freed yourself from it by making a principle of it, you were willing to destroy man's works and to fight him in order to add to his basic misery. Meanwhile, refusing to accept that despair and that tortured world, I merely wanted men to rediscover their solidarity in order to wage war against their revolting fate.

As you see, from the same principle we derived quite different codes, because along the way you gave up the lucid view and considered it more convenient (you would have said a matter of indifference) for another to do your thinking for you and for millions of Germans. Because you were tired of fighting heaven, you relaxed in that exhausting adventure in which you had to mutilate souls and destroy the world. In short, you chose injustice and sided with the gods. Your logic was merely apparent.

I, on the contrary, chose justice in order to remain faithful to the world. I continue to believe that this world has no ultimate meaning. But I know that something in it has a meaning and that is man, because he is the only creature to insist on having one. This world has at least the truth of man, and our task is to provide its justifications against fate itself. And it has no justification but man; hence he must be saved if we want to save the idea we have of life. With your scornful smile you will ask me: what do you mean by saving man? And with all my being I shout to you that I mean not mutilating him and yet giving a chance to the justice that man alone can conceive.

This is why we are fighting. This is why we first had to follow you on a path we didn't want and why at the end of that path we met defeat. For your despair constituted your strength. The moment despair is alone, pure, sure of itself, pitiless in its consequences, it has a merciless power. That is what crushed us while we were hesitating with our eyes still fixed on happy images. We thought that happiness was the greatest of conquests, a victory over the fate imposed upon us. Even in defeat this longing did not leave us.

But you did what was necessary, and we went down in history. And for five years it was no longer possible to enjoy the call of birds in the cool of the evening. We were forced to despair. We were cut off from the world because to each moment of the world clung a whole mass of mortal images. For five years the earth has not seen a single morning without death agonies, a single evening without prisons, a single noon without slaughters. Yes, we had to follow you. But our difficult achievement consisted in following you into war without forgetting happiness. And despite the clamors and the violence, we tried to preserve in our hearts the memory of a happy sea, of a remembered hill, the smile of a beloved face. For that matter, this was our best weapon, the one we shall never put away. For as soon as we lost it we should be as dead as you are. But we know now that the weapons of happiness cannot be forged without considerable time and too much blood.

We had to enter into your philosophy and be willing to resemble you somewhat. You chose a vague heroism, because it is the only value left in a world that has lost its meaning. And, having chosen it for yourselves, you chose it for everybody else and for us. We were forced to imitate you in order not to die. But we became aware then that our superiority over you consisted in our having a direction. Now that all that is about to end, we can tell you what we have learned—that heroism isn't much and that happiness is more difficult.

At present everything must be obvious to you; you know that we are enemies. You are the man of injustice, and there is nothing in the world that my heart loathes so much. But now I know the reasons for what was once merely a passion. I am fighting you because your logic is as criminal as your heart. And in the horror you have lavished upon us for four years, your reason plays as large a part as your instinct. This is why my condemnation will be sweeping; you are already dead as far as I am concerned. But at the very moment when I am judging your horrible behavior, I shall remember that you and we started out from the same solitude, that you and we, with all Europe, are caught in the same tragedy of the intelligence. And, despite yourselves, I shall still apply to you the name of man. In order to keep faith with ourselves, we are obliged to respect in you what you do not respect in others. For a long time that was your great advantage since you kill more easily than we do. And to the very end of time that will be the advantage of those who resemble you. But to the very end of time, we, who do not resemble you, shall have to bear witness so that mankind, despite its worst errors, may have its justification and its proof of innocence.

This is why, at the end of this combat, from the heart of this city that has come to resemble hell, despite all the tortures inflicted on our people, despite our disfigured dead and our villages peopled with orphans, I can tell you that at the very moment when we are going to destroy you without pity, we still feel no hatred for you. And even if tomorrow, like so many others, we had to die, we should still be without hatred. We cannot guarantee that we shall not be afraid; we shall simply try to be reasonable. But we can guarantee that we shall not hate anything. And we have come to terms with the only thing in the world I could loathe today, I assure you, and we want to destroy you in your power without mutilating you in your soul.

As for the advantage you had over us, you see that you continue to have it. But it likewise constitutes our superiority. And it is what makes this night easy for me. Our strength lies in thinking as you do about the essence of the world, in rejecting no aspect of the drama that is ours. But at the same time we have saved the idea of man at the end of this disaster of the intelligence, and that idea gives us the undying courage to believe in a rebirth. To be sure, the accusation we make against the world is not mitigated by this. We paid so dear for this new knowledge that our condition continues to seem desperate to us. Hundreds of thousands of men assassinated at dawn, the terrible walls of prisons, the soil of Europe reeking with millions of corpses of its sons—it took all that to pay for the acquisition of two or three slight distinctions which may have no other value than to help some among us to die more nobly. Yes, that is heart-breaking. But we have to prove that we do not deserve so much injustice. This is the task we have set ourselves; it will begin tomorrow. In this night of Europe filled with the breath of summer, millions of men, armed or unarmed, are getting ready for the fight. The dawn about to break will mark your final defeat. I know that heaven, which was indifferent to your horrible victories, will be equally indifferent to your just defeat. Even now I expect nothing from heaven. But we shall at least have helped save man from the solitude to which you wanted to relegate him. Because you scorned such faith in mankind, you are the men who, by thousands, are going to die solitary. Now, I can say farewell to you.

July 1944

ROBERT LOWELL

memories of west street and lepke

Only teaching on Tuesdays, book-worming
in pajamas fresh from the washer each morning,
I hog a whole house on Boston's
"hardly passionate Marlborough Street,"
where even the man
scavenging filth in the back alley trash cans,
has two children, a beach wagon, a helpmate,
and is a "young Republican."
I have a nine months' daughter,
young enough to be my granddaughter.
Like the sun she rises in her flame-flamingo infants' wear.

These are the tranquillized *Fifties,*
and I am forty. Ought I to regret my seedtime?
I was a fire-breathing Catholic C. O.,
and made my manic statement,
telling off the state and president, and then
sat waiting sentence in the bull pen
beside a Negro boy with curlicues
of marijuana in his hair.

Given a year,
I walked on the roof of the West Street Jail, a short
enclosure like my school soccer court,
and saw the Hudson River once a day
through sooty clothesline entanglements
and bleaching khaki tenements.
Strolling, I yammered metaphysics with Abramowitz,
a jaundice-yellow ("it's really tan")
and fly-weight pacifist,
so vegetarian,
he wore rope shoes and preferred fallen fruit.
He tried to convert Bioff and Brown,
the Hollywood pimps, to his diet.
Hairy, muscular, suburban,

wearing chocolate double-breasted suits,
they blew their tops and beat him black and blue.

I was so out of things, I'd never heard
of the Jehovah's Witnesses.
"Are you a C. O.?" I asked a fellow jailbird.
"No," he answered, "I'm a J.W."
He taught me the "hospital tuck,"
and pointed out the T shirted back
of *Murder Incorporated's* Czar Lepke,
there piling towels on a rack,
or dawdling off to his little segregated cell full
of things forbidden the common man:
a portable radio, a dresser, two toy American
flags tied together with a ribbon of Easter palm.
Flabby, bald, lobotomized,
he drifted in a sheepish calm,
where no agonizing reappraisal
jarred his concentration on the electric chair—
hanging like an oasis in his air
of lost connections. . . .

DEMETRIOS CAPETANAKIS

abel

My brother Cain, the wounded, liked to sit
Brushing my shoulder, by the staring water
Of life, or death, in cinemas half-lit
By scenes of peace that always turned to slaughter.

He liked to talk to me. His eager voice
Whispered the puzzle of his bleeding thirst,
Or prayed me not to make my final choice,
Unless we had a talk about it first.

And then he chose the final pain for me.
I do not blame his nature: he's my brother;
Nor what you call the times: our love was free,
Would be the same at any time; but rather

The ageless ambiguity of things
Which makes our life mean death, our love be hate.
My blood that streams across the bedroom sings:
"I am my brother opening the gate."

PIERRE GASCAR

the season of the dead

Dead though they be, the dead do not immediately become ageless. Theirs is not the only memory involved; they enter into a seasonal cycle, with an unfamiliar rhythm—ternary perhaps, slow in any case, with widely spaced oscillations and pauses; they hang for a while nailed to a great wheel, sinking and rising by turns; they have become, far beyond the horizons of memory, rays of a skeleton sun.

We had reached the first stage. We were opening up the graveyard—in the sense in which one speaks of opening up a trench; in this place, there had only been life before there was death. And this freshness was to persist for a long time, before the teeming dust of the charnel should dim it, before, eventually, when all the earth was trodden down, oblivion should spread with couch-grass and darnel, and the writing on the tombstones should have lost its meaning; and the arable land should regain what we had taken from it.

For a graveyard to become a real graveyard, many dead must be buried there, many years must pass, many feet must tread on it; the dead, in short, must make the ground their own. We were certainly far from that point. Our dead would be war dead, for whom we had to break open a grassy mound. It was all, in short, brimful of newness.

War dead. The formula had lost its heroic sense without becoming obsolete. The war had lately moved away from this spot. These men would die a belated and, as it were, accidental death, in silence and captivity, yielding up their arms for a second time. But could one still use the word "arms"?

From the slope of the mound where the new graveyard lay I could see them walking round and round within the barbed wire enclosure of the camp, looking less like soldiers than like people of every sort and condition brought together by their common look of sleeplessness, their unshaven cheeks and the cynical complicity of gangsters the morning after a raid. Following several abortive escapes through Germany, some thousand French soldiers had just been transferred to the disciplinary camp of Brodno in Volynia. It was a second captivity for them, a new imprisonment that was more bewilderingly outlandish and also more romantic. That word gives us a clue: it was an imprisonment for death.

I had been granted the title of gravedigger in advance of the functions. When you dig a ditch, it's because you have already found water. Just now there was nothing of that sort. The ditch we were digging was too long to have a tree planted in it, too deep to be one of those individual holes in which, at that time, throughout Europe, men in helmets were burrowing, forming the base of a monolithic monument which was hard to imagine, particularly here. It could only be a grave. Now we strengthened it with props, we covered it with planks. Nobody was dead. The grave was becoming a sort of snare, a trap in which Fate would finally be caught, into which a dead man would eventually creep. He would thus have been forestalled and would glide into the darkness through wide-open doors, while we would shrink back as he passed, hiding our earth-stained hands behind our backs.

The German N.C.O. had rounded us up in the camp. He needed six men. When he had got that number he took us to the gate and handed us over to an armed sentry. We skirted the wall outside the camp until we came to a small rough road which, a little farther on, led over the side of a hill. At this point a track took us to the verge of the forest. The N.C.O., riding a bicycle, had caught up with us. He went to cut a few switches from an elm tree.

"Who knows German?" he asked without turning round.

"I do."

He called me to him. He was trimming the leaves from the

switches with vigorous strokes of his penknife. I disliked the sight: swift-working fingers, pursed lips, and at the end of the supple, swaying branch a ridiculous tuft of leaves dancing as though before an imminent storm. There is no wretchedness like that of flogged men.

"There's to be a graveyard here . . ." he said to me, suddenly handing me the trimmed branches. "These are yours. Follow me and tell your mates to pull off some more branches."

I passed on the order and followed the N.C.O. to a place where the skirt of the wood dipped down into a narrow valley at the end of which lay a round pond like a hand mirror. The German dug the heel of his boot into the grass: "Here." As carefully as a gardner I planted a branch at the spot he showed me. Then he straightened his back and made a half-turn; staring straight in front of him, he walked forward, stopped and dug his heel into the grass, started off again and stopped again. My companions came up with their arms loaded with leafy branches. The task of planting began, and soon the branches stood lined up there in the still morning, marking the footsteps of the man as he doggedly staked his theoretical claim.

When the enclosure was thus demarcated, the German called me. We had to mark the site of the first grave. When this was set out, my companions, in a fit of zeal, immediately began to lift up clods of turf. Then the earth suddenly appeared as it really was; it lay there against the grass like a garment ready to be put on.

"That's enough, you can dig it tomorrow," the German told us. "We must always have one ready. Death comes quickly these days. War's a shocking thing."

He collected us together and the sentry took us back to the camp. As we were going through the gate one of us got from him, after some pleading, a leaf from his notebook with his signature. We rushed to the kitchens where extra rations of soup were sometimes distributed to the men who were working in gangs about the camp.

"Graveyard!" cried the prisoner who held the voucher, waving it. The man with the soup-ladle looked at us uncertainly for a moment, as though trying to remember to what burial ground this irregular privilege could suddenly have been allotted.

"Camp graveyard!" someone else repeated. The man took

the can that was held out to him and filled it. Death had spoken; moreover, death's voucher was in order.

From that day, and still more from the following day when the first grave had been dug and shored up, I began to look out for death in the faces of my comrades, in the weight of the hour, the color of the sky, the lines of the landscape. Here, the great spaces of Russia were already suggested; I had never known a sky under which one had such a sense of surrender.

Sometimes the earth, dried by the early spring sunshine, was blown so high by the wind that the horizon was darkened by a brown cloud, a storm cloud which would break up into impalpable dust, and under which the sunflowers glowed so luminously and appeared suddenly at such distances that you felt you were witnessing the brief, noisy revenge of a whole nation of pensive plants, condemned for the rest of their days to the dull quietness of sunshine.

Close to us, the town was shut in with a white wall above which rose a bulbous church spire, some roofs, and the white plume of smoke from a train, rising for a long time in the same spot, with a far-off whistle like a slaughtered factory.

We had reached Brodno one April morning. The melting snows and the rain had washed away so much earth from the unpaved streets that planks and duckboards had been thrown down everywhere to let people cross, haphazard and usually crooked, looking like wreckage left after a flood subsides. The sentries could no longer keep the column in order and we were all running from one plank to another, mingled with women wearing scarves on their heads and boots on their feet, with German soldiers, with men in threadbare caftans; and here and there jostling one of those strange villagers who stood motionless with rigid faces, their feet in the mud, idle as mourners, with white armlets on their arms as though in some plague-stricken city.

It might have been market day, and the animation in the main street of the village might have been merely the good-humored bustle of the population between a couple of showers, such as one sees also on certain snowy mornings, or on the eve of a holiday. . . . In any case, that first day, the star of David, drawn in blue ink on the armlets of those painfully deferential villagers who looked oddly Sundayfied in their dark threadbare town clothes amongst that crowd of peasants, seemed to me a symbol of penitence, somewhat mitigated, however, by its traditional character.

It was not until later on that their destiny was clearly revealed to me. Then, when I saw them in a group away from the crowd, they ceased to be mere landmarks; exposed to solitude as to a fire, that which had been diluted among so many and had passed almost unnoticed acquired sudden solidity. All at once, they became the mourners at a Passion: a procession of tortured victims, a mute delegation about to appeal to God.

A certain number of Jews had been detailed by the Germans to get the camp ready before our arrival. When we entered the gates they were still there, carefully putting the last touches to the fences, finishing the installation of our sordid equipment, and thus implacably imprisoning themselves, by virtue of some premonitory knowledge, within a universe with which they were soon to become wholly familiar.

The camp consisted of cavalry barracks built by the Red Army shortly after the occupation of Eastern Poland at the end of 1939. A huge bare space separated the three large brick-built main buildings from the whitewashed stables which housed the overflow of our column, according to that mode of military occupation that disdains all hierarchy of places—thus identifying itself with the bursting of dams, the blind and inexorable progress of disasters.

Inside every building, whether stable or barracks, wooden platforms, superimposed on one another, had been set up the whole length of the huge rooms, leaving only a narrow passage along the walls and another across the middle of the structure: tiered bunks like shelves in a department store, where the men were to sleep side by side. Our captivity thus disclosed that homicidal trend which (for practical rather than moral reasons) it usually refused to admit: for the Germans, the unit of spatial measurement was "a man's length."

The great typhus season was barely over at Brodno. It had decimated the thousands of Russian prisoners who had occupied the place before us and who had left their marks on the whitewashed walls—the print of abnormally filthy hands, bloodstains and splashed excrement—messages from those immured men jostling one another in the silent winter night, while death and frost exchanged rings: faintly-heard calls from far away. Because of the lingering typhus and the risk of propagating lice, we were given no straw.

We were given little of anything that first day. The Germans, except for a few sentries established in their watchtowers, had retired no one knew whither, as though it were understood that at the end of our trying journey we must be granted a day's truce, an unwonted Sunday that found us standing helpless, leaning against the typhus-ridden bunks with our meager bundles at our feet. A louse crawled up one's spine like a drop of sweat running the wrong way, and within one there was that great echoing vault, hunger.

In the afternoon, however, a few pots full of soup were thrust through the kitchen door. A thousand men lined up on the path of planks that led to it. Hardly any of us had a mess-tin, but a great rubbish dump full of empty food cans supplied our needs. When the cans were all used up we unscrewed the clouded glass globes covering the electric lamps in the building, and made empty flower-pots water tight by plugging the holes with bits of wood. When these uncouth vessels appeared in the queue they were greeted with shouts of envy, provoked rather by their capacity than by their grotesque character. A sort of carnival procession in search of soup took place, and the owner of an empty sardine-can might be seen gauging a piece of hollow brick half-buried in the mud, wondering if those four holes like organ-pipes might perhaps be stopped up at the base, and turning over the problem with his foot while the column moved on a few yards. Fine rain was falling.

"It's millet!" shouted a man coming towards us from the kitchens, clasping his brimming can in both hands.

A cry of joy, in an unknown voice: a fragmentary phrase, as though cut out of its context, which, uttered in the dying afternoon in the heart of the Volynian plain, seemed to have escaped from a speech begun very far away, many years earlier, and to have returned now—just as, in the hour of death, words half-heard long ago, neglected then and despised, recur to one's memory, suddenly whispering out their plaintive revenge, suddenly gleaming with a prodigious sheen because they hold the last drops of life.

It was not until much later that somebody died.

From the time of that first burial I felt certain that death would never move far from our threshold. A dead body is never buried as deep as one thinks; when a grave is dug, each blow of the pickax consolidates the boundaries of the underground world. Though you lie sepulchered in the earth, like a vessel sunk in quicksands, and the waves of darkness beat against you from below, your bones remain like an anchor cast.

That day a group of German soldiers accompanied the convoy. They were armed and helmeted. They fell into step with the handful of Frenchmen—the chaplain, the medical orderly, the *homme de confiance**—who were walking behind the *tarantass* on which the coffin was laid. They moved very fast and they seemed to be upon us in a few minutes, as we stood watching from the graveyard on the side of the hill (had they remembered to bring the cross and the ropes?); they were charging on us, a crowd of them, two by two, clad from head to foot; they were coming for us, making us realize in a flash what a terrible responsibility we had accepted when we dug that hole, what echoes our solitary toil had roused over there.

We had to face them, to lay the ropes down side by side on the spot where the coffin would be placed, to put down the two logs at the bottom of the grave on which it would lie so that we might afterwards haul up the cords, the ends of which would flap against the coffin for a minute like the pattering footsteps of a last animal escaping. The chaplain recited prayers. The medical orderly sounded Taps on a bugle, picked up somewhere or other. We grasped our ropes and, leaning over the grave, began to slacken them. At an order from their N.C.O. the German soldiers, who were presenting arms, raised the barrels of their guns towards the sky and fired a salvo.

There is always somebody there behind the target of silence. A shout or a word uttered too loud or too soon, and you hear a distant bush crying out with a human voice—you run towards a sort of dark animal only to see it clasp a white, human hand to its bleeding side; it's the tragedy of those hunting accidents where the victims, emerging from silence, are the friend or stranger—equally innocent—who happened to be passing by; there's always somebody passing just there, and we are never sufficiently aware of it.

The Germans' salvo re-echoed for a long time. We had lifted

* One of the French prisoners chosen by the rest to represent their interests in dealing with the Germans.

our heads again. Lower down, on the little road, some peasants and their women, coming back from the town, who had not witnessed the beginning of the ceremony (at that distance, in any case, they could not have observed its details) began to walk suddenly faster, casting a quick look back at us. Some women drew closer together and took each other's arms, a man stumbled in his haste, and all of them swiftly bowed their heads and refused to look at what was happening in our direction.

They seemed possessed not so much by anxiety as by a kind of shuddering anticipation, making them shun a spectacle which they dreaded as though it were contagious and hurry slightly despite their assumed indifference. They betrayed that tendency to deliberate withdrawal which, at that time, was making the whole region more deserted than any exodus could have done. Had we run towards them, clasped their hands, gazed into their faces crying "It's all right, we're alive!" they would no doubt still have turned away from us, terrified by fresh suspicions, feeling themselves irremediably compromised. . . . Now they had vanished. The Germans slung their rifles. We stood upright round the grave, like a row of shot puppets.

This incident and others less remarkable gave us a feeling of solidarity. We tried to secure official recognition for our team from the camp authorities by presenting a list of our names to every new sentry—to those that kept guard over the gates, those that supervised the kitchens, those that inspected our block. Every week we made out several lists, in case the camp administration should prove forgetful. We gave notice of our existence to remoter authorities, to prisoners' representatives, shock brigade headquarters, divisional commanders, with the stubborn persistence of minorities ceaselessly tormented by the nightmare of illegality.

We guessed that our proceedings met with secret opposition from the Germans, who were unwilling to give public recognition to this peculiar team, the granting of legal status to which would, for them, have been equivalent to admitting criminal premeditation—and from the prisoners too, since they did not need so realistic a reminder of the gruesome truth.

Between two deaths, it was only owing to the force of habit and the routinist mentality of the guardroom officer that we found a couple of sentries waiting each morning to take us to the graveyard. This, lying on the side of the hill amongst long grass, was in such sharp contrast to the almost African aridity of the camp as to enhance the feeling of separateness and even of exclusion which the failure of our advances to the administration had fostered in us. We belonged to another world, we were a team of ghosts returning every morning to a green peaceful place, we were workers in death's garden, characters in a long preparatory dream through which, from time to time, a man would suddenly break, leaping into his last sleep.

In the graveyard we led that orderly existence depicted in old paintings and, even more, in old tapestries and mosaics. A man sitting beside a clump of anemones, another cutting grass with a scythe; water, and somebody lying flat on his belly drinking, and somebody else with his eyes turned skyward, drawing water in a yellow jug. . . . The water was for me and Cordonat. We had chosen the job of watering the flowers and turf transplanted on to the first grave and amongst the clumps of shrubs that we had arranged within our enclosure.

Its boundaries were imaginary but real enough. We had no need to step outside them to fill our vessels at the pond which, from the graveside, could be seen between the branches, a little lower down; there, the radiance of the sky reflected in the water enfolded us so vividly, lit up both our faces so clearly, that any thought of flight could have been read on them from a distance, before we had made the slightest movement, before—risking everything to win everything—we had set the light quivering, like bells.

The only flight left to us was the flight of our eyes towards the wooded valley at the end of which the pond lay. The leaves and grass and tree trunks glowed in the shadow, through which sunbeams filtered and in which, far off, a single leaf, lit by the sun's direct fire, gleamed transparently, an evanescent landmark whose mysterious significance faded quickly as a cloud appeared.

Flowers grew at the very brink of the pond: violets, buttercups, dwarf forget-me-nots, reviving memories of old herbals; only the ladybug's carapace and the red umbrella of the toadstool were lacking to link up the springtime of the world with one's own childhood. When we had filled our bottles, Cordonat and I would linger there gazing at our surroundings, moved by our memories, and in an impulse of greedy sentimentality guessing at the beechnut under the beech leaf, the young acorn under the oak leaf, the mushroom under the toadstool and the snail under the moss.

Sometimes the sun hid. But we could not stir, for we had fallen down out of our dream to such a depth that our task—watering a few clumps of wood-sorrel in a remote corner of Volynia—appeared absurd to the point of unreality, like some purgatorial penance where the victims, expiating their own guilt or original sin, are forced to draw unending pails of water from a bottomless well, in a green landscape, tending death like a dwarf tree—just as we were doing here.

Actually, I did not know whether Cordonat's dream followed the same lines as my own. I had lately grown very fond of Cordonat, but he was so deeply consumed by nostalgia that maybe I only loved the shadow of the man. He was ten years older than I, married, with two children; home consists of what you miss most. This vineyard worker from Languedoc showed his Catalan ancestry in his lean, tanned face, with the look of an old torero relegated to the rear rank of a *cuadrilla,* his delicate aquiline nose and wrinkled forehead with white hair over the temples which predestined him for the loneliness of capitivity.

It so happened that, with the exception of myself, all the men of our graveyard team, who belonged to the most recent call-up, were natives of the South of France, and all showed a tendency to nostalgic melancholy which was highly appropriate not only to their new duties but to our peculiar isolation on the fringe of camp life. This distinction enhanced a characteristic which was common to all the prisoners of Brodno, who, by their repeated attempts to escape from Germany, had in effect escaped from their own kind. At a time when under cover of captivity countless acts of treachery were taking place, they had set up on the Ukranian border, in a corner of Europe where the rules of war were easily forgotten, a defiant Resistance movement, a group of "desert rats" whose most seditious song was the Marseillaise.

Homesickness creates its own mirages, which can supersede many a landscape. But that amidst which we were living now was becoming so cruelly vivid that it pierced through all illusory images; it underlay my companions' dreams like a sharp-pointed harrow. This became clear only by slow degrees.

When Cordonat and I were sitting by the pond, we would look up and see peasants and their wives on their way back from the town, passing along the path through the trees and bushes at the end of our valley. We would stand up to see them better and immediately they would hurry on and vanish from sight, imperceptibly accentuating the furtiveness of their way of walking, stooping a little and averting their eyes as though they were eager to avoid the sight of something unlucky or, more precisely, something compromising.

As we stood at the foot of this hillock, somewhat apart from the other prisoners, we must have seemed to be in one of those irregular situations which were not uncommon here, like cases of some infectious disease. Were we escaped prisoners, obdurate rebels? Were we in quarantine, or about to be shot? In any case we were obviously trying to make them our accomplices, determined to betray them into a word or a look and thus involve them in that contamination that always ended with a shower of bullets and blood splashed against a wall. And the forest in which, only a minute before, spring flowers had awakened childhood memories, now emerged as though from some Hercynian flexure, darker and denser, more mysterious and more ominous, because of the fear and hunger of men. Fear can blast reality.

But it was when we left the skirt of the forest and reached the plain where the town lay that this devastating power of fear seemed actually to color the whole landscape. The white road, the far-off white house fronts, the lack of shadows, all this was deprived of radiance by the subdued quality of the light; but it exuded a kind of stupor. At first, you noticed nothing.

But when we drew near we would suddenly catch sight of a man or woman standing motionless between two houses or two hedges, and turning towards us in an attitude of submission, like people who have been warned to prepare for any danger. The man or woman would stare at us as we passed with eyes that revealed neither curiosity nor envy nor dread: a gaze that was not dreamy, but enigmatically watchful. A few men, also dressed in threadbare town clothes, were filling up the holes in the pavement. They did not raise their heads as we went by; they kept on with their work, but performed only secondary, inessential tasks, like factory hands waiting for the bell to release them from work and staying at their posts only because they have to.

In every case we were aware that, as we approached (or more precisely as our sentries approached), some final inner process of preparation was taking place (but maybe it had long since been completed?) and that of the Germans had only to say "Come on!," load his gun or raise the butt to strike, for everything to take its inevitable, unaltering course. The tension of waiting was extreme.

They had long ago passed the stage when your pulse beats faster, spots dance before your eyes and sweat breaks out on your back; they had not left fear behind, but they had been married to it for so long that it had lost its original power. Fear shared their lives, and when we walked past with our sentries beside us it was Fear, that tireless companion, that began, in a burst of lunatic lucidity, to count the pebbles dropping into the hole in the pavement, the trees along the road, or the days dividing that instant from some past event or other—the fête at Tarnopol, or Easter 1933, or the day little Chaim passed his exam: some other spring day, some dateless day, some distant day that seemed to collect and hold all the happiness in life.

Sometimes, in the depth of their night, fear would flare up and wake them, like the suddenly remembered passion that throws husband and wife into each other's arms; then they would embrace their fear, foreseeing the coming of their death like the birth of a child, and their thoughts would set out in the next room the oblong covered cradle in which it would be laid. Morning would bring back their long lonely wait, tête-à-tête with fear. They tied around their arms the strip of white material with the star of David drawn on it. Often the armlet slipped down below the elbow, and hung round the forearm slack and rumpled and soiled like an old dressing that has grown loose and needs renewing. The wound is unhealed, but dry. But why should I speak of wounds? Hunger, cold, humiliation and fear leave corpses without stigmata. One morning we saw a man lying dead by the roadside on the way to the graveyard. There was no face; it was hidden in the grass. There was no distinguishing mark, save the armlet with the star of David. There was no blood. There is practically no blood in the whole of this tale of death.

One Monday morning two new sentries came up to join us at the camp gates. They belonged to a nondescript battalion in shabby uniforms which had been sent from somewhere in Poland by way of relief, and had arrived at Brodno a few days earlier: one of those nomadic divisions to which only inglorious duties are assigned, and whose soldiers get killed only in defeats.

Our two new sentries were a perfect example of the contrasts, exaggerated to the point of grotesqueness, which are always to be found among any group of belatedly conscripted men, since neither regulation dress nor *esprit de corps* nor conviction can replace the uniformity of youth. One of the two soldiers was long and thin, with a high-colored face; the other, short and squat, was pale.

Each morning, when we went into the enclosure, we would quickly dismiss and, one after the other, go and stand before the graves giving a military salute; it was the only solemn moment of the day. That morning, as I was walking after my comrades to pay my homage to the dead, I heard a click behind me: the taller of the two soldiers was loading his gun. We had been running rather quickly towards our dead, because it was Monday and we felt lively. He had been afraid we were trying to escape or mutiny. But we were merely hurrying towards the graves like workmen to the factory cloakroom, discarding discipline and, at the same time, hanging up our jackets on the crosses.

There were only three graves at this time. We made up for this by working on the flowerbeds, those other plots of consecrated, cultivated ground. Cordonat and I were already grasping our bottles, eager to resume our reveries beside the pond, at the bottom of which could be seen a rifle and a hand grenade thrown there by a fugitive Russian soldier. This filthy panoply, sunk deep in the mud, mingled with our reflected images when we bent over the water, as though we had not been haunted enough for the past two years by the memory of our discarded arms.

I went up to the short German soldier (the other had alarmed me by that performance with his rifle a little while before) and explained to him that it was our custom to go and draw water from the pond. He nodded, smiling but silent; then, before I went off, he said to me in French: "*Je suis curé.*"

The word, uttered with an accent that was in itself slightly ridiculous, had a kind of popular simplicity that, far from conferring any grandeur on it, seemed to relegate it to the vocabulary of anti-clericalism, made it sound like the admission of a comic anomaly. Such a statement, made by this embarrassed little man wearing a dreaded uniform in the depth of that nameless country, suggested the depressing exhibitionism of hermaphrodites, the sudden surprise of their disclosure. I could find nothing to reply.

"Protestant," he went on in his own language. "In France, you're mostly Catholics."

So he was a pastor. The rights of reason were restored—so

were those of the field-gray uniform, since I found it easier to associate the Protestant religion with the military profession. I acquiesced: we were, apparently, Catholics. Generously, the Germans granted us this valid historical qualification; we might graze on this reprieve. The little pastor, however, did not try to stop us from going to draw water for our flowers; he encouraged us to do so and walked along with us down the path leading to the pond.

Without giving me time to answer, he chattered in his own language, of which Cordonat understood barely a word. I had never before heard German spoken so volubly; it poured forth like a long-repressed confession, like a flood breaking the old barriers of prejudice and rationalism, and the clear waters rushed freely over me, carrying the harsh syllables like loose pebbles. He was a pastor at Marburg. His family came from the Rhineland and one of his ancestors was French. In the Rhineland they grew vines; the country was beautiful there. Marburg lay farther east; and there they still remembered Schiller and Goethe and Lessing (nowadays people seldom talk about Lessing). The pastor's wife was an invalid. On summer evenings he would go into the town cafés with his elder daughter. They were often taken for man and wife.

He went on talking. It was a sunny June morning. The Ukrainian wheat was springing up. By the side of the sandy roads, you could sometimes see sunflower blossoms thrown away by travelers after eating the seeds. And we carried on our Franco-Rhenish colloquy, squatting at the foot of the hillock, beside the pond, in the shade of the trees, while the peasant women, suspecting some fresh conflict, some subtle and wordy form of bullying, hurriedly passed by higher up, with a rustle of leaves under their bare feet.

In order to keep our hands occupied and to justify our long halt by the pond in the eyes of the other sentry, Cordonat and I had begun to scour our mess-tins. We always carried them about with us. I had fixed a small wire handle to mine so as to hook it to my belt. This habit was partly due to the constant hope of some windfall, some unexpected distribution of food, but also no doubt it expressed a sort of fetishistic attachment to the object that symbolized our age's exclusive concern with the search for food. These mess-tins, which had only been handed out to us on our second day in camp, were like little zinc bowls; we went about with barbers' basins hanging from our waists. As part of this instinctive cult, we felt bound to polish them scrupulously. Cordonat and I were particular about this, to the point of mania. It was largely because of the fine sand on the edge of the pond and also because we were waiting—waiting for better days to come.

"*Ydiom! Ydiom!*" ("Come on!") we heard a peasant woman on the hill above us calling to one of her companions, who must have been lingering in the exposed zone.

The little pastor kept on talking.

"What d'you think of all this?" I asked him.

"It's terrible," he said. "Yes, what's happening here is terrible."

That simple word assumed the value of a confession, of a dangerous secret shared. It was enough in those days (a look, a gesture, a change of expression would have been enough) to lift the hostile mask and reveal the pact beneath. However, I dared not venture further and I began pleading our cause, describing our destitution, making no major charge but only such obvious complaints as could give no serious offense to the Germans. The petty sufferings we endured acted as a convenient salve for one's conscience; I realized this as I spoke and I resented it. Even this graveyard, so sparsely populated and so lavishly decorated, had begun to look like "a nice place for a picnic," with its green turf overlying the great banqueting-halls of death.

"Terrible, terrible," the little pastor kept saying. It was the word he had used earlier. But it had lost its original beauty.

Back in camp, after the midday meal of soup, I waited impatiently for the two sentries to come and take us to the graveyard. I looked forward to seeing Ernst, the pastor (he had told me his name), with a feeling of mingled sympathy and curiosity that was practically friendship; it only needed to be called so.

I was not surprised when, on reaching the graveyard, Ernst took me into the forest, explaining to his mate that we were going to look for violet plants. It was high time, the last violets were fading. The other German appeared quite satisfied with this explanation. Since the morning, he had been so good-humored that I felt inclined to think that that sudden business with the rifle had been an automatic gesture; a gun never lets your hands stay idle. He had a long shrewd face.

"I'm a Socialist," he told my friends while I walked away with Ernst.

Cordonat watched me go; was he envying me or disowning

me? He sat there beside the pond like some lonely mythological figure.

But now the forest was opening up in front of me: that forest which hitherto I had known only in imagination, which had existed for me by virtue not of its copious foliage or its stalwart tree-trunks but of its contrasting gloom, the powerful way it shouldered the horizon and above all its secret contribution to the darkness that weighed me down. We walked on amidst serried plants; he carried his rifle in its sling, looking less like an armed soldier than like a tired huntsman, glad to have picked up a companion along the homeward road. But already the forest and its dangerous shadows had begun to suggest that the journey home would be an endless one, that our companionship was forever; once more, in the midst of a primeval forest, we were shackled together like those countless lonely damned couples—the prisoner and his guard, the body and its conscience, the hound and its prey, the wound and the knife, oneself and one's shadow.

"Well, when you're not too hungry in camp, what d'you like doing? You must have some sort of leisure. Oh, I know you don't like that word. But I don't know any other way to express the situation where I'd hope to find your real self—for hunger isn't really you, Peter. Well, what else is there?"

He pushed back from his hip the butt of his rifle, which kept swinging between us.

"I walk round the camp beside the barbed wire, or else I sleep, and when I find a book I read it. . . ."

"And sometimes you write, too. . . ."

I looked at Ernst suspiciously.

"A few days ago," he went on, "I was on guard in one of the watchtowers. I noticed you. You stopped to write something in a little note book. This morning I recognized you at once."

This disclosure irritated me.

"You see, I can't even be alone!" I cried. "Isn't that inhuman?"

"But you were alone. You were alone because at that moment I didn't know you, and you didn't know me. Really, nothing was happening at all."

He was beginning to sound a little too self-confident. It was a tone that did not seem natural to him; there was a sort of strained excitement about it. I did not pursue the matter; without answering I bent down to pick up my violet plants. Ernst stood in silence for a while then, returning to the words I had spoken a few minutes earlier, as though his mind had dwelt on them in spite of what had followed:

"Books," he repeated with a schoolmasterish air of satisfaction and longing. "They were my great refuge too, when I spent a few months in a concentration camp two years ago. I'd been appointed librarian, thank Heaven. . . . Look here," he went on in a livelier tone, as though what had been said previously was of no importance, "put down your violet plants. Come and I'll show you something."

He was giving me line enough, as fishermen say; but I was well and truly caught this time. I stood up. He had started off ahead of me along a path that led to the right. I caught up with him: "I suppose the camp was on account of your political ideas?"

"Political . . . well, that's a word we don't much care for. Rather on account of my moral views. However, they did let me out of that camp. It was just a warning. I need hardly tell you that I haven't changed. . . . You see that wall?"

I saw the wall. It was decrepit, overgrown with moss and briars, its stones falling apart, and it enclosed a space in which the forest seemed to go on, to judge by the treetops that appeared above it. We walked some way round the outside and came to a gap in the wall. Within the enclosure gray stones stood among trees which were slighter than those of the surrounding forest, contrary to my previous impression. Here and there, pale grass was growing; it had begun to take possession of the ground again. The upright stones marked Jewish graves, a hundred years old no doubt. Eastern religions lay their dead at the foot of slabs of slate, stumbling blocks for the encroaching wilderness. Time had jostled many and overthrown a few of these old battlements of death, monoliths on which Heaven had written its reckoning in the only tongue it has ever spoken.

Ernst knew a little Hebrew. His small plump hand was soon moving over the stone, beginning on the right as in fortune-telling by cards. He read out some long-distant date, lazily coiled up now with a caterpillar of moss lying in the concavity of the figures, some name, with the knowledgeable curiosity of an accountant who has discovered old statements, bills yellow with age that have been settled once and for all. His religion was based on the belief that death belongs to the past and, when he looked at a grave, whether worn down by time or black with leaf-mold, he would say to himself with visible gladness that "all that's over and done with." Meanwhile I was overwhelmed by the symbolism of these graves; on most of the stones there was carved a breaking branch—you could see the sharp points at the break and the two fragments about to separate forming an angle, a gaping angle like an elbow. It was like the sudden rending that takes place high up in the tree of life, its imminence revealed by the flight of a bird, of that other soul which has hitherto deafened us by its ceaseless twittering, whereas our real life lay in the roots. On the stone, the branch was endlessly breaking, it would never break; when death has come, has one finished dying? Ernst raised his head and straightened his back.

"I've been rereading your classics," he said to me with a smile.

I did not understand.

"I mean that this ancient, traditional burial ground, close by your own fresh and improvised one, is rather like the upper shelf in a library. . . ." He laid his hand on a carved stone. "The preceding words in the great book. . . ."

"Who can tell? Perhaps the moment of death is never over," I replied, thinking of the symbol of the broken branch. "Perhaps we are doomed to a perpetual leavetaking from that which was life and which lies in the depth of night, as eternal as the patient stars. Perhaps there is no more identity in death than in life. Each man dies in his own corner, each man stays dead in his own corner, alone and friendless. Every death invents death anew."

"But I believe in Heaven and in the communities of Heaven, where no echo of life is heard," replied Ernst joyfully. "In the peace of the Lord."

"I cannot and will not believe that those who are murdered here cease their cries the moment after. . . ."

"Their cries have been heard before," said Ernst. "What do you mean? Do you need to hear dead men's cries? Isn't it enough that God remembers them, that we remember them? I will tell you something: they are sleeping peacefully in the light, all in the same light."

"That's too easy an answer!" I cried. "That's just to make us feel at peace."

"Don't torture yourself," Ernst replied. "In any case, neither you nor I is to blame."

We were not to blame. I had taken up my violets again from the place where I had left them a short while before and, with this badge of innocence, my flowers refuting what Ernst's rifle might suggest, we made our way to the graveyard through the silent forest.

"Tomorrow we'll go for another walk," Ernst said. "We might take the others too. We'll find some pretext."

But next day we were deprived of any pretext. Two men had died in the camp. Graves had to be dug; the dead had to be buried.

Ernst directed our labors skilfully and with pensive dignity. It was he who taught us that in this part of Europe they lined the inside of graves with fir-branches. Not to lag behind in the matter of symbolism we decided to bury the dead facing towards France. As France happened to be on the farther side of the forest against which the first row of graves had been dug, we were obliged to lay the dead men the wrong way round, with their feet under the crosses.

These two deaths occurring simultaneously aroused our anxiety. Sanitary conditions within the camp had worsened; underfed and weakened by their sufferings during the escape, and the subsequent journeys from camp to camp, the men gathered in daily increasing numbers in a huge sickroom. A few French doctors had been sent to Brodno by way of reprisal; lacking any sort of medicaments, they went from one straw mattress to the next making useless diagnoses, reduced to the passive role of witnesses in this overcrowded world whose rhythm was the gallop of feverish pulses and where delirious ravings mingled in a crazy arabesque, while men sat coughing their lungs out.

We buried four men in the same week. June was nearly over; it was already summer. By now, the white roads of the invasion spread like a network over the Russian land, far east of Brodno, right up to the Don, then to the Volga, to the Kuban, milestoned with poisoned wells. The woods were full of hurriedly filled graves, and the smoke rose up straight and still from the countryside, while the front page of German illustrated papers showed bareheaded soldiers, with their sleeves rolled up, munching apples as they set off to conquer the world. Hope dried up suddenly, like a well.

The Germans' victorious summer, as it rolled eastward, left us stranded on that floor formed by the hardened sediments of their violence, their extortions, their acts of murder, which already disfigured the whole of Europe. The drift of war away from us had only removed the unusualness of these things; the things themselves remained, only instead of seeming improvised they had assumed a workmanlike character; ruins were now handmade, homes became prisons, murder was premeditated.

The Jews of Brodno had practically stopped working inside the camp, where everything was now in order. Those who were road menders spent their time vainly searching the roads for other holes to fill; the sawmill workers, whom we used to see on our way to the graveyard, kept on moving the same planks to and fro, with gestures that had become ominously slow. More and more frequently you could see men and women, wearers of the white armlet, standing motionless between houses or against a hedge, driven there by the somnambulism of fear.

Inside the camp the same fatal idleness impelled the French to line up against the barbed wire, with their empty knapsacks slung across their back and clogs on their bare feet. To Jews and Frenchmen alike (to the former particularly) going and staying were equally intolerable fates, and they would advance timidly towards the edge of the road or of the barbed wire, take one step back and move a little to one side, as though seeking some state intermediary between departure and immobility. They would stand on the verge of imagined flight, and in their thoughts would dig illusory tunnels through time.

The tunnels we were digging might well have served them as models. Only ours had no outlet.

"Indeed, yes, Peter, graves have outlets," Ernst told me.

He had just brought me the stories of Klemens von Brentano. Death having left us a brief respite, we had gone off for a walk in the forest. A little way behind us, my comrades were gathered round Otto, the other sentry.

"What's he saying?" they shouted to me. I turned round. Otto repeated the words he had just uttered.

"He says that at home he was the best marksman in the district," I translated.

"Yes, we got that, he won some competitions. But he said something about birds. . . ."

"He can kill a bird on a branch fifty meters off with one shot. He's ready to prove it to us presently."

Otto was smiling, his neck wrinkling. His boast sounded like a public tribute when repeated as an aside by somebody else. I went back to Ernst.

"He's a nuisance with his stories of good marksmanship! Shots would make too much noise in the forest and in these parts they mean only one thing. I was going to take you to see the girls who work where the new road's being made. If he shoots we shall find them all terrified. . . ."

The project had a frivolous ring but Ernst forestalled my questions:

"They are young Jewish girls, unfortunate creatures. I've made friends with one of them. Every evening I take her some bread—a little bread; it's my own bread—at least, part of my own bread," he added in some confusion, recalling the daily agony of sharing it, his hunger and his weakness.

"Why are we going to see them?" I asked him. "We can't do anything for them. You know that."

"You are French, and the point is this: these are girls from the cultured classes of Brodno. They are better dressed than the peasants, they don't speak the same language, they had relations in various other countries, and now they are isolated, as though by some terrible curse. Nothing can save them from their isolation. Even if tomorrow the peasants round here were to be persecuted, the girls would find no support amongst them, no sense of kinship, no co-operation. Believe me, they've always been exiles in the East, even before the Germans settled here. And perhaps only you and I share what they've got, what makes them different. So don't run away."

"How could I run away?" I pointed to his gun. Ernst reddened with anger and shook his head. Behind us, big Otto had seen my gesture: "Don't talk to the pastor about his gun," he called out to me. "He thinks it's a fishing rod."

I turned round. "Please note that I'm just as much a pacifist as he is," Otto said. "Only I know how to shoot!"

He burst out laughing. Cordonat was near him and beckoned to me. "Ask him to choose a biggish target," he said as I came up, "a rabbit, for instance, or a jay or a crow. Let's at least have something to get our teeth into!"

I passed on the request to Otto.

"But then it wouldn't be a demonstration," he cried. "It's got to be quite a tiny animal."

I tried to explain to him that he could still keep to the rules of the game if he stood farther away from his living target. The argument seemed likely to go on indefinitely.

Ernst walked on ahead of us, indifferent to our conversation, with his back a little bent, like a recluse, and in addition that pathetic look that small men have when they are unhappy. He was going forward through the forest without keeping to the paths, and the forest was growing thicker. Already, we felt cut off from the outside world here, just because the shadows were a little deeper and the ground was carpeted with dead leaves, moss, myrtles and nameless plants. For us, as for millions of others, war meant "the fear of roads." These enslaved men looked at you sometimes with eyes like horses'.

There was still the sky, the sky between the branches when you raised your head, an unyielding sky, still heavy with threats. Daylight is up there. I must be dreaming. It was as if when you pushed open the shutters after a night full of bad dreams the influx of light proved powerless to dispel the terrifying visions of the darkness from your eyes. And yet everything is there, quite real. You need a second or third awakening, the maneuvering of a whole set of sluice-gates, before the morning light yields what you expect of it—not so much truth as justice.

After a few minutes I caught up with Ernst. I was afraid of disappointing him by showing so little interest in the visit he had suggested to me. Perhaps he had given it up; the thought caused me no remorse, for he was a man with too clear a conscience, too easily moved to compassion. But even if I had interfered with the execution of his plans, I did not want him to think me indifferent or insensitive.

"I'm hungry," I said as I drew near him, so as to avoid further explanations.

"So am I. But we shall soon find these girls, and they'll give us some coffee—they make it out of roasted grain. That'll help to appease our hunger. Afterwards we'll go and fell the trees. And then Otto will have plenty of time to fire his shots."

The trees that we were to fell were intended to build a fence round the graveyard. Ernst had discovered this excuse to justify our walks. We were now on a path that led down to the verge of the forest. The new road that was being made skirted it at this point and the workmen had set up a few huts for their gear and for the canteen. Eight Jewish girls worked here under German orders on various tasks, and two of them kept the canteen.

These were the girls we saw first when Ernst, telling his mate we were going to get some coffee, led me towards the hut. The two girls had come out over the threshold. They were wearing faded summer dresses whose original colors suggested Western fashions and cheap mass production. That was enough to introduce into this woodland setting an urban note which would have struck one as strange even without the added impression of bewilderment and weariness conveyed by the pale faces and wild eyes of the two girls. In spite of their youth, their features were devoid of charm. Beautiful faces were rare in this war; those faces which were daily taken from one were like commonplace relatives full of modest virtues, known intimately and loved and now gone into the night, unforgettable faces with their freckles and their tear-stained eyes.

When they recognized Ernst the two girls nodded gently. They stayed close together on the doorstep. Ernst spoke to them, calling them by their names. We were Frenchmen, he told them, prisoners too, hungry and unhappy. "Nothing was happening." We looked at each other, helplessly. What conversation could we hold? Everything had been said before we opened our mouths. It was not to one another that we must listen but to the far-off heavens, to which someday perhaps would rise the noise of our deliverance.

"We can't give you coffee," said one of the girls to Ernst. "The *Meister* hasn't given us any grain today."

Ernst had poked his head inside the hut to peer round. "Who's that?" he asked in a whisper. I looked too. In a corner of the room a man in black was leaning over a basin, with his back towards us. He was dipping a rag in water and from time to time raising it to his face. One could guess from the stiff hunching of his shoulders and the timidity betrayed by his slow awkward gestures that he felt our eyes upon him.

"It's a man from the sawmill," quickly replied one of the girls. "He hurt his face at work."

"But he doesn't work up here," said Ernst. "If the *Meister* finds him here there'll be a row."

"He'll go away when you've gone," said the smaller of the two girls, speaking for the first time and with an ill-disguised nervousness. She was dirty, with untidy red hair hanging down each side of her face. "The other sentinel mustn't see him," she went on in a low voice. "Please, Herr Pastor, be kind and take your Frenchman farther off."

"Where is Lidia?" asked Ernst.

"She's working on the dump trucks," said the other girl. "She's being punished because she broke the cord of the siren this morning."

"It's not fair!" went on the smaller girl, with bitterness. "The cord was rotten. When she tried to stop the siren, at seven o'clock, the cord broke off in her hand. The siren went on wailing long after everybody was at work. All the steam was being wasted. The *Meister* called it insubordination. It's not fair. . . . Yesterday they hanged four more men at Tarnopol."

"The way that siren went on wailing," said her friend. "There was something sinister about it—it was like a warning. But what was the use of warning us? How could we move? What could we do?" she added anxiously.

Ernst did not answer. He stood with downcast eyes.

"Perhaps I'll come back tonight," he said after a while. "Tell Lidia. God be with you."

We joined the group of prisoners who were waiting for us, guarded by Otto, and plunged once more into the forest.

"Somebody must have hit him," muttered Ernst as I walked at his side. "I'm speaking of that man we saw in the hut," he added, with a look at me. "He didn't want us to see the blood."

"Why not?"

"Because they feel that to let their blood be seen is not only a confession of weakness, of impotence, but moreover it marks them out as belonging to the scattered herd of blood-stained victims who are being ruthlessly hunted down. While they are whole, they'll carry on as long as their luck holds; when they're wounded, they go out to meet their own death. The order of things that has been established here is all-embracing, Peter. If a civilian—if one of these civilians is found with blood on him, the authorities think the worst. Where did he get it, who gave him leave to move about? Why is he branded with that mark, and why is he not with the herd of the dead? There's something suspicious about it. That man was well aware of this. He was hiding. He'd 'stolen' a beating. . . ."

"Do you think those girls are really in danger?"

While I was asking Ernst this question I realized that I had no wish to learn from him whether their danger was great or small. For the last few minutes I had experienced that slight nausea which, at the time, was more effective than any outward sign in warning me of imminent peril. Before Ernst could answer me a shot rang out behind us. Otto lowered his rifle and Cordonat ran towards a bush: "It's a jay!" he called out to me.

But I was observing the amazement created all around us, in the lonely forest, by the sudden report. I thought I caught sight of a gray figure disappearing swiftly between distant tree trunks. Then everything was as it had been, unmoving. I did not want to talk any more, and Ernst seemed not to want to either. That rifleshot had been like a blow struck with a clenched fist on a table, a call to order, silencing all chatter, even the private chatter of the heart. Otto was looking at us with a smile. He was looking at Ernst and myself. The bullet had passed just over our heads. He stopped smiling just as I was about to speak, to try and break out of that clear-cut circle which henceforward would enclose the three of us and within which we were now bound to one another by the dangerous silence that had followed our commonplace words.

The dead used to be brought to us in the morning, like mail that comes with habitual irregularity and provides no surprises; their belongings had to be classified, bills of lading for ships that have long since put out to sea; a cross had to be provided, with a name and a date. Now the coffins no longer showed those once ever-present wooden faces like those of eyeless suits of armor. Now a dead man in his coffin was no longer a human being wrapped in a door.

All we knew of the dead was their weight. However, this varied enough to arouse in us occasionally a sort of suspicion that somehow seemed to rarefy this inert merchandise. Unconsciously one was led to think in terms of a soul. A dead body that felt exceptionally heavy or, on the other hand, too light, reassumed some semblance of personality, smuggled in, as it were, in that unexpected gap between the weight of an "average" corpse and that of this particular corpse.

Things had begun to take their course. We might have been tempted to open the coffin, to examine the inscrutable face, to question the dead man's friends and search out his past history. But it was too late; the coffin was being lowered on its ropes, it lay at the bottom of the grave on the two supports we had placed there; the body was laid down, laid on its andirons and already more than half consumed with oblivion, loaded with ashes.

By now our burial ground comprised seventeen graves. The flowers had grown and we were preparing to open a new section. It would be another row of graves set below the first, which lay alongside the edge of the forest. We were thus tackling the second third of the graveyard, for its limits had been strictly set from the beginning. Hardly two months had passed since our arrival at Brodno and we were already beginning to wonder if the graveyard would last out as long as we did, or if it would be full before we left the camp, so that someday we might find ourselves confronted with an overflow of dead bodies which would have to be disposed of in a hasty, slapdash, sacrilegious way.

We foresaw that times would have changed by then; we might have a snowy winter, for instance, full of urgent tasks, and the fortunes of war would be drooping like a bent head. The limits of the burial ground, in a word, were those of our future, of our hope; all summer was contained within them. This summer had begun radiantly.

Fed by marshlands, fanned by the great wind blowing off the plain, the forest was aglow with its thousands of tree trunks—beeches and birches for the most part—and its millions of leaves; carpeted with monkshood and borage, it projected into the middle of the wide wilderness, somewhat like a mirage no doubt, but above all like a narrow concession made to the surrounding landscape, to the past, and, in a more practical sense, to the dead.

We had gone through it now in all directions. As soon as a funeral was over Ernst and Otto would take us off to the hamlets that lay on the other side of the forest. There we would buy food from the peasants in exchange for linen and military garments from our Red Cross parcels; the barter took place swiftly and in silence, as though between thieves. We brought home a few fowls or rabbits, which we hurriedly slaughtered in the forest, using our knees and cursing one another, while the sentries guarded the paths.

We would wipe our hands with leaves. Then the dead creature had to be slipped inside one's trousers, between one's legs, held up by strings tied round the head and feet and wound round one's waist. The volume of the body, the feel of fur or feather, the temporary invasion of the lice they harbored, the smell of blood and a lingering warmth made us feel as though we were saddled with some ludicrous female sexual appendage, as though we had given birth to something hairy and shapeless that obliged us to walk clumsily, with straddled legs.

This stratagem enabled us to get back into the camp safely; I had no hesitation about resorting to it under the eyes of Ernst, since the very vulgarity of my movements, my grotesque gait, freed me from the mental complicity that bound me to him. It was a sort of revenge against despair. Sometimes, on the way back, we would catch a distant glimpse of the men and women at work on the new road. Ernst pointed out Lidia to me; she was wearing a light-colored dress and pushing a dump truck full of earth. Rain was threatening: "She's going to get soaked to the skin," Ernst muttered.

"Why Lidia?" I asked.

"Yes, why Lidia . . ." he echoed, in torment, his head downcast.

"I meant why are you particularly interested in her?" It was hard to keep up this tone with a barely dead fowl stuck between your thighs.

"One has to make a choice, Peter," Ernst mumured. "One can't suffer tortures on every side at once. Mind you, that doesn't mean. . . ."

Otto was behind us, though far enough not to catch our words. I felt sure that if we went on talking like this he would soon shoot at a jay, a magpie, the first bird he saw. There's always one ready to fly off from an empty branch over your head, a little way in front of you or to one side. At every work, like involuntary beaters, we "put up" a covey of pretexts, birds with strange plumage and taunting cries. I turned round; Otto was smiling. Since I had begun carrying slaughtered animals between my legs his smile had grown broader; I was a fellow. Suddenly his smile froze: "Halt!" he called to me, pointing into the depths of the forest. Two figures were rapidly disappearing between the trees.

"Partisans," he said, hurriedly smiling again.

The word "partisans," as he spoke it, seemed to indicate some species of big game, rare and practically invulnerable, some solitary stag or boar shaking the unmysterious undergrowth with its startled gallop. Yet my heart had leaped. One morning, when we reached the burial ground, we caught sight of black smoke drifting over a hamlet in the plain. Otto explained to me that some patisans, having been given a poor reception there in the night, had burned it by way of reprisal. After that the open German cars that drove through Brodno assumed a warlike aspect, despite their gleaming nickel and brightly polished bodies. For beside the officers they were carrying sat two helmeted soldiers armed with Tommy guns.

We did not see them for long; the partisans seemed to have disappeared. In the villages, the Germans had distributed arms and formed militias. A watchman blew a bugle at the first alarm; it was a sort of long wail in the depth of the night which, generally without cause, made those who had taken refuge in treachery stir in their uneasy sleep. During the day Ukrainian policemen passed along the little path below the graveyard. They wore a black uniform with pink, yellow or white braid and badges of the same colors in checks, circles or triangles, like the gaudy signals of some obscure code hung out on the semaphores of terror.

The Germans acknowledged the stiff salutes of these liveried men with a nonchalant air. The Jews shrank back when they drew near: the Ukrainian policemen had the wild cruelty of certain sheep dogs, and above all their eyes and their voices recalled traditional pogroms. A few days earlier they had killed three prisoners who had escaped from the camp, shooting them down in the wood.

When they passed near us Cordonat would taunt them under his breath in the patois of Languedoc. These muttered insults showed the total disconnectedness of everything; what mazes of recent history one would have to explore to account for this absurd conflict between a Ukrainian peasant dressed in a stage uniform and a *vigneron* from the South of France who, before the war, used to vote anti-Communist and who was now talking, in his patois, about joining the Volynian partisans.

Otto made fun of the Ukrainian policemen out loud when they had gone past us, and embarked on a conversation with Cordonat in which gestures to a large extent filled the gaps in their vocabulary; after a lengthy exchange of naïvely pacifist opinions, they had ended by discussing hunting, poaching and mushrooms.

Ernst appeared to be growing somewhat mistrustful of his companion. In order to be able to speak freely to me he evolved the plan of taking me almost every day to the sawmill to get our woodcutting tools sharpened. I had never expressed any wish for these tête-à-tête conversations. They only lasted, actually, during the time we took to walk from the burial ground to the sawmill. This sawmill was worked on behalf of the Germans by a Jewish employer and his men. I met there the man with the wounded face of whom we had caught sight a few days earlier in the girls' hut.

I had asked the boss of the sawmill for a glass of water, as he stood talking to us in front of the workshop door. He turned round and asked someone inside, whom I could not see, to bring me one. A few minutes later Isaac Lebovitch came up to me carrying a glass of water. It was a glass of fine quality, patterned with a double ring, the remnant of a set no doubt, and its fragility and bourgeois origin made me uneasy. In this token of hospitality I recognized an object which might have been a family heirloom of my own.

Isaac Lebovitch (he was soon to tell me his name) seemed to be about thirty years old. He had a long face with a lean beak of a nose. His dark curly hair, already sparse, grew low on his forehead. He stood beside us while I was emptying my glass.

"It may be that our hour has struck," the master of the sawmill was saying to Ernst. "It may be that the end of our race is in sight. There are things written up there," he added, pointing to the sky which was empty of birds, empty of hope.

I noticed a vine climbing round the door of the sawmill. In that region where vines had never been cultivated it looked strange, like a Biblical symbol.

". . . And yet," the sawmill boss was saying, "I myself fought during the last war in the Austro-Hungarian army. I was an N.C.O. and I won a medal. That means I was on your side, doesn't it?"

I felt embarrassed as I listened to his words. He was quite an old man, no sort of rebel against order or established authority, ready to accept a strict social hierarchy and even a certain degree of victimization to which his religion exposed him. . . . But not this, not what was happening now! These things were on the scale of a cosmogony. Or worse: they took you into a universe which perhaps had always existed behind the solid rampart of the dead, and of which the metaphors of traditional rhetoric only gave you superficial glimpses: where the bread was, literally, snatched from one's mouth, where one could not keep body and soul together, where one really was bled white and died like a dog.

Like novice sorcerers inexpert in the magic of words, we now beheld the essential realities of hell, escaping from the dry husks of their formulae, come crowding towards us and over us: the black death of the plague, the bread of affliction, the pride of a louse. . . . Seeing that Ernst was listening, with a look of deep distress, to the old man's words, Lebovitch plucked up courage to speak to me. He first addressed me in German, asking me whereabouts in France I lived, what sort of job I had, whether my relatives over there suffered as much from the German occupation as the people here did; then he suddenly spoke a sentence in English.

It was quite an ordinary sentence like "Life isn't good here." There was really no need to wrap it up in the secrecy of another language, since it was no more compromising than the words that had preceded it; and no doubt he had only had recourse to these English words for the sake of their foreignness. A language does not always remain intact; when it has been forced to express monstrous orders, bitter curses and the mutterings of murderers, it retains for a long time those insidious distortions, those sheer slopes of speech from the top of which one looks down dizzily. In those days the German language was like a landscape full of ravines, from the depths of which rose tragic echoes.

"No, life isn't good here," I answered in German. "But out there in the forest. . . ."

"I don't go there any more. The other day. . . ." Lebovitch showed me the dry wound on his forehead. "Besides, you saw. . . ."

"Probably you didn't go far enough, you didn't venture into the depths. . . ."

"I had just gone to see Lidia," said Lebovitch, surprised by my remark. "I have no reason to go farther. You're liable to meet the partisans. . . ."

"That's just what I meant."

He stayed silent for a moment. We had moved a little farther off and had turned our backs on Ernst and the old man. Lebovitch stepped still farther to one side and, realizing that he wanted me to come away from the other two, I went up beside him.

"The partisans," he said with an anxious air. "I'll tell you this: we don't know much about them. If they saw me coming up to them they might shoot me down. And how could I live in that forest? I've got no strength left," he gasped, striking his thin chest with his fist." And then there's so much violence, so much bloodshed every day, and all those farms set on fire. . . . After all, we're managing to hold out here. I've held out up till now. Perhaps we've been through the hardest part now. Listen, I may perhaps be dead tomorrow but I think it's better for me to save my strength. Don't you think that's best for you too?"

It would have been cruel to tell him that the dangers that threatened us seemed less terrible than his own, and I left him to his patience.

"That girl you call Lidia, who works on the new road," I remarked, "isn't she the one my sentry knows?"

"He ought to stop trying to see her. She told me so. It's likely do her a lot of harm. I think she's had herself sent to the dump trucks on purpose because of him, so that he can't try to see her during the daytime. What's he want with her, anyway? He knows that relations of that sort are forbidden. He'll only get her hanged, and himself after her."

"He wants to help her."

Lebovitch grasped me by the arm, after making sure that the other two could not see him: "Let me tell you this, Frenchman: the Germans can help nobody, d'you understand, nobody. They couldn't if they wanted to, they couldn't any longer. Imagine a hedgehog struggling to stop being a hedgehog; you wouldn't want to go near him then!"

Ernst called me. The tools were ready. We had to get back to the graveyard. As I left Lebovitch I was careful not to tell him that we would soon be back. It was no doubt bad for him and his friends for us to be seen at the sawmill too often. We must each keep to his own solitude; fraternization had become conspiracy.

As we walked back, I spoke to Ernst about Lebovitch. "He's a friend of your Lidia's," I told him. "He's afraid that your interest in her may compromise her in the eyes of the German authorities."

"He's wrong," replied Ernst in an offhand manner. "You know I'm a pastor, and although I'm not a chaplain, the Commandant, who comes from my home town (only yesterday he was asking me for news of my family), gives me tacit permission to make some approaches to these people in a priestly capacity; to behave with a little more humanity, in other words. . . ."

"Humanity," I echoed.

"I know what you're thinking, Peter," murmured Ernst. "Well, even if your thoughts correspond to the reality, what about it? Won't you ever understand?" he cried, appealing, far beyond me, to some unknown body of critics. "We are all lost. There's nothing for us to fall back on; there never will be. Even the earth has begun to fail us. In such conditions, who can forbid me to love in whatever way I can? Who can forbid me? This is the last form of priesthood open to me, Peter—the last power I've got. It's inadequate and clumsy, it needs to be exercised upon a living object, a single object. . . ."

His lips went on moving. I said nothing. I would not have known what to say. And then Otto was already watching us come, from the top of the burial ground; the evening sun was behind his back and we could not see his face. He was standing motionless with his rifle on his shoulder. Behind him the graves were casting their shadows to one side, like beasts of burden relieved of their packs.

From that time on, discovering into what abysses I might be dragged if I followed Ernst, I fell back on the position of safety provided by the graveyard. Here was the only innocent place. Here we seemed to find a sort of immunity. When an officer came to inspect us we each bent as low as possible over a grave, assiduously weeding it as though pressed for time, without raising our heads, and the visitor refrained from speaking to us, wondering (probably for the first time in his life) if we were acting thus in response to some urgent appeal from the dead, such as he himself might perhaps have heard (it suddenly came back to him) in the middle of the night, in the days when he still felt remorse.

"The weeds are the white hair of the dead," Cordonat would say, and his words savored of that senile cult whose hold on us grew in proportion to the dangers that threatened us.

These dangers now assumed the shapes and sunburned faces of S.S. men and military policemen, a few detachments of whom had recently arrived in the region of Brodno. But it was above all the growing silence of that summer, the pallor of the sun at certain hours, the oppressive heat that secretly frightened us. Our religion, which had never actually been a cult of the dead, was becoming a cult of the grave. As we dug and then filled up our pits, we appeased some haunting dream of underground.

With our twenty-two dead, we had already opened up and explored a real labyrinth. We were familiar with its passages, its detours, its angles. It was a sort of deep-down landscape. We knew just where a tangle of hanging roots clutched clods of earth, where you could catch the smell of a distant spring, where you passed over a slab of granite. In the course of our work of excavation we had grown used to the coolness of this universe of the dead and we found our way about it mentally with the help of these particularities of structure rather than with the help of the names of the dead men who had drifted there accidentally, like foreign bodies.

This longing for the depths, unsatisfied by our task of weeding on the surface of the graves, impelled Cordonat and myself to try and open up a trench which would run a few yards into the forest and drain away the rain water that poured down on to the graves and scored deep furrows in their unstable earth. Since we now no longer left the burial ground to walk in the forest, which was patrolled by the soldiers who had recently come to Brodno, I was looking for an occupation.

Digging this trench had another very different result; it was through this narrow channel that I happened on something that I had been anxiously anticipating for many months. It began under my feet, like a forest fire. Right at the start, we had got on fairly fast with our trench and were now digging in the sandy soil of the forest, among the live roots of trees. Below us our comrades were lying beside the graves, plucking the weeds from off the dead with one hand. Otto and Ernst were sitting in the shade of the trees, Ernst reading *Louis Lambert*, which had just been sent to me and which I had lent him. As we worked, Cordonat was telling me about his *landes*. When we stopped to change tools, for we used pick and spade in turn, we divided up a little tobacco. The war seemed endless but here, at this precise moment, under this white silent sky, it had a flavor of patience, a flavor of sand; it bore the same relation to life as a fine sand to a coarser sand.

It was not with the pickax but with the sharp edge of the spade that I cut open the arm of the corpse. It was lying flush with the side of the trench and as I was leveling the walls I struck right into the flesh. It was pink, like certain roots, like a thick root covered with black cloth instead of bark. My blow had ripped off a bit of the sleeve. I started back, spellbound with horror. Cordonat came up and then called the sentries. Everybody was soon gathered round the unknown corpse. A little earth had crumbled away and his elbow and wounded arm were now projecting into the void; he was literally emerging from a wall.

"Cover it up with earth," said Otto.

"We'll make a cross of branches," murmured Ernst.

They went back into the graveyard with our comrades; the problem of burying this corpse was beyond them. It is easy, it is even tempting to throw earth on a dead body. Often, after our burials, we managed, using boards and spades, to push into the hole at one go most of the heaped-up earth that lay at its brink. Here, one would have had to cover over the arm that projected from the wall of earth, to enclose it in an overhanging recess. We therefore decided to fill up our trench and start it again lower down, skirting round the corpse. I did not know what name to give it. But all the indications (the color of the clothes, their "civilian" appearance) suggested that the body was that of a Jew who had been killed there before our arrival or during one night, or maybe on a Sunday, very hurriedly no doubt, in a hush like that of a suicide.

I felt slightly sick. It was very hot. We were working with fierce concentration now, in silence. A few hours later, when we were digging our trench at some distance from the corpse, Cordonat, who was wielding his pickax ahead of me, suddenly started back. A sickly, intolerable smell arose; he had just uncovered a second body. This one was lying at the bottom of the trench, slightly askew and concealed by a thin layer of earth, so that Cordonat had trodden on it before—surprised by the elasticity of the soil—he exposed its clothing and upper part of a moldering face.

I was overwhelmed by the somber horror of it and the truth it revealed. This was death—these liquefying muscles, this half-eaten eye, those teeth like a dead sheep's; death, no longer decked with grasses, no longer ensconced in the coolness of a vault, no longer lying sepulchred in stone, but sprawling in a bog full of bones, wrapped in a drowned man's clothes, with its hair caught in the earth.

And it was as though, looking beyond the idealized dead with whom I had hitherto populated my labyrinths, my underground retreats, I had discovered the state of insane desolation to which we are reduced when life is done. Death had become "a dead thing," no more; just as some being once endowed with great dignity and feminine mystery may, after a slow degeneration, surrender to the grossest drunkenness and fall asleep on the bare ground, wrapped in rags; here, the rags were flesh. Death was this: a dead mole, a mass of putrefaction sleeping, its scalp covered with hair or maybe with fur: wreckage stranded in the cul-de-sac of an unfinished tunnel: surrender at the end of a blind alley.

Cordonat discovered three more bodies. We had struck the middle of a charnel, a heap of corpses lying side by side in all directions, in the middle of the wood; a sort of subterranean bivouac which even now, when he had exposed it to the light, lost none of its clandestine character. We shouted, but in vain; this time nobody came to us. We turned over the earth till we were exhausted in an effort to cover up the bodies. We were practicing our craft of gravediggers in sudden isolation. And now it had assumed a wildly excessive character; we were gravediggers possessed by feverish delirium. Night was falling. We had ceased to care who these men were, who had killed them or when; they were irregular troops on the fringe of the army of the dead, they were "partisans" of another sort. We should never have finished burying them.

Their very position close by our own graveyard cruelly emphasized its prudent orderliness. Our dead, meekly laid out in rows, suddenly seemed to exude servility and treachery, wearing their coffins like a wooden livery.

The appalling stench of these accidentally exhumed corpses persisted for a long time in the forest, and spread over our graveyard. It was as though our own dead had awakened for a moment, had turned over in their graves, like wild animals hazily glimpsed in the sultry torpor that precedes a storm. There could be no doubt that something was going to happen. The smell warned one that the tide was about to turn.

The thundery heat and the horror of my discoveries made me feverish. Back in camp, I lay prostrate for several days on the wooden bed. Myriads of fleas had invaded the barrack-rooms and were frenziedly attacking us, while in the shadow of my clothes I traced the searing passage of my lice. Towards evening Cordonat brought me a little water. This was so scarce that at the slightest shower all the men would rush outside clutching vessels, bareheaded, like ecstatic beggars, and when the rain stopped they sprawled on the ground, still jostling one another, round the spitting gutters. Then my fever dropped. When I went back to the burial ground the first trains had begun to pass.

A railway line ran over the plain that we overlooked from our mound. It was only a few hundred yards away. Until then we had paid little attention to it, for the traffic was slight or nonexistent. During my absence it had increased without my noticing it; these trains sounded no whistles. If they had, I should have heard them from my bed in the camp; I should have questioned my comrades and they could have enlightened me, for from certain windows in the building you could see a section of the line, beyond the station which was hidden by houses.

The first trains had gone past behind us, full of stifled cries and shouts, like those trains that pass all lit up, crammed with human destinies and snatched out of the night with a howl while, framed in the window of a little house near the railway, a man in his shirt sleeves stands talking under a lamp, with his back turned, and then walks off to the other end of the room. And now, from the graveyard, I could see them coming, panting in the heat of the day, interminable convoys that had started a long time ago, long freight trains trickling slowly through the summer marshaling-yards, collecting men on leave and refugees like a herd of lowing cattle.

I could hear their rumbling long before they appeared past the tip of the forest, and then when they were in sight (sometimes almost before) I could hear another sound, superimposed and as elusive as a singing in one's ears, a buzzing in one's head or the murmur in a sea shell: the sound of people calling and weeping.

The trains consisted of some twenty freight cars sandwiched between two passenger coaches, one next the engine and one at the rear. At the windows of these two coaches (they were old ones, green, with bulging bodywork) stood uniformed Germans smoking cigars. All the rest of the train was an inferno.

The cries seemed transparent against the silence, like flames in the blaze of summer. What they were shouting, these men and women and children heaped together in the closed vans, I could not tell. The cries were wordless. The human voice, hovering over the infinite expanse of suffering like a bird over the infinite sea, rose or fell, ran through the whole gamut of the wind before it faded into the distance, leaving behind it that same serene sky, that store of blue that bewildered birds and dying men can never exhaust. On the side of each van a narrow panel was open near the roof, framing four or five faces pressed close together, with other halves and quarters of faces visible between them and at the edges, the clusters of eyes expressing terror.

But it was more than terror, it was a sort of death-agony of fear; the time for beating their breasts was over and now they watched the interminable unrolling of that luminous landscape which they were seeing for the last time, where there was a man standing free and motionless in the middle of a field, and trees, and a harvester, and the impartial summer sun, while your child was suffocating, pressed between your legs in the overcrowded van and weeping with thirst and fright. Here and there a child was hoisted up to the narrow opening. When its head projected the German guards in the first carriage would fire shots. You had to stand still there in front of the opening and bear silent witness to what was going on in the dense darkness of the van: women fainting, old men unable to lie down, newborn babies turning blue, crazed mothers howling—while you watched the symbols of peace slowly filing past.

The trains followed one another at short intervals. Empty trains came back. Beside the narrow openings the deported victims had hung vessels in the hope of collecting water—mess-tins, blue enamel mugs—like pathetic domestic talismans which a mocking Fate kept jingling hollowly as the train disappeared in the dusty distance. They had no thought of displaying sacred draperies or waving oriflammes at this window; death was yet another journey, and they set out armed with water bottles.

Empty trains came back. I recognized them by the sound of the engine's panting.

"Now then, get busy, boys," Otto would tell us.

We had been given a third sentry. Brodno was crammed with troops and they had to be made use of. Ernst was some distance away from us, pale, his lips tight.

"Do you know why they're being taken off and where they're being taken to?" I asked the sentry, whom I did not know.

"Delousing," he answered calmly. "Got to make an end of this Jewish vermin. It's quickly done. It happens some thirty miles away. I'm told it's with electricity or gas. Oh, they don't suffer anything. In one second they're in Heaven."

This man, as I learned later, was an accountant from Dresden. He might just as well have been a blacksmith from Brunswick, a cobbler from Rostock, a peasant from Malchin, a professor from Ingolstadt, a postman from Cuxhaven or a navvy from Bayreuth; he would have used the same language. And he did use the same language under all these different aspects, shifting from one to another like an agile actor impelled by Evil, altering his voice to suit each of these thousands of masks, imbuing it with the atmosphere of profound calm appropriate to Ingolstadt, Malchin, Bayreuth and countless other equally humane cities, and repeating, "Oh, they don't suffer, they don't suffer!"

Trains came down from the far depths of Volynia and the Ukraine, loaded with death agonies, with tears and lamentations. At one stop, farther up, the German guards had tossed dead children onto the roofs of the vans; nothing had to be left by the way, for each train was like the tooth of a rake. High up in the wall of the van, a little to the left in the narrow opening, there was a face; it seemed not living, but painted—painted white, with yellow hair, with a mouth that moved feebly and eyes that did not move at all: the face of a woman whose dead child was lying above her head; and beside the opening the little blue enamel mug, useless henceforward, shaken by every jolt of the train. Death can never appease this pain; this stream of black grief will flow for ever.

Towards the end of the morning I succeeded in drawing near to Ernst, who had moved away from the other two soldiers.

"It had started three months ago, at Brest Litovsk, when I was there," he told me in a low, tense voice. "But it wasn't on this scale. In a few days, tomorrow maybe, they'll begin on the people of this place. Do you think she ought to go away? To take refuge in the woods?"

He was looking at me bewilderedly, seeming more like a priest than ever with his smooth, babyish face, his indirect glance.

"It's probably the only chance they've got left," I muttered, bending towards the turf on the grave, since the new sentry was slowly coming towards us.

"But you've seen her: she's not strong, she'll never stand up to such an ordeal!" cried Ernst, without noticing that the soldier was now standing quite close to him.

The soldier looked at Ernst in some surprise and then went off, humming. I stood silent.

"Won't you speak to me, Peter?" asked Ernst humbly. "You're saying to yourself: He thinks only of her. . . ."

"I mistrust the other sentry," I answered. "You're exposing yourself unnecessarily. If you're willing to run the risk, throw away your gun and go off into the forest with her."

"I've thought of that," said Ernst, hanging his head. "I've thought of that. And then nothing gets done. You're horrified and you stay where you are. In this war, every man looks after himself. But we ought to realize that there can't be any true life afterwards for us, who have endured these sights. For me, there'll be no more life, Peter, do you hear, no more life. . . ."

His two companions called him and he went off abruptly. I lifted my head. Down below, there were only empty trains passing along the line. Towards evening all traffic ceased. Ernst did not speak another word to me as we went back to the camp. And I never saw him again.

Next day, when our gang turned up at the guardhouse, the Germans sent us back to our barracks. Soon rumors reached us: the Jews of Brodno were going to be taken away in their turn. Towards noon, looking out of the windows of our building, we saw the first procession of doomed victims appear on the little road leading to the station. Many of them—nursing what hopes, trusting in what promises?—had brought bundles and suitcases. The hastily knotted bundles frequently let drop underclothes or scraps of cloth that nobody had time to pick up, since the soldiers were continually hurrying on the procession, with curses on their lips and rifle butts raised. Other victims, arriving later, thus found themselves confronted with a scene of dispossession whose causes were as yet unknown to them, with the signs of ominous disorder.

The same signs were visible within their own group, where old men, children and adults were mingled; clearly there had been no attempt to sort them out, as had always happened hitherto before the removal of groups of workers or some other utilitarian deportation. The German soldiers from time to time struck at the sides of the column, but as we could only see them from a distance their gestures seemed to be slowed down: silent, clumsy blows, aimed low, more like stealthy misdeeds than like acts of violence. I had turned away from the window.

"Here are more of them!" somebody cried behind me.

Should I see Lidia, her friends, Lebovitch or the old man from the sawmill in this group, or the man who mended the road, or the fair woman who often stood waiting between two houses? Their packs made their silhouettes misshapen. Some of the women hugged them against their stomachs like bundles of washing. The dust was rising and I could not make them out clearly.

Somebody said: "It's their children they're carrying. . . ."

Somebody said: "One of them has fallen. The guards are hitting him. . . . Now he's up; he's starting off again. . . ." Somebody said: "Oh, look at that woman running to catch up with the group!"

The untiring commentaries, despite transient notes of pity, disclosed a sort of detachment, for passionate feeling will not allow you to see things through to the end, whereas these men followed the whole business with the mournful eagerness of witnesses. Evening drew on. I lay stretched out on the wooden bunk. At my side Cordonat was smoking in silence. Later on, flickering lights and distant rumblings rent the night. It was a stifling night, tense with anguish, and you could not tell whether those distant flares came from thunderclouds or from armed men on the march, carrying torches.

The arrests went on all next day. We were told by sentries that the cottage doors had been smashed in with axes and the inhabitants cleared out. Towards noon stifled cries were heard from the direction of the station. The victims, who had spent all night packed together in the vans standing in the sidings, were clamoring for water. By evening not a single train was left in the station. One man was walking along the track, bending down from time to time to check the rails. He went off into the distance, till he was almost invisible. Beyond, the pure sky grew deeper.

It was not until three days later that we set out once more on the road to the burial ground. Two new sentries accompanied us. The road was empty, and most of the houses shut up. In one of them some Poles were setting up a canteen. A few men were working in front of the sawmill. I recognized none of them.

At least we still had our dead, that faithful flock, each of whom we could call by his name without raising up a murdered man's face staring wide-eyed in the darkness. Our dead were already beginning to get used to their earth. After each of our absences they had "put on green," as we said when the grass had once more invaded the graves. Our cult of the dead consisted in wiping away the shadow of the meadow, day by day. And once more the sentries surrendered.

They had come to the graveyard armed with mistrust. But here, amongst the dead, we got the better of them. In front of our tidy graves, so tirelessly tended, their antagonism dropped: our accounts were in order. The liquidations (in the business sense of the word) which the Germans were carrying on all round us took place only spasmodically, as though at an auction, in an atmosphere of anger and excess which, once the payment had been exacted, increased the insatiable credit of the murderers with a debt of bitter resentment; they found it hard to forgive their victims. Our dead, on the other hand, had needed no dunning. Although the Germans were never paid fast enough, these had not worn out their patience like the others; nobody was conscious of having forced them to die.

Then, too, they seemed to be lying at attention under their three feet of earth in properly dressed lines, whereas the others, who had been shot point-blank, hid their heads in the crook of their arms; they had to be pulled by the hair, in fact it was an endless business bringing them to heel.

When the charm of the graveyard had worked, I plucked up courage to ask one of the two soldiers if he knew what had become of Ernst.

"Oh, the little pastor!" he replied. "He got punished. He's been sent to a disciplinary company. He knew a Jewess. They even say he burst out crying in the Commandant's office. Oh, don't talk to me about such people! Anyhow, I'm a Bavarian myself, so you see I'm of the same religion as you. I'm a Catholic, yes, but one's country comes first! Now get along and see to your graves."

I had not had time to inquire about the fate of Otto. In any case I was not deeply concerned about it. I felt calmer; the punishment inflicted on Ernst seemed a light one. Moreover, it cemented our friendship more firmly. He stood beside me now in the rebels' camp, like those guests at a party whom you've expected for a long time, wondering whether they'll come, and who suddenly appear, all made up and grotesquely disguised, with their familiar kindly, serious eyes looking at you from under their hats, when the music has already started and the dark wine is being poured out all round you.

All this was happening in 1942. Our friendship needed some discipline, imposed from without, naturally. I was thinking of Lidia, too. Her relations with Ernst seemed to me solid ground, but there were stars, too. They still wheel round in my dreams. I do not know what became of them on earth, but in the map of heaven, and in the map of my heart, I know where to look for the distant glimmer of that unattainable love.

We never went back to the new road. Our kingdom grew narrower. No more walks in the forest; we went down to the pond only with sentries on either side of us, and we were forbidden to linger there; we were more than ever confined to the burial ground. Otto and Ernst had already passed into a previous existence, threatened with oblivion, when we got news of the former: he sent us a corpse.

This was a fellow that I knew fairly well, a sullen-faced lad from Lyons obsessed by the urge to escape. Seeking an opportunity, he had asked me a few days earlier to let him take the place of a member of our gang who was too sick to leave the camp. He hoped to be able to make an easy getaway from the graveyard. I managed to get him accepted by our sentries. Underneath his uniform he was wearing some sort of escape outfit, and round his ankles there dangled long white laces belonging presumably to the linen trousers formerly issued to the French army. These were only too obvious. Silent, his jaws stiff with anxiety or determination, he thus attracted the guards' attention immediately. They never took their eyes off him and, that evening, he came back to the camp with us.

A few days later he got himself engaged in a gang of "road commandos" (prisoners employed on road-mending at some distance from the town) guarded by several sentries, among whom was Otto. Otto, being indirectly involved in Ernst's punishment, had been posted in charge of this detachment, which performed the duties of a gang of convicts and was rated as such. One evening, as the group was about to pass through the town on its way back to the camp, the young Lyonnais broke ranks abruptly and began to run off into the fields. Otto promptly shouldered his gun and fired. The fugitive dropped; the bullet had gone in through his back and pierced his heart.

It was our first violent death. On the day of the funeral the Germans sent a wreath of fir-branches tied with a red ribbon. The wooden cross bore the inscription FALLEN instead of DIED. Our graveyard had been sorely in need of this heroic note, as I suddenly realized; it was as though it had received the Military Cross.

"You shall soon have some stones, too," a sentry told me. "I know that in the camp they've been asking for a stone-mason. It's the Jews' tombstones you're going to get; their graveyard's full of them, down there in the forest. We shall use them for the roads too. You people can't complain, your graveyard's much finer than the one where our own men are buried. . . ."

It was quite true. With its always green turf, its flowerbeds, its carefully sanded paths edged with small black fir trees which we had transplanted, with its rustic fence of birch boughs, against the dark background of the forest edge, our graveyard seemed an "idyllic" place, as the Germans put it. On Sunday the soldiers from the garrison used to come and photograph it. The more we adorned it the greater grew its fame, and it aroused a wave of curiosity like that which carries crowds to gaze at certain baroque works of art or at others which, devoid of any art, are yet prodogies of patience and skill: houses built of bottle ends, ships made of matches, walking sticks carved to fantastic excess—monstrous triumphs of persistence and time.

On the fringe of the war, on the fringe of the massacres, on the fringe of Europe, sheltering behind our prodigious burial-ground, we seemed like hollow-eyed gardeners, sitters in the sun, fanatical weeders, busily working over the dead as over some piece of embroidery.

But the thought of those stones horrified us. We did not want to rob the Jews of their gravestones; that savored of sacrilege, and also of an incipient complicity with the Germans; and anyhow it "wasn't playing fair." We had made our graveyard out of earth and grass and to bring in marble would have been cheating. I went to lay the problem before the prisoners' French representative, the *homme de confiance* as we called him. He promised me to protest to the Germans.

A few days later, in one corner of the camp, I saw a man sitting on the ground sawing and planing a tombstone on which was carved a breaking branch.

He seemed in some doubt. Should each of the slabs of marble or granite intended for the graves (merely for epitaphs, not for funerary flagstones) represent an open book, a cushion (he could quite well picture a cushion slightly hollowed out by the weight of an absent head) or a coat of arms? He asked for my opinion. I told him angrily that I wasn't interested in his stones, and that they should never cross the threshold of the graveyard. However, he went on cutting them, full of delight at getting back to his trade, heaping them one on the other when they were ready, although the Germans were now busy with something else and never came to ask for them. In any case, he could not have handed them over as they were, for the essential part of the inscription was missing.

Though my ill-will discouraged him at first, he soon tried to get from one of us the names of the dead and the dates which he needed. He met with the same refusal. Besides ourselves, only the Germans possessed these essential facts, but no prisoner had access to their offices. Thenceforward, he began a patient investigation, going from one building to the next, questioning the men on the deaths that had taken place there. I soon got wind of this. It made me angry. The stonemason's obstinacy, although of a purely professional character, had begun to look like an intrusion into our field. For the last few months we had managed to keep our tasks secret, and now I felt this secrecy threatened by the publicity that he was causing by his noisy investigation of our past.

One day I saw him turn up at the graveyard, following a funeral. The man we were burying that day had come most opportunely in the nick of time, after the lad from Lyons, who, having introduced an appropriately heroic note into the place, had since seemed to be inaugurating a sequence of violent deaths. For here the latest corpse set the tone; it was in front of the latest corpse that we made our military salutes each morning; it was his bare, sparsely sown grave that attracted the attention (albeit vacuous) of visitors. It seemed important therefore that the tone thus set should not be, for too long, that of violent death: after all, a habit is easily acquired. And so I should have been quite glad to welcome this newcomer who restored order to things, had I not perceived, among the handful of Frenchmen walking behind the cart, the stonemason, sporting a swordbelt.

He had probably managed to slip into the procession by posing as one of the dead man's friends; he may even have been one really. . . . But we were already convinced of one thing: he had come to the graveyard to take measurements and pick up names. We decided to keep an eye on him, and we buried the corpse in a state of nervous tension although, in the depths of our innocent hearts, we had longed for it. We did not take our eyes off the man during the whole ceremony which, with its dying bugle-call and the report of arms fired into the sky, was like that which marks the close of a war. When the burial was over the Germans and the Frenchmen who had formed the procession hung about. As the fame of our graveyard increased, funerals had tended to become, for those who were able to attend them, a sort of summer excursion, a trip into the country from which you might well picture yourself returning with armsful of flowers picked on the spot. The stonemason had moved towards the first row of graves. I followed him. He was already taking a notebook out of his pocket.

"What are you doing there?" I asked him, my voice distorted with anger.

"I've been told to make tombstones!" he said, very loud. "You shan't prevent me! They don't belong to you, after all!" he added, indicating the graves of the dead.

"More than to you, anyhow!" I answered. "We wouldn't go and put stolen stones on their graves. . . ."

"Stolen?" He shook his head. "They're given to us and it's not our business to ask where they come from. . . . Well, I know, of course!" he went on, seeing that I was about to answer. "And so what? Would you rather see them laid on the roads?"

"Yes, I'd rather see them laid on the roads. I suppose you get soup and bread from the Germans for doing this job?"

"Oh, don't you talk about that!" cried the stonemason. He brought his angry face close to mine. "Everybody in the camp knows what you've wangled with your famous graveyard!" He stopped suddenly.

"Well then, tell me! Tell me!" I cried.

"Listen to me," went on the stonemason in a quieter voice. "Can't we make peace?"

Everything seemed conducive to this. The heat of the hour had led Frenchmen and Germans, in separate groups, to sit down beside the graves, where the forest trees cast their shade. Only our words disturbed the silence.

"Don't expect to get the names of the dead, whatever happens," I answered.

"You can keep them," said the stonemason, sitting down. He was a thin-faced man a little older than myself, with short grayish hair. "We're an obstinate pair. After all, I understand your feelings; you don't want it to be said that those stones had names taken off them in order to carve these on. Well, I'd never have had the courage to take them off myself if they hadn't been written in Hebrew. But in Hebrew they mean nothing! I'm not even sure that they were names and dates. And then the stones were there in the camp, without anybody lying beneath them. Put yourself in my place! I'm bored, I need to keep my hand in for after the war, and I'm presented with tools and stones! But it's all right; I give up the names," he added, pulling out his tobacco pouch and handing it to me.

I rolled a cigarette and he did the same.

"I give up the names," he went on, puffing at his cigarette, "but all the same, something really ought to be done with those stones—they're not all in good condition, you know, some of them are molding away. Besides, the dead people or their relations, if there are any left, wouldn't see any harm in our making use of these stones now that the Germans have pulled them up. They'd surely like that better than to see them crushed and scattered on the roads. . . . After all, we're on the same side as they are, aren't we? . . . So this is what I thought. Let's not talk of carving names on them, but let's make them into little ornaments, cornerstones for instance. We must think of our own dead too. I needn't comment on what you've done for them; it's quite unbelievable. But after all, there's nothing permanent about it. Suppose they take us off into Germany next month; after a single winter there'll be no sign of your graves. The rains and the melting snows will have washed all the earth away, and grass and briars will have grown over it. But with stones . . . Oh, I'm not suggesting making monuments," he cried, raising his hand to forestall objections. "I assure you, very little is needed. And I'm speaking from experience—I'm in the trade. A little pyramid at each corner of the grave for instance, or a ball on a little pedestal if you prefer, although that's much harder to make, or else carved corners joined together with chains, only unluckily we haven't any chains . . . well, you get the idea, something not very high, firmly fastened into the ground, preferably with cement, and above all something decently made. . . ."

But I was no longer listening to him. For the last few minutes I had been listening to the rumble of a train and now it was growing louder. The train was about to emerge round the tip of the wood. I could tell, without waiting for it to roll past before my eyes, what sort of freight it carried. Its slow, jolting sound warned me of the other sounds that would follow although for the moment a contrary wind delayed them. I should soon hear the weeping, the cries of despair. The silence, no doubt, was due to the wind; but perhaps, too, those who were being transported, knowing what fate awaited them, had deliberately refrained from sending out their lamentations into that empty, sun-baked plain, in which the great migrations of death had never yet awakened any lasting echo.

And so it all began again. Every day one or two convoys crossed the plain, and then were no more to be seen; and when night fell a train would rumble, too slowly, through the silence. New processions appeared on the little road that led to the station. They were smaller and more infrequent than the previous ones and seemed to be made up of belated recruits, of survivors from some ancient and now almost forgotten disaster, of beggars or vagrants rounded up in the middle of their wasted summer. Nothing rolled out of the bundles this time; nobody seemed to be in a hurry now, and the soldiers who struck at the sides of the column did so with the lazy indifference of cowherds.

The massacre was drawing to a close, but it lingered interminably like the raw gleam of a lurid sunset on walls, between patches of shadow. We said to ourselves: "Surely this must be the end of these torments." The plain seemed to have nothing left to offer death save its quota of vagrants. We were wrong. On the contrary, those whom the Germans were now dispatching to be slaughtered had been taken from the ranks of a scattered resistance movement which, up till now, without our knowledge, had been fighting to the last ditch for the right to live.

If they seemed wearier than those who had gone before them along the same road that led between darkly gleaming slagheaps and through engine-sheds to Calvary, it was because they had suffered a twofold defeat. They had been surrounded in the forest, they had been arrested at night on the roads or among the brambles in the ravines, where for so long they had been wandering round and round in dazed despair. Now, in the evenings near the graveyard, we often caught sight of nonchalant armed soldiers making their way in extended line into the forest, and bending down from time to time to pick a strawberry. Brodno was encircled with a military cordon, and the whole region was being combed step by step.

This state of siege, of which we shortly felt the oppressive effects, brought back a certain animation around the camp and around our graveyard. The inhabitants—Poles, Ukrainians and Ruthenians—realizing that for the moment the Germans had no designs on them, suddenly felt the need to move around in all directions within the circle that hemmed them in. They came to look at the graveyard, the fame of which had reached them. They stood still at some distance from it, motionless, communicating with one another by gestures.

One evening two girls came forward as far as the verge of the forest, close to the spot where we had discovered the charnel.

One of them was plain and awkward; the other was slender and seemed younger. The brightness of her blue-green eyes disturbed me. They shouted to the soldiers that they were Polish. The setting, the gathering dusk and my own troubled heart made the younger girl's smile seem like that of a vision. To the German who, with one foot on a grave, asked them their names and ages, she called out "Maria!" and there was still joy in her voice. I had gone up to the sentry; the girl looked at me and waved to me as she went off. Next day as we made our way to the graveyard I caught sight of her at the door of the new canteen and we made signs of greeting to each other.

From that time on I clung to her image. The first rains of autumn had begun; the graveyard had ceased to be a garden and was once more a burial ground. The earth sank under one's feet; it was deep again, and heavy, like a morass. Autumn promised to be a season rich in deaths. More trains came through from the further end of the plain, with white faces framed in the narrow windows, trains full of condemned creatures who, this time, uttered no cries of thirst but stood motionless, clutching their despair between their hands like a twisted handkerchief. My mind was fixed on her image.

I turned to it again when new processions appeared on the road leading to the station or when, towards evening, groups of soldiers made their way into the forest with more speed than usual. Three or four times a day, whether we were going to the graveyard or coming away from it. Maria, standing at the door of the Polish canteen, would watch me thoughtfully and smile at me. My friends nudged one another but let fall no word. From their dealings with the dead they had learned to respect mysteries. And this was undoubtedly a mystery—my devotion to the image of this girl about whom I knew nothing to suggest that she was worthy of it surprised me more than it surprised them. I pushed back my hair from my forehead—it was damp from the drizzling rain—and stood upright; there were still many things to which I should have to bear witness later, many sufferings to be shared, many hopes to be nurtured, many steps to be taken which would add up to something someday. But as soon as I had reached the graveyard and was standing under the branches at the edge of the forest, where raindrops rustled, the image recurred.

One morning I was sunk in this sort of reverie when Cordonat called me. He led me to the end of the last row of graves where, covered with planks and with an old tarpaulin to keep off the rain water, the spare grave lay empty, awaiting its corpse. He had just been inspecting it and had found there, besides more subtle traces which, as an expert poacher, he had picked out, a cigarette end of unfamiliar origin. It was rolled in a scrap of paper from a child's exercise book and made of coarse unripe tobacco, presumably taken from one of the plants which, in those penurious times, the peasants used to grow outside their houses.

"It wasn't there last night," Cordonat told me. "For several days I'd noticed that somebody had been taking up and putting back the planks and the tarpaulin during the night. So I began to keep an eye on the grave. The other proofs are more tricky, you might not believe them. But this one! There's no possible doubt about it: a man comes to sleep in our grave at night."

"Well, what then?" I asked.

"Well, so much the better," he cried. "It must be a hunted man. For once, let this graveyard be some use to a living man!" (Cordonat had never been really enthusiastic about the graveyard.) "Only we ought to help him. This evening, for instance, we might leave him some provisions."

I did not doubt Cordonat's charitable intentions, but I also suspected that he was anxious to secure a further proof by this method. We had lately been receiving a little food from France and we were able, without too great a sacrifice, to deposit in the grave for the benefit of the stranger who inhabited it a handful of sugar, a piece of chocolate or a few army biscuits deducted from our store of provisions, which were meticulously arranged and counted, dry and crumbly as rats' provender. When evening came, before leaving the graveyard we slipped a parcel between the planks and then replaced them as before. Next day the parcel had disappeared. Cordonat found at the bottom of the grave a scrap of paper on which a message of thanks was penciled, in English. The two words had been written with a trembling hand, no doubt by the first light that filtered through the parted planks as dawn brought back panic.

That evening our gift was made up merely of a few cigarettes. I added a message: "Who are you?" Although the answer consisted only of two initials, it was clear and it did not surprise me. It was written on a piece of packing paper: I.L. An arrow invited me to turn over the page: "You know me Peter= [the arithmetical sign *equals*] I know you. Keep quiet, both of you, keep quiet. Thank You." I had recognized Lebovitch. But how could he know that it was I who had put the cigarettes there and that only one other knew the secret?

"During the day he must stay hidden by the edge of the forest and watch us," said Cordonat.

It would have been madly imprudent, and the Germans would have discovered him long ago; Cordonat admitted it. These communications through the trap door of a grave, these notes with their anguished laconicism, the condition of "semi-survival" in which Lebovitch existed and the second sight with which he seemed to be endowed—all these things concurred to give me the impression that our continual contact with death was beginning to open for us a sort of wicket gate into its domain. I almost forgot Maria. Sometimes, in the evening, she would walk a little way along the road below the graveyard just as we had slipped a few provisions into the grave and were replacing the planks, the tarpaulin and the stones that held it down with furtive care, as though we were laying snares. Cordonat rediscovered the pleasures of his poaching days. I would stand up and wave to Maria. The sentries were amused by my performance and it distracted their attention from the mysterious tasks which we were performing over the empty grave.

"How do you live?" I wrote to Lebovitch, leaving him a few sheets of blank paper. His answers grew longer but also more obscure. He lived with difficulty. During the day he remained hidden, no doubt, in the high branches of a tree, for he wrote: "I am very high up. Do not look for me. A glance might betray me. I see them come to and fro. Please tell me what is happening about the dogs [these last words were underlined]. How soon will autumn be here? Have I the right to try and escape from God's will? Anyhow all this is unendurable and I shall not hold out much longer! If only they would let me speak! I should be exempted. Yes, they should let me speak! Have you heard tell in the village of anyone being exempted? Keep quiet! Thank you."

During the days that followed I had difficulty in preventing Cordonat from staring up at the tree tops on the forest border; he would have attracted the guards' attention. Instinctively, as one accustomed to roaming the woods and starting animals from their lair, he found it an exciting game to hunt for Lebovitch's aerial shelter. One morning I surprised him sitting down with his back turned to the forest and staring into a pocket mirror concealed in his hand which he was slowly turning in all directions.

"I tell you he's not found a perch in any of these trees," he told me, putting back his little mirror into his pocket. "Even if he'd been well camouflaged I'd have discovered him. There's no foliage thick enough to conceal a man. He'd have been obliged to surround himself with other branches, cut off from other parts of the tree; and believe me, I know from experience that the color of leaves changes as soon as they're cut. Ask him about it, once and for all. . . ."

I wrote a note to Lebovitch to this effect, accompanying it with a handful of army biscuits.

"I can't tell you where I am," replied Lebovitch. "You haven't told me anything about the dogs. And the exemptions? Do they ever exempt anybody? Yesterday three more trains went past. During the night there were luminous things drawn on the carriages! You can have *no idea of it.* [The last words were underlined.] This morning I vomited because of all the raw mushrooms I'd eaten. God rises early just now. So does the wind! Couldn't they have pity on me? Tell me if it's humanly possible?"

"We shan't learn anything more," said Cordonat when I had read him this letter.

The incoherence of these notes depressed him. We were too close to the world beyond death not to be aware of its dank breath when speech became so sparing and sibylline, when a human being's presence proved so elusive, while these brief messages expressed a tortured silence pierced by a thousand exclamation marks, like nails. We continued to offer food to this Egyptian tomb, which a couple of days later had to remove farther off; death provided Lebovitch with a new neighbor.

Cordonat offered to dig the spare grave into which, that same evening, Lebovitch would creep to rest, and at the bottom of the grave he arranged a little pile of earth for the sleeper to lay his head on. I helped him in this task which, as we soon admitted to one another, filled us with a strange uneasiness; we had the feeling that we were preparing to bury an unseen friend. The present that we left in the grave that evening was more generous than usual. I avoided putting any message with it, however. The tone of the answers distressed me.

Lebovitch broke silence only on the second morning (he must have written his notes during the day, up in his tree or inside some unknown retreat). He had been deeply touched by Cordonat's thoughtfulness in providing the earthen pillow. Perhaps, also, by the nearness of a newly dead Frenchman, whose burial he must have watched, since he never took his eyes off the graveyard. He wrote: "I know that one day there will be no more morning. Last night I went on knocking for an hour against the earth, on the side where all the others are lying. I say an hour, but my watch has stopped. I wanted to go on knocking all night. As long as I'm knocking I'm alive. Even here, where I am now, at this moment, I'm knocking. And I keep saying: have mercy, have mercy! They've killed them all, Peter, killed them all! What is loneliness?"

I could no longer keep up this dialogue, and I could hardly bear the abstract presence that now filled my narrow universe. I could no longer look with confidence at the forest trees or into the hollow grave, nor gaze out over the plain where one of those trains was always dawdling. Like those tireless birds that drop to the ground like stones and as soon as they have touched it dart back to perch on one of a hundred quivering branches, then dizzily gravitate to the ground once more and once more rebound upward, as though in avid quest not of earthly or aerial prey but of pure trajectories, of secretly deliberate flights, of prophetic tangents, or as though irrevocably doomed to this endless to-and-fro, Lebovitch moved between the grave and the treetops every day; he was only fit for shooting down.

Yet I would have liked to save him. His talk of exemptions, although I had at first put it down to insanity (and I was beginning to find out how rich and full was insanity's account compared with the meager bankbooks of reason), had made an impression on my mind. I felt I must sound the Germans, or Maria, who doubtless knew what was happening in the village now.

The Germans told me that the fate of the Jews of Brodno (and elsewhere too) was old history now. "Let's talk of Maria instead," they said to me. "You're keen on her, aren't you, you rascal?"

I endured their mockery. As it happened I was anxious to speak to Maria. If she passed along the road tomorrow, might I not beckon to her to come? I'd only want a couple of minutes with her. I felt infinitely sorry for myself. Evening with its swift black clouds was falling over Volynia and its crowd of dead, over the distant fires of war, and I was standing there, eager to strike my pitiful bargain—two minutes of that time!—I was standing there with Lebovitch at my back, weighing me down, his hard hands against my shoulders. The Germans made fun of my anxiety. "Maybe," they said, sending me back to my graves. I slipped a note into the pit: "In two days I'll know for sure about the exemptions."

Next evening Maria appeared on the road with her friend. "You can call her," cried the sentries, laughing. I called her. She saw me. I beckoned to her to meet me at the graveyard gate. But she shook her head with a smile. She walked away. I had turned white with vexation to which, in the depths of my heart, I gave a bitter name. On the new message that I found in the grave Lebovitch wrote: "I'm knocking harder than ever, Peter. It's the only thing to do: knock, knock, knock!" He said nothing more about exemptions.

A few trains full of condemned victims still passed through the plain. When the sound of them had faded away I still seemed to hear behind me the dull persistent rhythm of blows hammered against the earth, against a tree trunk, mingled with the throbbing of my temples, the tapping of summer's last woodpecker, a far-off woodcutter's blows and the rumble of a passing cart, in a soothing confusion.

Summer drew to a close. In the darkened countryside all life was slowed down; even the great convoys of death became more infrequent—those harvests, too, had been gathered in. But the dawn of a new season was less like the morning after a bad dream or the lucid astonishment of life than the final draining away of all blood, the last stage of a slow hemorrhage behind which a few tears of lymph trickle, like mourners at life's funeral. Autumn brought a prospect of exhausted silence, of a world pruned of living sounds, of the reign of total death. What had I left to delay this consummation, when every gust of wind in the branches of the trees, every leaf blown away, every corner of the naked sky, reminded me of its imminence?

It was from that moment that the life of Lebovitch, his dwindled, precarious existence, became for me the last remaining symbol of a denial of death—of that death which was so visibly being consummated all around me. I renewed our dialogue. I sent him urgent messages: "Where were the rest? What had happened to him? and indeed, who was he?" I urged him to tell me about his own past and that of all the others.

For nothing makes you feel so impoverished as the death of strangers; dying, they testify to death without yielding anything of their lives that might compensate for the enhanced importance of darkness. Thus what did he know of Lidia's fate? He must tell me; the survival of all my hopes depended on it.

These questions remained unanswered. Lidia sank in her turn, with all the others, like them consecrated to death, behind those distant horizons of memory where, even after we have forgotten everything, there lingers a pale light, an endless comforting twilight, a thin streak of radiance which will perhaps serve us for eyes when our eyes are closed in death. Lebovitch soon caught up with Lidia on that dark slope where never, not in all eternity, should I be able to reach them.

One morning on arriving at the graveyard we found that the planks covering the empty grave had been thrown to one side. At the bottom of the grave there lay a black jacket without an armlet. One of its pockets was full of acorns. I knew then that Lebovitch would never come back. Had he been surprised in his sleep or, in a fit of madness, had he suddenly rushed out into the forest to meet his murderers? I raised my head. Clouds were rising towards the west. The wind had got up. My companions were taking away the dead leaves that fell on the graves. In the flowerbeds the summer flowers had turned black. Soon no more convoys passed along the railway over the plain, which in the mornings was drowned in mist. There were no more soldiers to be seen patrolling the woods, where the trees were growing bare. Autumn was really there now.

Maria chose this time to visit the burial-ground. I had been waiting for her there for a long time, secretly convinced that she would come. One evening she came along the ill-paved road, her thin summer dress clinging to her in the wind. She walked slowly, her face uplifted, quietly resolute, and her fair hair was fluttering over her brow. A violent fit of trembling possessed me. I turned towards the single sentry who now guarded us. He was a prematurely old man, full of melancholy resignation. He knew about my romance, and nodded his head.

I darted towards Maria like a dog let off the leash. Seeing me come, she hurried forward without taking her eyes off me and, passing the gate of the graveyard, quickly made for the edge of the forest. The sky had grown dark and the wind was blowing stronger. I only caught up with her under the trees. I seized hold of her arm, and she drew me on involuntarily while I spoke to her in breathless tones. I did not know what I was saying; I was in a sort of ecstasy.

Suddenly I drew her to me and pressed her closely. My face groped feverishly for the hollow of her shoulder. For so long I had been waiting for this moment of blindness, of oblivion, this ultimate salvation! It was the only refuge within which to break the heavy, clipped wings that thought had set growing on one's temples, the only place where the mind, like a heavy-furred moth dazzled by the great light of death, could for an instant assuage its longing to return to the warm, original darkness of its chrysalis. . . . Frightened by the desperate wildness of my movement, Maria sharply withdrew from my arms, kissed me on the lips and fled. For a moment I tried to follow her. Then I leaned against a tree. Within me and about me a great silence had fallen. After a moment I wiped away my tears and went back to my dead.

AFTERWORD

the helpers

No joke is more exhausted and less funny than the income-tax joke. The little frightened man who sits up all night to get his returns in before the Big Bad State gets a deputy out for him, how familiar he is, and how essentially fictive, we tell ourselves. If we think about it, it probably occurs to us that he belongs to a world that has largely vanished, the world of the lascivious traveling salesman, the virile iceman, and the naughty adolescents behind the barn or deep in the pasture. Today every town with a population of 100 has a discount house, no one gets ice, and the kids all have sports cars, or at the very least Daddy's Rambler when they want it.

The truth is, there is nothing dated about the frightened man filling out his tax forms, nor is there anything particularly comic about the situation. The jokes have no particular significance because their butt is a Caspar Milquetoast who is frightened by anything, and they are dated because they have not accommodated themselves to the present, for they have left out an essential element of the new situation, the "helper." If today ". . . even the man/scavenging filth in the back alley trash cans,/has two children, a beach wagon, a helpmate," he no doubt has an accountant as well, for who would voyage through the labyrinth of the tax laws, which are surely more complicated and more complicated and more important than the road to Paradise, without a guide?

I have gone to some doctors who tediously explained the nature of my problem as though I had come to them for knowledge. I go to the doctor for two things, a cure and a pair of trained hands, and I will usually settle for either. There are times when one must put the responsibility for one's body or mind or both into qualified hands; after all one is not an expert trained to cope with one's serious problems. And one trots off to the accountant with precisely the same need.

Although my income is by no means vast or its sources complex, I went for help a few years ago to a certified public accountant who had been recommended by a friend. I had delayed until the last possible moment and so had to be accommodated during irregular hours. On a Sunday morning in early April I rose in the elevator from the clammy lobby of an old downtown office building, hoping I would like my accountant as I had come to like my doctor and my dentist. On the phone he had seemed a bit irritated that I had waited so long to make an appointment, and doubtless he would have preferred to spend such a pleasant morning with his family. I found his office in the dark, marbled catacomb of the sixth floor and knocked. The door was opened by a dark, short, unshaven man in his early forties carrying a cup of coffee; he wore a checked sport shirt and a pair of denim trousers no longer adequate around the waist, and he looked thoroughly unprofessional. As he ushered me into his inner office, explaining unnecessarily why the girls were off today, I wondered if I had come to the right place. Seated behind his enormous glass-topped desk, surrounded by an army of musty unreadable tax volumes, and with his gold-framed glasses riding low on the bridge of his nose, he lifted my hopes. And when his hand came gently forward with a "what have we today?" I handed over my tax forms with an enormous sense of relief.

The next hour was one of the most surprising hours of my life. Never have I tried so desperately and so cunningly to place the burden of a guilt I felt to be mine onto another man, and never have I been so surgically foiled. For, of course, Mr. Harris, as I shall call him, was a professional. What were my medical expenses? he would ask barely looking up from the forms over which he poised with a drawing pencil honed down to the thinness of a needle, and when I would answer a bit too quickly, he would ask with the slightest suggestion of a smile, "Are you sure? Remember, Philip, it is not me they'll drag out of bed."

"Nobody's going to drag me out of bed."

No, of course not. It had merely been a convenient figure of speech. "Do you have the receipts for those travel expenses? Even your old plane ticket will help. Do you have anything from the hotels?" No, I didn't. I must remember that the burden of proof was mine; did I want to forget those expenses? No, I'd spent the money, and I wanted to get what was mine. Yes, I was entitled to that, he let me know, especially if I could prove the nature and size of the expenditures. His hand, pencil poised and ready, hovered over a blank line until I said, "Yes, I want what's mine."

It was rather amazing, he commented, how I always seemed to spend money in round figures. "Isn't that something? You bought exactly $100 worth of books last year." And so I added a dollar and twenty-seven cents here and subtracted some change there to make it all seem a bit less predictable and a little more believable. Finally, he leaned back in his chair with a satisfied look and consulted his watch; in less than an hour he'd saved me $187. The form was before me and the tip of his pencil indicated where I was to sign, and I did so immediately, feeling that I had hesitated too often in the past fifty-two minutes.

"And I sign here," he said smiling, though even his sunniest moments were touched by the blue shadow of his beard. "Now you'll go to jail with me," I said. No, fortunately he wouldn't. The $187 was mine, and if there was a crime that was mine also.

"Seriously," I said, and I was serious, "if I'm in error about any of this, or if I can't prove that these were my expenses, what are my chances of getting in trouble?"

"Very small," he said. "You don't earn enough to merit an investigation. Very small and very real."

"Very real?"

"Yes."

"What do you mean?"

"Well, if they want to get you, they can. You can't prove

most of this. They might think you're honest, but they've got to have proof."

"What might they do if they investigated me? What sort of punishment would they deal out if they found against me?"

"I can't say; they're very arbitrary about it."

"Why that's terrifying," I said.

Of course it was terrifying; that was exactly the point, it was supposed to be terrifying. No, he wasn't kidding, and he seemed not the least surprised at my shock. This was a small part of a planned campaign of terror. How could he be sure? It served no other function than to terrorize the great mass of Americans. He'd seen its effects on hundreds of people: "The tax situation scares the hell out of everyone, me included." And he'd seen the campaign grow; the State, he assured me, was making more demands each year, and their punishments were becoming increasingly inconsistent. "If people can't be made to love the law, they'll be made to fear it; after all the government has got to have this money." He told me that he had had some clients who had suggested they pay more than the law required so as to be certain they would not be harassed, but even payment in excess guaranteed nothing, in fact it might only arouse suspicion. "A planned campaign of terror." All the accountants in America knew this, so did all the lawyers. "It's common knowledge," he said, politely ushering me to the door.

Again, I hadn't come for knowledge, but that's what I'd gotten, and as I clicked down the dark hall toward the elevator, I wondered what great truth of my life on earth the real estate agent in 621 could give me if I knocked on his door, or the chiropractor in 617, or the insurance broker in 611. What little hidden nuggets of my private life were a matter of public fact to these experts? When I emerged from the cold lobby below I was not nearly as overjoyed by the bright spring sunshine as I should have been. It was as though the day were too bright, the sunlight too revealing.

But only for a moment. I am a free man in a free society, I told myself; the police and the armed forces are my servants and the great network of the state protects me. The dialogue went on, for I knew that when at dawn the jet fighters boomed over and their vibrations shuddered the foundations of my house, I did not leap from nightmare with any sense of security, and the reality into which I wakened was more detailed and awesome than my dreams.

If as the years go by I come to accommodate the jets, if my body and my mind learn to sleep through the morning blast, what violence will I have allowed to be perpetrated upon myself? Whether I sleep or wake, something is being done to me, and long ago I surrendered the notion I could stop it.

No doubt men can live in the most unspeakable circumstances, I tell myself so as to defend what is left of me, and often having faced the violent and terrible they gain a measure of nobility deprived the average little man running from his average little problems. Today, it does not seem terribly difficult merely to survive; some say it is all too easy, and that what Americans lack is the minute-by-minute challenge of the frontier, for out of such circumstances are born men of substance, toughness, vision. Maybe. But I think of the men I knew who came back from the POW camps of World War II, men who took their plates into the corner and ate with their backs to their mothers and wives. The price that many of them paid to endure in a world of beasts was to become beasts. One former prisoner of war told me that he had been home six months before he realized that it was the manner in which he ate that was making the evening meal a traumatic experience for his family. "I knew something was wrong, everybody was upset and nervous before we ate, and then one night I heard the kind of noises I was making. I sounded like a dog." Part of the horror of deprivation is that one no longer knows of what one is deprived.

We do not live in POW camps, the defense answers; we do not live in a world in which the forces of society have declared themselves for death, for suppression, a world in which terror is no longer hidden in anonymity but walks the streets at broad noon, uniformed and efficient. All this is true, but invisibility and subtlety rarely make an evil less dangerous. And how can one deal with an external evil if one can no longer deal with oneself? If day by day I surrender to the "helpers" the responsibility for and the knowledge of my body, my mind, my finances, my defense, my rights, what do I leave myself? What significant choices can I make living in a medium-sized American town with three television channels?

PHILIP LEVINE

2

on youth in an organized society

JAMES BALDWIN

equal in paris

On the 19th of December, in 1949, when I had been living in Paris for a little over a year, I was arrested as a receiver of stolen goods and spent eight days in prison. My arrest came about through an American tourist whom I had met twice in New York, who had been given my name and address and told to look me up. I was then living on the top floor of a ludicrously grim hotel on the rue du Bac, one of those enormous dark, cold, and hideous establishments in which Paris abounds that seem to breathe forth, in their airless, humid, stone-cold halls, the weak light, scurrying chambermaids, and creaking stairs, an odor of gentility long long dead. The place was run by an ancient Frenchman dressed in an elegant black suit which was green with age, who cannot properly be described as bewildered or even as being in a state of shock, since he had really stopped breathing around 1910. There he sat at his desk in the weirdly lit, fantastically furnished lobby, day in and day out, greeting each one of his extremely impoverished and *louche* lodgers with a stately inclination of the head that he had no doubt been taught in some impossibly remote time was the proper way for a *propriétaire* to greet his guests. If it had not been for his daughter, an extremely hardheaded *tricoteuse*—the inclination of *her* head was chilling and abrupt, like the downbeat of an ax—the hotel would certainly have gone bankrupt long before. It was said that this old man had not gone farther than the door of his hotel for thirty years, which was not at all difficult to believe. He looked as though the daylight would have killed him.

I did not, of course, spend much of my time in this palace. The moment I began living in French hotels I understood the necessity of French cafés. This made it rather difficult to look me up, for as soon as I was out of bed I hopefully took notebook and fountain pen off to the upstairs room of the Flore, where I consumed rather a lot of coffee and, as evening approached, rather a lot of alcohol, but did not get much writing done. But one night, in one of the cafés of St. Germain des Près, I was discovered by this New Yorker and only because we found ourselves in Paris we immediately established the illusion that we had been fast friends back in the good old U.S.A. This illusion proved itself too thin to support an evening's drinking, but by that time it was too late. I had committed myself to getting him a room in my hotel the next day, for he was living in one of the nest of hotels near the Gare St. Lazare, where, he said, the *propriétaire* was a thief, his wife a repressed nymphomaniac, the chambermaids "pigs," and the rent a crime. Americans are always talking this way about the French and so it did not occur to me that he meant what he said or that he would take into his own hands the means of avenging himself on the French Republic. It did not occur to me, either, that the means which he *did* take could possibly have brought about such dire results, results which were not less dire for being also comic-opera.

It came as the last of a series of disasters which had perhaps been made inevitable by the fact that I had come to Paris originally with a little over forty dollars in my pockets, nothing in the bank, and no grasp whatever of the French language. It developed, shortly, that I had no grasp of the French character either. I considered the French an ancient, intelligent, and cultured race, which indeed they are. I did not know, however, that ancient glories imply, at least in the middle of the present century, present fatigue and, quite probably, paranoia; that there is a limit to the role of the intelligence in human affairs; and that no people come into possession of a culture without having paid a heavy price for it. This price they cannot, of course, assess, but it is revealed in their personalities and in their institutions. The very word "institutions," from my side of the ocean, where, it seemed to me, we suffered so cruelly from the lack of them, had a pleasant ring, as of safety and order and common sense; one had to come into contact with these institutions in order to understand that they were also outmoded, exasperating, completely impersonal, and very often cruel. Similarly, the personality which had seemed from a distance to be so large and free had to be dealt with before one could see that, if it was large, it was also inflexible and, for the foreigner, full of strange, high, dusty rooms which could not be inhabited. One had, in short, to come into contact with an alien culture in order to understand that a culture was not a community basket-weaving project, nor yet an act of God; was something neither desirable nor undesirable in itself, being inevitable, being nothing more or less than the recorded and visible effects on a body of people of the vicissitudes with which they had been forced to deal. And their great men are revealed as simply another of these vicissitudes, even if, quite against their will, the brief battle of their great men with them has left them richer.

When my American friend left his hotel to move to mine, he took with him, out of pique, a bedsheet belonging to the hotel and put it in his suitcase. When he arrived at my hotel I borrowed the sheet, since my own were filthy and the chambermaid showed no sign of bringing me any clean ones, and put it on my bed. The sheets belonging to *my* hotel I put out in the hall, congratulating myself on having thus forced on the attention of the Grand Hôtel de Bac the unpleasant state of its linen. Thereafter, since, as it turned out, we kept very different hours—I got up at noon, when, as I gathered by meeting him on the stairs one day, he was only just getting in—my new-found friend and I saw very little of each other.

On the evening of the 19th I was sitting thinking melancholy thoughts about Christmas and staring at the walls of my room. I imagine that I had sold something or that someone had sent me a Christmas present, for I remember that I had a little money. In those days in Paris, though I floated, so to speak, on a sea of acquaintances, I knew almost no one. Many people were eliminated from my orbit by virtue of the fact that they had more money than I did, which placed me, in my own eyes, in the humiliating role of a free-loader; and other people were eliminated by virtue of the fact that they enjoyed their poverty, shrilly insisting that this wretched round of hotel rooms, bad food, humiliating concierges, and unpaid bills was the Great Adventure. It couldn't, however, for me, end soon enough, this Great Adventure; there was a real question in my mind as to which would end soonest, the Great Adventure or me. This meant, however, that there were many evenings when I sat in my room, knowing that I couldn't work there, and not knowing what to do, or whom to see. On this particular evening I went down and knocked on the American's door.

There were two Frenchmen standing in the room, who immediately introduced themselves to me as policemen; which did not worry me. I had got used to policemen in Paris bobbing up at the most improbable times and places, asking to see one's *carte d'identité*. These policemen, however, showed very little interest in my papers. They were looking for something else. I could not imagine what this would be and, since I knew I certainly didn't have it, I scarcely followed the conversation they were having with my friend. I gathered that they were looking for some kind of gangster and since I wasn't a gangster and knew that gangsterism was not, insofar as he had one, my friend's style, I was sure that the two policemen would presently bow and say *Merci, messieurs,* and leave. For by this time, I remember very clearly, I was dying to have a drink and go to dinner.

I did not have a drink or go to dinner for many days after this, and when I did my outraged stomach promptly heaved everything up again. For now one of the policemen began to exhibit the most vivid interest in me and asked, very politely, if he might see my room. To which we mounted, making, I remember, the most civilized small talk on the way and even continuing it for some moments after we were in the room in which there was certainly nothing to be seen but the familiar poverty and disorder of that precarious group of people of whatever age, race, country, calling, or intention which Paris recognizes as *les étudiants* and sometimes, more ironically and precisely, as *les nonconformistes.* Then he moved to my bed, and in a terrible flash, not quite an instant before he lifted the bedspread, I understood what he was looking for. We looked at the sheet, on which I read, for the first time, lettered in the most brilliant scarlet I have ever seen, the name of the hotel from which it had been stolen. It was the first time the word *stolen* entered my mind. I had certainly seen the hotel monogram the day I put the sheet on the bed. It had simply meant nothing to me. In New York I had seen hotel monograms on everything from silver to soap and towels. Taking things from New York hotels was practically a custom, though, I suddenly realized, I had never known anyone to take a *sheet.* Sadly, and without a word to me, the inspector took the sheet from the bed, folded it under his arm, and we started back downstairs. I understood that I was under arrest.

And so we passed through the lobby, four of us, two of us very clearly criminal, under the eyes of the old man and his daughter, neither of whom said a word, into the streets where a light rain was falling. And I asked, in French, "But is this very serious?"

For I was thinking, it is, after all, only a sheet, not even new.

"No," said one of them. "It's not serious."

"It's nothing at all," said the other.

I took this to mean that we would receive a reprimand at the police station and be allowed to go to dinner. Later on I concluded that they were not being hypocritical or even trying to comfort us.

They meant exactly what they said. It was only that they spoke another language.

In Paris everything is very slow. Also, when dealing with the bureaucracy, the man you are talking to is never the man you have to see. The man you have to see has just gone off to Belgium, or is busy with his family, or has just discovered that he is a cuckold; he will be in next Tuesday at three o'clock, or sometime in the course of the afternoon, or possibly tomorrow, or, possibly, in the next five minutes. But if he is coming in the next five minutes he will be far too busy to be able to see you today. So that I suppose I was not really astonished to learn at the commissariat that nothing could possibly be done about us before The Man arrived in the morning. But no, we could not go off and have dinner and come back in the morning. Of course he knew that we *would* come back—that was not the question. Indeed, there was no question: we would simply have to stay there for the night. We were placed in a cell which rather resembled a chicken coop. It was now about seven in the evening and I relinquished the thought of dinner and began to think of lunch.

I discouraged the chatter of my New York friend and this left me alone with my thoughts. I was beginning to be frightened and I bent all my energies, therefore, to keeping my panic under control. I began to realize that I was in a country I knew nothing about, in the hands of a people I did not understand at all. In a similar situation in New York I would have had some idea of what to do because I would have had some idea of what to expect. I am not speaking now of legality which, like most of the poor, I had never for an instant trusted, but of the temperament of the people with whom I had to deal. I had become very accomplished in New York at guessing and, therefore, to a limited extent manipulating to my advantage the reactions of the white world. But this was not New York. None of my old weapons could serve me here. I did not know what they saw when they looked at me. I knew very well what Americans saw when they looked at me and this allowed me to play endless and sinister variations on the role which they had assigned me; since I knew that it was, for them, of the utmost importance that they never be confronted with what, in their own personalities, made this role so necessary and gratifying to them, I knew that they could never call my hand or, indeed, afford to know what I was doing; so that I moved into every crucial situation with the deadly and rather desperate advantages of bitterly accumulated perception, of pride and contempt. This is an awful sword and shield to carry through the world, and the discovery that, in the game I was playing, I did myself a violence of which the world, at its most ferocious, would scarcely have been capable, was what had driven me out of New York. It was a strange feeling, in this situation, after a year in Paris, to discover that my weapons would never again serve me as they had.

It was quite clear to me that the Frenchmen in whose hands I found myself were no better or worse than their American counterparts. Certainly their uniforms frightened me quite as much, and their impersonality, and the threat, always very keenly felt by the poor, of violence, was as present in that commissariat as it had ever been for me in any police station. And I had seen, for example, what Paris policemen could do to Arab peanut vendors. The only difference here was that I did not understand these people, did not know what techniques their cruelty took, did not know enough about their personalities to see danger coming, to ward it off, did not know on what ground to meet it. That evening in the commissariat I was not a despised black man. They would simply have laughed at me if I had behaved like one. For them, I was an American. And here it was they who had the advantage, for that word, *Américain,* gave them some idea, far from inaccurate, of what to expect from me. In order to corroborate none of their ironical expectations I said nothing and did nothing—which was not the way any Frenchman, white or black, would have reacted. The question thrusting up from the bottom of my mind was not *what* I was, but *who.* And this question, since a *what* can get by with skill but *who* demands resources, was my first real intimation of what humility must mean.

In the morning it was still raining. Between nine and ten o'clock a black Citroën took us off to the Ile de la Cité, to the great, gray Préfecture. I realize now that the questions I put to the various policemen who escorted us were always answered in such a way as to corroborate what I wished to hear. This was not out of politeness, but simply out of indifference—or, possibly, an ironical pity—since each of the policemen knew very well that nothing would speed or halt the machine in which I had become entangled. They knew I did not know this and there was certainly no point in their telling me. In one way or another I would certainly come out at the other side—for they also knew that being found with a stolen bedsheet in one's possession was not a crime punishable by the guillotine. (They had the advantage over me there, too, for there were certainly moments later on when I was not so sure.) If I did *not* come out at the other side—well, that was just too bad. So, to my question, put while we were in the Citroën—"Will it be over today?"—I received a "*Oui, bien sûr.*" He was not lying. As it turned out, the *procès-verbal* was over that day. Trying to be realistic, I dismissed, in the Citroën, all thoughts of lunch and pushed my mind ahead to dinner.

At the Préfecture we were first placed in a tiny cell, in which it was almost impossible either to sit or to lie down. After a couple of hours of this we were taken down to an office, where, for the first time, I encountered the owner of the bedsheet and where the *procès-verbal* took place. This was simply an interrogation, quite chillingly clipped and efficient (so that there was, shortly, no doubt in one's own mind that one *should* be treated as a criminal), which was recorded by a secretary. When it was over, this report was given to us to sign. One had, of course, no choice but to sign it, even though my mastery of written French was very far from certain. We were being held, according to the law in France, incommunicado, and all my angry demands to be allowed to speak to my embassy or to see a lawyer met with a stony "*Oui, oui. Plus tard.*" The *procès-verbal* over, we were taken back to the cell, before which, shortly, passed the owner of the bedsheet. He said he hoped we had slept well, gave a vindictive wink, and disappeared.

By this time there was only one thing clear: that we had no way of controlling the sequence of events and could not possibly guess what this sequence would be. It seemed to me, since what I regarded as the high point—the *procès-verbal*—had been passed and since the hotel-keeper was once again in possession of his sheet, that we might reasonably expect to be released from police custody in a matter of hours. We had been detained now for what would soon be twenty-four hours, during which time I had learned only that the official charge against me was *receleur*. My mental shifting, between lunch and dinner, to say nothing of the physical lack of either of these delights, was beginning to make me dizzy. The steady chatter of my friend from New York, who was determined to keep my spirits up, made me feel murderous; I was praying that some power would release us from this freezing pile of stone before the impulse became the act. And I was beginning to wonder what was happening in that beautiful city, Paris, which lived outside these walls. I wondered how long it would take before anyone casually asked, "But where's Jimmy? He hasn't been around"—and realized, knowing the people I knew, that it would take several days.

Quite late in the afternoon we were taken from our cells; handcuffed, each to a separate officer; led through a maze of steps and corridors to the top of the building; fingerprinted; photographed. As in movies I had seen, I was placed against a wall, facing an old-fashioned camera, behind which stood one of the most completely cruel and indifferent faces I had ever seen, while someone next to me and, therefore, just outside my line of vision, read off in a voice from which all human feeling, even feeling of the most base description, had long since fled, what must be called my public characteristics—which, at that time and in that place, seemed anything but that. He might have been roaring to the hostile world secrets which I could barely, in the privacy of midnight, utter to myself. But he was only reading off my height, my features, my approximate weight, my color—that color which, in the United States, had often, odd as it may sound, been my salvation—the color of my hair, my age, my nationality. A light then flashed, the photographer and I staring at each other as though there was murder in our hearts, and then it was over. Handcuffed again, I was led downstairs to the bottom of the building, into a great enclosed shed in which had been gathered the very scrapings off the Paris streets. Old, old men, so ruined and old that life in them seemed really to prove the miracle of the quickening power of the Holy Ghost—for clearly their life was no longer their affair, it was no longer even their burden, they were simply the clay which had once been touched. And men not so old, with faces the color of lead and the consistency of oatmeal, eyes that made me think of stale *café-au-lait* spiked with arsenic, bodies which could take in food and water—any food and water—and pass it out, but which could not do anything more, except possibly, at midnight, along the riverbank where rats scurried, rape. And young men, harder and crueler than the Paris stones, older by some five to seven years. And North Africans, old and young, who seemed the only living people in this place because they yet retained the grace to be bewildered. But they were not bewildered by being in this shed: they were simply bewildered because they were no longer in North Africa. There was a great hole in the center of this shed which was the common toilet. Near it, though it was impossible to get very far from it, stood an old man with white hair, eating a piece of camembert. It was at this point, probably, that thought, for me, stopped, that physiology, if one may say so, took over. I found myself incapable of saying a word, not because I was afraid I would cry but because I was afraid I would vomit. And I did not think any longer of the city of Paris but my mind flew back to that home from which I had fled. I was sure that I would never see it any more. And it must have seemed to me that my flight from home was the cruelest trick I had ever played on myself, since it had led me here, down to a lower point than any I could ever in my life have imagined—lower, far, than anything I had seen in that Harlem which I had so hated and so loved, the escape from which had soon become the greatest direction of my life. After we had been here an hour or so a functionary came and opened the door and called out our names. And I was sure that *this* was my release. But I was handcuffed again and led out of the Préfecture into the streets—it was dark now, it was still raining—and before the steps of the Préfecture stood the great police wagon, doors facing me, wide open. The handcuffs were taken off, I entered the wagon, which was peculiarly constructed. It was divided by a narrow aisle, and on each side of the aisle was a series of narrow doors. These doors opened on a narrow cubicle, beyond which was a door which opened onto another narrow cubicle: three or four cubicles, each private, with a locking door. I was placed in one of them; I remember there was a small vent just above my head which let in a little light. The door of my cubicle was locked from the outside. I had no idea where this wagon was taking me and, as it began to move, I began to cry. I suppose I cried all the way to prison, the prison called Fresnes, which is twelve kilometers outside of Paris.

For reasons I have no way at all of understanding, prisoners whose last initial is A, B, or C are always sent to Fresnes; everybody else is sent to a prison called, rather cynically it seems to me, La Santé. I will, obviously, never be allowed to enter La Santé, but I was told by people who certainly seemed to know that it was infinitely more unbearable than Fresnes. This arouses in me, until today, a positive storm of curiosity concerning what I promptly began to think of as The Other Prison. My colleague in crime, occurring lower in the alphabet, had been sent there and I confess that the minute he was gone I missed him. I missed him because he was not French and because he was the only person in the world who knew that the story I told was true.

For, once locked in, divested of shoelaces, belt, watch, money, papers, nailfile, in a freezing cell in which both the window and the toilet were broken, with six other adventurers, the story I told of *l'affaire du drap de lit* elicited only the wildest amusement or the most suspicious disbelief. Among the people who shared my cell the first three days no one, it is true, had been arrested for anything much more serious—or, at least, not serious in my eyes. I remember that there was a boy who had stolen a knitted sweater from a *monoprix*, who would probably, it was agreed, receive a six-month sentence. There was an older man there who had been arrested for some kind of petty larceny. There were two North Africans, vivid, brutish, and beautiful, who alternated between gaiety and fury, not at the fact of their arrest but at the state of the cell. None poured as much emotional energy into the fact of their arrest as I did; they took it, as I would have liked to take it, as simply another unlucky happening in a very dirty world. For, though I had grown accustomed to thinking of myself as looking upon the world with a hard, penetrating eye, the truth was that they were far more realistic about the world than I, and more nearly right about it. The gap between us, which only a gesture I made could have bridged, grew steadily, during thirty-six hours, wider. I could not make any gesture simply because they frightened me. I was unable to accept my imprisonment as a fact, even as a temporary fact. I could not, even for a moment, accept my present companions as *my* companions. And they, of course, felt this and put it down, with perfect justice, to the fact that I was an American.

There was nothing to do all day long. It appeared that we would one day come to trial but no one knew when. We were awakened at seven-thirty by a rapping on what I believe is called the Judas, that small opening in the door of the cell which allows the guards to survey the prisoners. At this rapping we rose from the floor—we slept on straw pallets and each of us was covered with one thin blanket—and moved to the door of the cell. We peered through the opening into the center of the prison, which was, as I remember, three tiers high, all gray stone and gunmetal steel, precisely that prison I had seen in movies, except that, in the movies, I had not known that it was cold in prison. I had not known that when one's shoelaces and belt have been removed one is, in the strangest way, demoralized. The necessity of shuffling and the necessity of holding up one's trousers with one hand turn one into a rag doll. And the movies fail, of course, to give one any idea of what prison food is like. Along the corridor, at seven-thirty, came three men, each pushing before him a great garbage can, mounted on wheels. In the garbage can of the first was the bread—this was passed to one through the small opening in the door. In the can of the second was the coffee. In the can of the third was what was always called *la soupe,* a pallid paste of potatoes which had certainly been bubbling on the back of the prison stove long before that first, so momentous revolution. Naturally, it was cold by this time and, starving as I was, I could not eat it. I drank the coffee—which was not coffee—because it was hot, and spent the rest of the day, huddled in my blanket, munching on the bread. It was not the French bread one bought in bakeries. In the evening the same procession returned. At ten-thirty the lights went out. I had a recurring dream, each night, a nightmare which always involved my mother's fried chicken. At the moment I was about to eat it came the rapping at the door. Silence is really all I remember of those first three days, silence and the color gray.

I am not sure now whether it was on the third or the fourth day that I was taken to trial for the first time. The days had nothing, obviously, to distinguish them from one another. I remember that I was very much aware that Christmas Day was approaching and I wondered if I was really going to spend Christmas Day in prison. And I remember that the first trial came the day before Christmas Eve.

On the morning of the first trial I was awakened by hearing my name called. I was told, hanging in a kind of void between my mother's fried chicken and the cold prison floor, "*Vous préparez. Vous êtes extrait*"—which simply terrified me, since I did not know what interpretation to put on the word "*extrait,*" and since my cellmates had been amusing themselves with me by telling terrible stories about the inefficiency of French prisons, an inefficiency so extreme that it had often happened that someone who was supposed to be taken out and tried found himself on the wrong line and was guillotined instead. The best way of putting my reaction to this is to say that, though I knew they were teasing me, it was simply not possible for me to totally *dis*-believe them. As far as I was concerned, once in the hands of the law in France, anything could happen. I shuffled along with the others who were *extrait* to the center of the prison, trying, rather, to linger in the office, which seemed the only warm spot in the whole world, and found myself again in that dreadful wagon, and was carried again to the Ile de la Cité, this time to the Palais de Justice. The entire day, except for ten minutes, was spent in one of the cells, first waiting to be tried, then waiting to be taken back to prison.

For I was *not* tried that day. By and by I was hand-cuffed and led through the halls, upstairs to the courtroom where I found my New York friend. We were placed together, both stage-whisperingly certain that this was the end of our ordeal. Nevertheless, while I waited for our case to be called, my eyes searched the courtroom, looking for a face I knew, hoping, anyway, that there was someone there who knew *me*, who would carry to someone outside the news that I was in trouble. But there was no one I knew there and I had had time to realize that there was probably only one man in Paris who could help me, an American patent attorney for whom I had worked as an office boy. He could have helped me because he had a quiet solid position and some prestige and would have testified that, while working for him, I had handled large sums of money regularly, which made it rather unlikely that I would stoop to trafficking in bedsheets. However, he was somewhere in Paris, probably at this very moment enjoying a snack and a glass of wine and as far as the possibility of reaching him was concerned, he might as well have been on Mars. I tried to watch the proceedings and to make my mind a blank. But the proceedings were not reassuring. The boy, for example, who had stolen the sweater *did* receive a six-month sentence. It seemed to me that all the sentences meted out that day were excessive; though, again, it seemed that all the people who were sentenced that day had made, or clearly were going to make, crime their career. This seemed to be the opinion of the judge, who scarcely looked at the prisoners or listened to them; it seemed to be the opinion of the prisoners, who scarcely bothered to speak in their own behalf; it seemed to be the opinion of the lawyers, state lawyers for the most part, who were defending them. The great impulse of the courtroom seemed to be to put these people where they could not be seen—and not because they were offended at the crimes, unless, indeed, they were offended that the crimes were so petty, but because they did not wish to know that their society could be counted on to produce, probably in greater and greater numbers, a whole body of people for whom crime was the only possible career. Any society inevitably produces its criminals, but a society at once rigid and unstable can do nothing whatever to alleviate the poverty of its lowest members, cannot present to the hypothetical young man at the crucial moment that so-well-advertised right path. And the fact, perhaps, that the French are the earth's least sentimental people and must also be numbered among the most proud aggravates the plight of their lowest, youngest, and unluckiest members, for it means that the idea of rehabilitation is scarcely real to them. I confess that this attitude on their part raises in me sentiments of exasperation, admiration, and despair, revealing as it does, in both the best and the worst sense, their renowned and spectacular hard-headedness.

Finally our case was called and we rose. We gave our names. At the point that it developed that we were American the proceedings ceased, a hurried consultation took place between the judge and what I took to be several lawyers. Someone called out for an interpreter. The arresting officer had forgotten to mention our nationalities and there was, therefore, no interpreter in the court. Even if our French had been better than it was we would not have been allowed to stand trial without an interpreter. Before I clearly understood what was happening, I was handcuffed again and led out of the courtroom. The trial had been set back for the 27th of December.

I have sometimes wondered if I would *ever* have got out of prison if it had not been for the older man who had been arrested for the mysterious petty larceny. He was acquitted that day and when he returned to the cell—for he could not be released until morning—he found me sitting numbly on the floor, having just been prevented, by the sight of a man, all blood, being carried back to *his* cell on a stretcher, from seizing the bars and screaming until they let me out. The sight of the man on the stretcher proved, however, that screaming would not do much for me. The petty-larceny man went around asking if he could do anything in the world outside for those he was leaving behind. When he came to me I, at first, responded, "No, nothing"—for I suppose I had by now retreated into the attitude, the earliest I remember, that of my father, which was simply (since I had lost his God) that nothing could help me. And I suppose I will remember with gratitude until I die the fact that the man now insisted: "*Mais, êtes-vous sûr?*" Then it swept over me that he was going *outside* and he instantly became my first contact since the Lord alone knew how long with the outside world. At the same time, I remember, I did not really believe that he would help me. There was no reason why he should. But I gave him the phone number of my attorney friend and my own name.

So, in the middle of the next day, Christmas Eve, I shuffled downstairs again, to meet my visitor. He looked extremely well fed and sane and clean. He told me I had nothing to worry about any more. Only not even he could do anything to make the mill of justice grind any faster. He would, however, send me a lawyer of his acquaintance who would defend me on the 27th, and he would himself, along with several other people, appear as a character witness. He gave me a package of Lucky Strikes (which the turnkey took from me on the way upstairs) and said that, though it was doubtful that there would be an celebration in the prison, he would see to it that I got a fine Christmas dinner when I got out. And this, somehow, seemed very funny. I remember being astonished at the discovery that I was actually laughing. I was, too, I imagine, also rather disappointed that my hair had not turned white, that my face was clearly not going to bear any marks of tragedy, disappointed at bottom, no doubt, to realize, facing him in that room, that far worse things had happened to most people and that, indeed, to paraphrase my mother, if this was the worst thing that ever happened to me I could consider myself among the luckiest people ever to be born. He injected—my visitor—into my solitary nightmare common sense, the world, and the hint of blacker things to come.

The next day, Christmas, unable to endure my cell, and feeling that, after all, the day demanded a gesture, I asked to be allowed to go to Mass, hoping to hear some music. But I found myself, for a freezing hour and a half, locked in exactly the same kind of cubicle as in the wagon which had first brought me to prison, peering through a slot placed at the level of the eye at an old Frenchman, hatted, overcoated, muffled, and gloved, preaching in this language which I did not understand, to this row of wooden boxes, the story of Jesus Christ's love for men.

The next day, the 26th, I spent learning a peculiar kind of game, played with match-sticks, with my cellmates. For, since I no longer felt that I would stay in this cell forever, I was beginning to be able to make peace with it for a time. On the 27th I went again to trial and, as had been predicted, the case against us was dismissed.

The story of the *drap de lit,* finally told, caused great merriment in the courtroom, whereupon my friend decided that the French were "great." I was chilled by their merriment, even though it was meant to warm me. It could only remind me of the laughter I had often heard at home, laughter which I had sometimes deliberately elicited. This laughter is the laughter of those who consider themselves to be at a safe remove from all the wretched, for whom the pain of the living is not real. I had heard it so often in my native land that I had resolved to find a place where I would never hear it any more. In some deep, black, stony, and liberating way, my life, in my own eyes, began during that first year in Paris, when it was borne in on me that this laughter is universal and never can be stilled.

ALAN SILLITOE

the loneliness of the long-distance runner

As soon as I got to Borstal they made me a long-distance cross-country runner. I suppose they thought I was just the build for it because I was long and skinny for my age (and still am) and in any case I didn't mind it much, to tell you the truth, because running had always been made much of in our family, especially running away from the police. I've always been a good runner, quick and with a big stride as well, the only trouble being that no matter how fast I run, and I did a very fair lick even though I do say so myself, it didn't stop me getting caught by the cops after that bakery job.

You might think it a bit rare, having long-distance cross-country runners in Borstal, thinking that the first thing a long-distance cross-country runner would do when they set him loose at them fields and woods would be to run as far away from the place as he could get on a bellyful of Borstal slumgullion—but you're wrong, and I'll tell you why. The first thing is that them bastards over us aren't as daft as they most of the time look, and for another thing I'm not so daft as I would look if I tried to make a break for it on my long-distance running, because to abscond and then get caught is nothing but a mug's game, and I'm not falling for it. Cunning is what counts in this life, and even that you've got to use in the slyest way you can; I'm telling you straight: they're cunning, and I'm cunning. If only 'them' and 'us' had the same ideas we'd get on like a house on fire, but they don't see eye to eye with us and we don't see eye to eye with them, so that's how it stands and how it will always stand. The one fact is that all of us are cunning, and because of this there's no love lost between us. So the thing is that they know I won't try to get away from them: they sit there like spiders in that crumbly manor house, perched like jumped-up jackdaws on the roof, watching out over the drives and fields like German generals from the tops of tanks. And even when I jog-trot on behind a wood and they can't see me anymore they know my sweeping-brush head will bob along that hedge-top in an hour's time and that I'll report to the bloke on the gate. Because when on a raw and frosty morning I get up at five o'clock and stand shivering my belly off on the stone floor and all the rest still have another hour to snooze before the bells go, I slink downstairs through all the corridors to the big outside door with a permit running-card in my fist, I feel like the first and last man on the world, both at once, if you can believe what I'm trying to say. I feel like the first man because I've hardly got a stitch on and am sent against the frozen fields in a shimmy and shorts—even the first poor bastard dropped on to the earth in midwinter knew how to make a suit of leaves, or how to skin a pterodactyl for a topcoat. But there I am, frozen stiff, with nothing to get me warm except a couple of hours' long-distance running before breakfast, not even a slice of bread-and-sheepdip. They're training me up fine for the big sports day when all the pig-faced snotty-nosed dukes and ladies—who can't add two and two together and would mess themselves like loonies if they didn't have slavies to beck-and-call—come and make speeches to us about sports being just the thing to get us leading an honest life and keep our itching finger-ends off them shop locks and safe handles and hairgrips to open gas meters. They give us a bit of blue ribbon and a cup for a prize after we've shagged ourselves out running or jumping, like race horses, only we don't get so well looked-after as race horses, that's the only thing.

So there I am, standing in the doorway in shimmy and shorts, not even a dry crust in my guts, looking out at frosty flowers on the ground. I suppose you think this is enough to make me cry? Not likely. Just because I feel like the first bloke in the world wouldn't make me bawl. It makes me feel fifty times better than when I'm cooped up in that dormitory with three hundred others. No, it's sometimes when I stand there feeling like the *last* man in the world that I don't feel so good. I feel like the last man in the world because I think that all those three hundred sleepers behind me are dead. They sleep so well I think that every scruffy head's kicked the bucket in the night and I'm the only one left, and when I look out into the bushes and frozen ponds I have the feeling that it's going to get colder and colder until everything I can see, meaning my red arms as well, is going to be covered with a thousand miles of ice, all the earth, right up to the sky and over every bit of land and sea. So I try to kick this feeling out and act like I'm steamed up enough to get this feeling in me, I take a flying leap out of the doorway, and off I trot.

I'm in Essex. It's supposed to be a good Borstal, at least that's what the governor said to me when I got here from Nottingham. "We want to trust you while you are in this establishment," he said, smoothing out his newspaper with lily-white workless hands, while I read the big words upside down: *Daily Telegraph.* "If you play ball with us, we'll play ball with you." (Honest to God, you'd have thought it was going to be one long tennis match.) "We want hard honest work and we want good athletics," he said as well. "And if you give us both these things you can be sure we'll do right by you and send you back into the world an honest man." Well, I could have died laughing, especially when straight after this I hear the barking sergeant-major's voice calling me and two others to attention and marching us off like we was Grenadier Guards. And when the governor kept saying how 'we' wanted you to do this, and 'we' wanted you to do that, I kept looking round for the other blokes, wondering how many of them there was. Of course, I knew there were thousands of them, but as far as I knew only one was in the room. And there *are* thousands of them, all over the poxeaten country, in shops, offices, railway stations, cars, houses, pubs—In-law blokes like you and them, all on the watch for Out-law blokes like me and us—and waiting to 'phone for the coppers as soon as we make a false move. And it'll always be there, I'll tell you that now, because I haven't finished making all my false moves yet, and I dare say I won't until I kick the bucket. If the In-laws are hoping to stop me making false moves they're wasting their time. They might as well stand me up against a wall and let fly with a dozen rifles. That's the only way they'll stop me, and a few million others. Because I've been doing a lot of thinking since coming here. They can spy on us all day to see if we're pulling our puddings and if we're working good or doing our 'athletics' but they can't make an X-ray of our guts to find out what we're telling ourselves. I've been asking myself all sorts of questions, and thinking about my life up to now. And I like doing all this. It's a treat. It passes the time away and don't make Borstal seem half so bad as the boys in our street used to say it was. And this long-distance running lark is the best of all, because it makes me think so good that I learn things even better than when I'm on my bed at night. And apart from that, what with thinking so much while I'm running I'm getting to be one of the best runners in the Bostal. I can go my five miles round better than anybody else I know.

So as soon as I tell myself I'm the first man ever to be dropped into the world, and as soon as I take that first flying leap out into the frosty grass of an early morning when even birds haven't the heart to whistle, I get to thinking, and that's what I like. I go my rounds in a dream, turning at lane or footpath corners without knowing I'm turning, leaping brooks without knowing they're there, and shouting good morning to the early cow-milker without seeing him. It's a treat, being a long-distance runner, out in the world by yourself with not a soul to make you bad-tempered or tell you what to do or that there's a shop to break and enter a bit back from the next street. Sometimes I think that I've never been so free as during that couple of hours when I'm trotting up the path out of the gates and turning by that bare-faced, big-bellied oak tree at the lane end. Everything's dead, but good, because it's dead before coming alive, not dead after being alive. That's how I look at it. Mind you, I often feel frozen stiff at first. I can't feel my hands or feet or flesh at all, like I'm a ghost who wouldn't know the earth was under him if he didn't see it now and again through the mist. But even though some people would call this frost-pain suffering if they wrote about it to their mams in a letter, I don't, because I know that in half an hour I'm going to be warm, that by the time I get to the main road and am turning on to the wheatfield footpath by the bus stop I'm going to feel as hot as a potbellied stove and as happy as a dog with a tin tail.

It's a good life, I'm saying to myself, if you don't give in to coppers and Borstal-bosses and the rest of them bastard-faced In-laws. Trot-trot-trot. Puff-puff-puff. Slap-slap-slap go my feet on the hard soil. Swish-swish-swish as my arms and side catch the bare branches of a bush. For I'm seventeen now, and when they let me out of this—if I don't make a break and see that things turn out otherwise—they'll try to get me in the army, and what's the difference between the army and this place I'm in now? They can't kid me, the bastards. I've seen the barracks near where I live, and if there weren't swaddies on guard outside with rifles you wouldn't know the difference between their high walls and the place I'm in now. Even though the swaddies come out at odd times a week for a pint of ale, so what? Don't I come out three mornings a week on my long-distance running, which is fifty times better than boozing. When they first said that I was to do my long-distance running without a guard pedalling beside me on a bike I couldn't believe it; but they called it a progressive and modern place, though they can't kid me because I know it's just like any other Borstal, going by the stories I've heard, except that they let me trot about like this. Borstal's Borstal no matter what they do; but anyway I moaned about it being a bit thick sending me out so early to run five miles on an empty stomach, until they talked me round to thinking it wasn't so bad—which I knew all the time—until they called me a good sport and patted me on the back when I said I'd do it and that I'd try to win them the Borstal Blue Ribbon Prize Cup For Long Distance Cross Country Running (All England). And now the governor talks to me when he comes on his rounds, almost as he'd talk to his prize race horse, if he had one.

"All right, Smith?" he asks.

"Yes, sir," I answer.

He flicks his grey moustache: "How's the running coming along?"

"I've set myself to trot round the grounds after dinner just to keep my hand in, sir," I tell him.

The pot-bellied pop-eyed bastard gets pleased at this: "Good show. I know you'll get us that cup," he says.

And I swear under my breath: "Like boggery, I will." No, I won't get them that cup, even though the stupid tash-twitching bastard has all his hopes in me. Because what does his barmy hope mean? I ask myself. Trot-trot-trot, slap-slap-slap, over the stream and into the wood where it's almost dark and frosty-dew twigs sting my legs. It don't mean a bloody thing to me, only to him, and it means as much to him as it would mean to me if I picked up the racing paper and put my bet on a hoss I didn't know, had never seen, and didn't care a sod if I ever did see. That's what it means to him. And I'll lose that race, because I'm not a race horse at all, and I'll let him know it when I'm about to get out—if I don't sling my hook even before the race. By Christ I will. I'm a human being and I've got thoughts and secrets and bloody life inside me that he doesn't know is there, and he'll never know what's there because he's stupid. I suppose you'll laugh at this, me saying the governor's a stupid bastard when I know hardly how to write and he can read and write and add-up like a professor. But what I say is true right enough. He's stupid, and I'm not, because I can see further into the likes of him than he can see into the likes of me. Admitted, we're both cunning, but I'm more cunning and I'll win in the end even if I die in gaol at eighty-two, because I'll have more fun and fire out of my life than he'll ever get out of his. He's read a thousand books I suppose, and for all I know he might even have written a few, but I know for a dead cert, as sure as I'm sitting here, that what I'm scribbling down is worth a million to what he could ever scribble down. I don't care what anybody says, but that's the truth and can't be denied. I know when he talks to me and I look into his army mug that I'm alive and he's dead. He's as dead as a doornail. If he ran ten yards he'd drop dead. If he got ten yards into what goes on in my guts he'd drop dead as well—with surprise. At the moment it's dead blokes like him as have the whip-hand over blokes like me, and I'm almost dead sure it'll always be like that, but even so, by Christ, I'd rather be like I am—always on the run and breaking into shops for a packet of fags and a jar of jam—than have the whip-hand over somebody else and be dead from the toe nails up. Maybe as soon as you get the whip-hand over somebody you do go dead. By God, to say that last sentence has needed a few hundred miles of long-distance running. I could no more have said that at first than I could have took a million-pound note from my back pocket. But it's true, you know, now I think of it again, and has always been true, and always will be true, and I'm surer of it every time I see the governor open that door and say Goodmorning lads.

As I run and see my smoky breath going out into the air as if I had ten cigars stuck in different parts of my body I think more on the little speech the governor made when I first came. Honesty.

Be honest. I laughed so much one morning I went ten minutes down in my timing because I had to stop and get rid of the stitch in my side. The governor was so worried when I got back late that he sent me to the doctor's for an X-ray and heart check. Be honest. It's like saying: Be dead, like me, and then you'll have no more pain of leaving your nice slummy house for Borstal or prison. Be honest and settle down in a cosy six pounds a week job. Well, even with all this long-distance running I haven't yet been able to decide what he means by this, although I'm just about beginning to—and I don't like what it means. Because after all my thinking I found that it adds up to something that can't be true about me, being born and brought up as I was. Because another thing people like the governor will never understand is that I *am* honest, that I've never been anything else but honest, and that I'll always be honest. Sounds funny. But it's true because I know what honest means according to me and he only knows what it means according to him. I think my honesty is the only sort in the world, and he thinks his is the only sort in the world as well. That's why this dirty great walled-up and fenced-up manor house in the middle of nowhere has been used to coop-up blokes like me. And if I had the whip-hand I wouldn't even bother to build a place like this to put all the cops, governors, posh whores, penpushers, army officers, Members of Parliament in; no, I'd stick them up against a wall and let them have it, like they'd have done with blokes like us years ago, that is, if they'd ever known what it means to be honest, which they don't and never will so help me God Almighty.

I was nearly eighteen months in Borstal before I thought about getting out. I can't tell you much about what it was like there because I haven't got the hang of describing buildings or saying how many crumby chairs and slatted windows make a room. Neither can I do much complaining, because to tell you the truth I didn't suffer in Borstal at all. I gave the same answer a pal of mine gave when someone asked him how much he hated it in the army. "I didn't hate it," he said. "They fed me, gave me a suit, and pocket-money, which was a bloody sight more than I ever got before, unless I worked myself to death for it, and most of the time they wouldn't let me work but sent me to the dole office twice a week." Well, that's more or less what I say. Borstal didn't hurt me in that respect, so since I've got no complaints I don't have to describe what they gave us to eat, what the dorms were like, or how they treated us. But in another way Borstal does something to me. No, it doesn't get my back up, because it's always been up, right from when I was born. What it does do is show me what they've been trying to frighten me with. They've got other things as well, like prison and, in the end, the rope. It's like me rushing up to thump a man and snatch the coat off his back when, suddenly, I pull up because he whips out a knife and lifts it to stick me like a pig if I come too close. That knife is Borstal, clink, the rope. But once you've seen the knife you learn a bit of unarmed combat. You have to, because you'll never get that sort of knife in your own hands, and this unarmed combat doesn't amount to much. Still, there it is, and you keep on rushing up to this man, knife or not, hoping to get one of your hands on his wrist and the other on his elbow both at the same time, and press back until he drops the knife.

You see, by sending me to Borstal they've shown me the knife, and from now on I know something I didn't know before: that it's war between me and them. I always knew this, naturally, because I was in Remand Homes as well and the boys there told me a lot about their brothers in Borstal, but it was only touch and go then, like kittens, like boxing-gloves, like dobbie. But now that they've shown me the knife, whether I ever pinch another thing in my life again or not, I know who my enemies are and what war is. They can drop all the atom bombs they like for all I care: I'll never call it war and wear a soldier's uniform, because I'm in a different sort of war, that they think is child's play. The war they think is war is suicide, and those that go and get killed in war should be put in clink for attempted suicide because that's the feeling in blokes' minds when they rush to join up or let themselves be called up. I know, because I've thought how good it would be sometimes to do myself in and the easiest way to do it, it occurred to me, was to hope for a big war so's I could join up and get killed. But I got past that when I knew I already was in a war of my own, that I was born into one, that I grew up hearing the sound of 'old soldiers' who'd been over the top at Dartmoor, half-killed at Lincoln, trapped in no-man's-land at Borstal, that sounded louder than any Jerry bombs. Government wars aren't my wars; they've got nowt to do with me, because my own war's all that I'll ever be bothered about. I remember when I was fourteen and I went out into the country with three of my cousins, all about the same age, who later went to different Borstals, and then to different regiments, from which they soon deserted, and then to different gaols where they still are as far as I know. But anyway, we were all kids then, and wanted to go out to the woods for a change, to get away from the roads of stinking hot tar one summer. We climbed over fences and went through fields, scrumping a few sour apples on our way, until we saw the wood about a mile off. Up Collier's Pad we heard another lot of kids talking in high-school voices behind a hedge. We crept up on them and peeped through the brambles, and saw they were eating a picnic, a real posh spread out of baskets and flasks and towels. There must have been about seven of them, lads and girls sent out by their mams and dads for the afternoon. So we went on our bellies through the hedge like crocodiles and surrounded them, and then dashed into the middle, scattering the fire and batting their tabs and snatching up all there was to eat, then running off over Cherry Orchard fields into the wood, with a man chasing us who'd come up while we were ransacking their picnic. We got away all right, and had a good feed into the bargain, because we'd been clambed to death and couldn't wait long enough to get our chops ripping into them thin lettuce and ham sandwiches and creamy cakes.

Well, I'll always feel during every bit of my life like those daft kids should have felt before we broke them up. But they never dreamed that what happened was going to happen, just like the governor of this Borstal who spouts to us about honesty and all that wappy stuff don't know a bloody thing, while I know every minute of my life that a big boot is always likely to smash any nice picnic I might be barmy and dishonest enough to make for myself. I admit that there've been times when I've thought of telling the governer all this so as to put him on his guard, but when I've got as close as seeing him I've changed my mind, thinking to let him either find out for himself or go through the same mill as I've gone through. I'm not hard-hearted (in fact I've helped a few blokes in my time with the odd quid, lie, fag, or shelter from the rain when they've been on the run) but I'm boggered if I'm going to risk being put in the cells just for trying to give the governor a bit of advice he don't deserve. If my heart's soft I know the sort of people I'm going to save it for. And any advice I'd give the governor wouldn't do him the least bit of good; it'd only trip him up sooner than if he wasn't told at all, which I suppose is what I want to happen. But for the time being I'll let things go on as they are, which is something else I've learned in the last year or two. (It's a good job I can only think of these things as fast as I can write with this stub of pencil that's clutched in my paw, otherwise I'd have dropped the whole thing weeks ago.)

By the time I'm half-way through my morning course, when after a frost-bitten dawn I can see a phlegmy bit of sunlight hanging from the bare twigs of beech and sycamore, and when I've measured my half-way mark by the short-cut scrimmage down the steep bush-covered bank and into the sunken lane, when still there's not a soul in sight and not a sound except the neighing of a piebald foal in a cottage stable that I can't see, I get to thinking the deepest and daftest of all. The governor would have a fit if he could see me sliding down the bank because I could break my neck or ankle, but I can't not do it because it's the only risk I take and the only excitement I ever get, flying flat-out like one of them pterodactyls from the 'Lost World' I once heard on the wireless, crazy like a cut-balled cockerel, scratching myself to bits and almost letting myself go but not quite. It's the most wonderful minute because there's not one thought or word or picture of anything in my head while I'm going down. I'm empty, as empty as I was before I was born, and I don't let myself go, I suppose, because whatever it is that's farthest down inside me don't want me to die or hurt myself bad. And it's daft to think deep, you know, because it gets you nowhere, though deep is what I am when I've passed this half-way mark because the long-distance run of an early morning makes me think that every run like this is a life—a little life, I know—but a life as full of misery and happiness and things happening as you can ever get really around yourself—and I remember that after a lot of these runs I thought that it didn't need much know-how to tell how a life was going to end once it had got well started. But as usual I was wrong, caught first by the cops and then by my own bad brain, I could never trust myself to fly scot-free over these traps, was always tripped up sooner or later no matter how many I got over to the good without even knowing it. Looking back I suppose them big trees put their branches to their snouts and gave each other the wink, and there I was whizzing down the bank and not seeing a bloody thing.

II

I don't say to myself: "You shouldn't have done the job and then you'd have stayed away from Borstal"; no, what I ram into my runner-brain is that my luck had no right to scram just when I was on my way to making the coppers think I hadn't done the job after all. The time was autumn and the night foggy enough to set me and my mate Mike roaming the streets when we should have been rooted in front of the telly or stuck into a plush posh seat at the pictures, but I was restless after six weeks away from any sort of work, and well you might ask me why I'd been bone-idle for so long because normally I sweated my thin guts out on a milling-machine with the rest of them, but you see, my dad died from cancer of the throat, and mam collected a cool five hundred in insurance and benefits from the factory where he'd worked, "for your bereavement," they said, or words like that.

Now I believe, and my mam must have thought the same, that a wad of crisp blue-back fivers ain't a sight of good to a living soul unless they're flying out of your hand into some shopkeeper's till, and the shopkeeper is passing you tip-top things in exchange over the counter, so as soon as she got the money, mam took me and my five brothers and sisters out to town and got us dolled-up in new clothes. Then she ordered a twenty-one-inch telly, a new carpet because the old one was covered with blood from dad's dying and wouldn't wash out, and took a taxi home with bags of grub and a new fur coat. And do you know—you wain't believe me when I tell you—she'd still near three hundred left in her bulging handbag the next day, so how could any of us go to work after that? Poor old dad, he didn't get a look in, and he was the one who'd done the suffering and dying for such a lot of lolly.

Night after night we sat in front of the telly with a ham sandwich in one hand, a bar of chocolate in the other, and a bottle of lemonade between our boots, while mam was with some fancy-man upstairs on the new bed she'd ordered, and I'd never known a family as happy as ours was in that couple of months when we'd got all the money we needed. And when the dough ran out I didn't think about anything much, but just roamed the streets—looking for another job, I told mam—hoping I suppose to get my hands on another five hundred nicker so's the nice life we'd got used to could go on and on for ever. Because it's surprising how quick you can get used to a different life. To begin with, the adverts on the telly had shown us how much more there was in the world to buy than we'd ever dreamed of when we'd looked into shop windows but hadn't seen all there was to see because we didn't have the money to buy it with anyway. And the telly made all these things seem twenty times better than we'd ever thought they were. Even adverts at the cinema were cool and tame, because now we were seeing them in private at home. We used to cock our noses up at things in shops that didn't move, but suddenly we saw their real value because they jumped and glittered around the screen and had some pasty-faced tart going head over heels to get her nail-polished grabbers on to them or her lipstick lips over them, not like the crumby adverts you saw on posters or in newspapers as dead as doornails; these were flickering around loose, half-open packets and tins, making you think that all you had to do was finish opening them before they were yours, like seeing an unlocked safe through a shop window with the man gone away for a cup of tea without thinking to guard his lolly. The films they showed were good as well, in that way, because we couldn't get our eyes unglued from the cops chasing the robbers who had satchel-bags crammed with cash and looked like getting away to spend it—until the last moment. I always hoped they would end up free to blow the lot, and could never stop wanting to put my hand out, smash into the screen (it only looked a bit of rag-screen like at the pictures) and get the copper in a half-nelson so's he'd stop following the bloke with the money-bags. Even when he'd knocked off a couple of bank clerks I hoped he wouldn't get nabbed. In fact then I wished more than ever he wouldn't because it meant the hot-chair if he did, and I wouldn't wish that on anybody no matter what they'd done, because I'd read in a book where the hot-chair worn't a quick death at all, but that you just sat there scorching to death until you were dead. And it was when these cops were chasing the crooks that we played some good tricks with the telly, because when one of them opened his big gob to spout about getting their man I'd turn the sound down and see his mouth move like a goldfish or mackerel or a minnow mimicking what they were supposed to be acting—it was so funny the whole family nearly went into fits on the brand-new carpet that hadn't yet found its way to the bedroom. It was the best of all though when we did it to some Tory telling us about how good his government was going to be if we kept on voting for them—their slack chops rolling, opening and bumbling, hands lifting to twitch moustaches and touching their buttonholes to make sure the flower hadn't wilted, so that you could see they didn't mean a word they said, especially with not a murmur coming out because we'd cut off the sound. When the governor of the Borstal first talked to me I was reminded of those times so much that I nearly killed myself trying not to laugh. Yes, we played so many good stunts on the box of tricks that mam used to call us the Telly Boys, we got so clever at it.

My pal Mike got let off with probation because it was his first job—anyway the first they ever knew about—and because they said he would never have done it if it hadn't been for me talking him into it. They said I was a menace to honest lads like Mike—hands in his pockets so that they looked stone-empty, head bent forward at if looking for half-crowns to fill 'em with, a ripped jersey on and his hair falling into his eyes so that he could go up to women and ask them for a shilling because he was hungry—and that I was the brains behind the job, the guiding light when it came to making up anybody's mind, but I swear to God I worn't owt like that because really I ain't got no more brains than a gnat after hiding the money in the place I did. And I—being cranky like I am—got sent to Borstal because to tell you the honest truth I'd been to Remand Homes before—though that's another story and I suppose if ever I tell it it'll be just as boring as this one is. I was glad though that Mike got away with it, and I only hope he always will, not like silly bastard me.

So on this foggy night we tore ourselves away from the telly and slammed the front door behind us, setting off up our wide street like slow tugs on a river that'd broken their hooters, for we didn't know where the housefronts began what with the perishing cold mist all around. I was snatched to death without an overcoat: mam had forgotten to buy me one in the scrummage of shopping, and by the time I thought to remind her of it the dough was all gone. So we whistled 'The Teddy Boys Picnic' to keep us warm, and I told myself that I'd get a coat soon if it was the last thing I did. Mike said he thought the same about himself, adding that he'd also get some brand-new glasses with gold rims, to wear instead of the wire frames they'd given him at the school clinic years ago. He didn't twig it was foggy at first and cleaned his glasses every time I pulled him back from a lamp-post or car, but when he saw the lights on Alfreton Road looking like octopus eyes he put them in his pocket and didn't wear them again until we did the job. We hadn't got two ha-pennies between us, and though we weren't hungry we wished we'd got a bob or two when we passed the fish and chip shops because the delicious sniffs of salt and vinegar and frying fat made our mouths water. I don't mind telling you we walked the town from one end to the other and if our eyes worn't glued to the ground looking for lost wallets and watches they was swivelling around house windows and shop doors in case we saw something easy and worth nipping into.

Neither of us said as much as this to each other, but I know for a fact that that was what we was thinking. What I don't know—and as sure as I sit here I know I'll never know—is which of us was the first bastard to latch his peepers on to that baker's backyard. Oh yes, it's all right me telling myself it was me, but the truth is that I've never known whether it was Mike or not, because I do know that I didn't see the open window until he stabbed me in the ribs and pointed it out. "See it?" he said.

"Yes," I told him, "so let's get cracking."

"But what about the wall though?" he whispered, looking a bit closer.

"On your shoulders," I chipped in.

His eyes were already up there: "Will you be able to reach?" It was the only time he ever showed any life.

"Leave it to me," I said, ever-ready. "I can reach anywhere from your ham-hock shoulders."

Mike was a nipper compared to me, but underneath the scruffy draught-board jersey he wore were muscles as hard as iron, and you wouldn't think to see him walking down the street with glasses on and hands in pockets that he'd harm a fly, but I never liked to get on the wrong side of him in a fight because he's the sort that don't say a word for weeks on end—sits plugged in front of the telly, or reads a cowboy book, or just sleeps—when suddenly BIFF—half kills somebody for almost nothing at all, such as beating him in a race for the last Football Post on a Saturday night, pushing in before him at a bus stop, or bumping into him when he was day-dreaming about Dolly-on-the-Tub next door. I saw him set on a bloke once for no more than fixing him in a funny way with his eyes, and it turned out that the bloke was cockeyed but nobody knew it because he'd just that day come to live in our street. At other times none of these things would matter a bit, and I suppose the only reason why I was pals with him was because I didn't say much from one month's end to another either.

He puts his hands up in the air like he was being covered with a Gatling-Gun, and moved to the wall like he was going to be mowed down, and I climbed up him like he was a stile or step-ladder, and there he stood, the palms of his upshot maulers flat and turned out so's I could step on 'em like they was the adjustable jack-spanner under a car, not a sound of a breath nor the shiver of a flinch coming from him. I lost no time in any case, took my coat from between my teeth, chucked it up to the glass-topped wall (where the glass worn't too sharp because the jags had been worn down by years of accidental stones) and was sitting astraddle before I knew where I was. Then down the other side, with my legs rammed up into my throat when I hit the ground, the crack coming about as hard as when you fall after a high parachute drop, that one of my mates told me was like jumping off a twelve-foot wall, which this must have been. Then I picked up my bits and pieces and opened the gate for Mike, who was still grinning and full of life because the hardest part of the job was already done. "I came, I broke, I entered," like that clever-dick Borstal song.

I didn't think about anything at all, as usual, because I never do when I'm busy, when I'm draining pipes, looting sacks, yaling locks, lifting latches, forcing my bony hands and lanky legs into making something move, hardly feeling my lungs going in-whiff and out-whaff, not realizing whether my mouth is clamped tight or gaping, whether I'm hungry, itching from scabies, or whether my flies are open and flashing dirty words like muck and spit into the late-night final fog. And when I don't know anything about all this then how can I honest-to-God say I think of anything at such times? When I'm wondering what's the best way to get a window open or how to force a door, how can I be thinking or have anything on my mind? That's what the four-eyed white-smocked bloke with the note-book couldn't understand when he asked me questions for day and days after I got to Borstal; and I couldn't explain it to him then like I'm writing it down now; and even if I'd been able to maybe he still wouldn't have caught on because I don't know whether I can understand it myself even at this moment, though I'm doing my best you can bet.

So before I knew where I was I was inside the baker's office watching Mike picking up that cash box after he'd struck a match to see where it was, wearing a tailor-made fifty-shilling grin on his square crew-cut nut as his paws closed over the box like he'd squash it to nothing. "Out," he suddenly said, shaking it so's it rattled. "Let's scram."

"Maybe there's some more," I said, pulling half a dozen drawers out of a rollertop desk.

"No," he said, like he'd already been twenty years in the game, "this is the lot," patting his tin box, "this is it."

I pulled out another few drawers, full of bills, books and letters. "How do you know, you loony sod?"

He barged past me like a bull at a gate. "Because I do."

Right or wrong, we'd both got to stick together and do the same thing. I looked at an ever-loving babe of a brand-new typewriter, but knew it was too traceable, so blew it a kiss, and went out after him. "Hang on," I said, pulling the door to, "we're in no hurry."

"Not much we aren't," he says over his shoulder.

"We've got months to splash the lolly," I whispered as we crossed the yard, "only don't let that gate creak too much or you'll have the narks tuning-in."

"You think I'm barmy?" he said, creaking the gate so that the whole street heard.

I don't know about Mike, but now I started to think, of how we'd get back safe through the streets with that money-box up my jumper. Because he'd clapped it into my hand as soon as we'd got to the main road, which might have meant that he'd started thinking as well, which only goes to show how you don't know what's in anybody else's mind unless you think about things yourself. But as far as my thinking went at that moment it wasn't up to much, only a bit of fright that wouldn't budge not even with a hot blow-lamp, about what we'd say if a copper asked us where we were off to with that hump in my guts.

"What is it?" he'd ask, and I'd say: "A growth." "What do you mean, a growth, my lad?" he'd say back, narky like. I'd cough and clutch myself like I was in the most tripe-twisting pain in the world, and screw my eyes up like I was on my way to the hospital, and Mike would take my arm like he was the best pal I'd got. "Cancer," I'd manage to say to Narker, which would make his slow punch-drunk brain suspect a thing or two. "A lad of your age?" So I'd groan again, and hope to make him feel a real bully of a bastard, which would be impossible, but anyway: "It's in the family. Dad died of it last month, and I'll die of it next month by the feel of it." "What, did he have it in the guts?" "No, in the throat. But it's got me in the stomach." Groan and cough. "Well, you shouldn't be out like this if you've got cancer, you should be in the hospital."

I'd get ratty now: "That's where I'm trying to go if only you'd let me and stop asking so many questions. Aren't I, Mike?" Grunt from Mike as he unslung his cosh. Then just in time the copper would tell us to get on our way, kind and considerate all of a sudden, saying that the outpatient department of the hospital closes at twelve, so hadn't he better call us a taxi? He would if we liked, he says, and he'd pay for it as well. But we tell him not to bother, that he's a good bloke even if he is a copper, that we know a short cut anyway. Then just as we're turning a corner he gets it into his big batchy head that we're going the opposite way to the hospital, and calls us back. So we'd start to run . . . If you can call all that thinking.

Up in my room Mike rips open that money-box with a hammer and chisel, and before we know where we are we've got seventy-eight pounds fifteen and fourpence ha'penny *each* lying all over my bed like tea spread out on Christmas Day: cake and trifle, salad and sandwiches, jam tarts and bars of chocolate: all shared and shared alike between Mike and me because we believed in equal work and equal pay, just like the comrades my dad was in until he couldn't do a stroke anymore and had no breath left to argue with. I thought how good it was that blokes like that poor baker didn't stash all his cash in one of the big marble-fronted banks that take up every corner of the town, how lucky for us that he didn't trust them no matter how many millions of tons of concrete or how many iron bars and boxes they were made of, or how many coppers kept their blue pop-eyed peepers glued on to them, how smashing it was that he believed in money-boxes when so many shopkeepers thought it old-fashioned and tried to be modern by using a bank, which wouldn't give a couple of sincere, honest, hardworking, conscientious blokes like Mike and me a chance.

Now you'd think, and I'd think, and anybody with a bit of imagination would think, that we'd done as clean a job as could ever be done, that, with the baker's shop being at least a mile from where we lived, and with not a soul having seen us, and what with the fog and the fact that we weren't more than five minutes in the place, that the coppers should never have been able to trace us. But then, you'd be wrong, I'd be wrong, and everybody else would be wrong, no matter how much imagination was diced out between us.

Even so, Mike and I didn't splash the money about, because that would have made people think straightaway that we'd latched on to something that didn't belong to us. Which wouldn't do at all, because even in a street like ours there are people who love to do a good turn for the coppers, though I never know why they do. Some people are so mean-gutted that even if they've only got tuppence more than you and they think you're the sort that would take it if you have half the chance, they'd get you put inside if they saw you ripping lead out of a lavatory, even if it weren't their lavatory—just to keep their tuppence out of your reach. And so we didn't do anything to let on about how rich we were, nothing like going down town and coming back dressed in brand-new Teddy boy suits and carrying a set of skiffle-drums like another pal of ours who'd done a factory office about six months before. No, we took the odd bobs and pennies out and folded the notes into bundles and stuffed them up the drainpipe outside the door in the backyard. "Nobody'll ever think of looking for it there," I said to Mike. "We'll keep it doggo for a week or two, then take a few quid a week out till it's all gone. We might be thieving bastards, but we're not green."

Some days later a plain-clothes dick knocked at the door. And asked for me. I was still in bed, at eleven o'clock, and had to unroll myself from the comfortable black sheets when I heard mam calling me. "A man to see you," she said. "Hurry up, or he'll be gone."

I could hear her keeping him at the back door, nattering about how fine it had been but how it looked like rain since early this morning—and he didn't answer her except to snap out a snotty yes or no. I scrambled into my trousers and wondered why he'd come—knowing it was a copper because 'a man to see you' always meant just that in our house—and if I'd had any idea that one had gone to Mike's house as well at the same time I'd have twigged it to be because of that hundred and fifty quid's worth of paper stuffed up the drainpipe outside the back door about ten inches away from that plain-clothed copper's boot, where mam still talked to him thinking she was doing me a favour, and I wishing to God she'd ask him in, though on second thoughts realizing that that would seem more suspicious than keeping him outside, because they know we hate their guts and smell a rat if they think we're trying to be nice to them. Mam wasn't born yesterday, I thought, thumping my way down the creaking stairs.

I'd seen him before: Borstal Bernard in nicky-hat, Remand Home Ronald in rowing-boat boots, Probation Pete in a pit-prop mackintosh, three-months clink in collar and tie (all this out of a

Borstal skiffle-ballad that my new mate made up, and I'd tell you it in full but it doesn't belong in this story), a 'tec who'd never had as much in his pockets as that drainpipe had up its jackses. He was like Hitler in the face, right down to the paint-brush tash, except that being six-foot tall made him seem worse. But I straightened my shoulders to look into his illiterate blue eyes—like I always do with any copper.

Then he started asking me questions, and my mother from behind said: "He's never left that television set for the last three months, so you've got nowt on him, mate. You might as well look for somebody else, because you're wasting the rates you get out of my rent and the income-tax that comes out of my pay-packet standing there like that"—which was a laugh because she'd never paid either to my knowledge, and never would, I hoped.

"Well, you know where Papplewick Street is, don't you?" the copper asked me, taking no notice of mam.

"Ain't it off Alfreton Road?" I asked him back, helpful and bright.

"You know there's a baker's half-way down on the left-hand side, don't you?"

"Ain't it next door to a pub, then?" I wanted to know.

He answered me sharp: "No, it bloody well ain't." Coppers always lose their tempers as quick as this, and more often than not they gain nothing by it. "Then I don't know it," I told him, saved by the bell.

He slid his big boot round and round on the doorstep. "Where were you last Friday night?" Back in the ring, but this was worse than a boxing match.

I didn't like him trying to accuse me of something he wasn't sure I'd done. "Was I at that baker's you mentioned? Or in the pub next door?"

"You'll get five years in Borstal if you don't give me a straight answer," he said, unbuttoning his mac even though it was cold where he was standing.

"I was glued to the telly, like mam says," I swore blind. But he went on and on with his looney questions: "Have you got a television?"

The things he asked wouldn't have taken in a kid of two, and what else could I say to the last one except: "Has the aerial fell down? Or would you like to come in and see it?"

He was liking me even less for saying that. "We know you weren't listening to the television set last Friday, and so do you, don't you?"

"P'raps not, but I was *looking* at it, because sometimes we turn the sound down for a bit of fun." I could hear mam laughing from the kitchen, and I hoped Mike's mam was doing the same if the cops had gone to him as well.

"We know you weren't in the house," he said, starting up again, cranking himself with the handle. They always say 'We' 'We', never 'I' 'I'—as if they feel braver and righter knowing there's a lot of them against only one.

"I've got witnesses," I said to him. "Mam for one. Her fancy-man, for two. Ain't that enough? I can get you a dozen more, or thirteen altogether, if it was a baker's that got robbed."

"I don't want no lies," he said, not catching on about the baker's dozen. Where do they scrape cops up from anyway? "All I want is to get from you where you put that money."

Don't get mad, I kept saying to myself, don't get mad—hearing mam setting out cups and saucers and putting the pan on the stove for bacon. I stood back and waved him inside like I was a butler. "Come and search the house. If you've got a warrant."

"Listen, my lad," he said, like the dirty bullying jumped-up bastard he was, "I don't want too much of your lip, because if we get you down to the Guildhall you'll get a few bruises and black-eyes for your trouble." And I knew he wasn't kidding either, because I'd heard about all them sort of tricks. I hoped one day though that him and all his pals would be the ones to get the black-eyes and kicks; you never knew. It might come sooner than anybody thinks, like in Hungary. "Tell me where the money is, and I'll get you off with probation."

"What money?" I asked him, because I'd heard that one before as well.

"You know what money."

"Do I look as though I'd know owt about money?" I said, pushing my fist through a hole in my shirt.

"The money that was pinched, that you know all about," he said. "You can't trick me, so it's no use trying."

"Was it three-and-eightpence ha'penny?" I asked.

"You thieving young bastard. We'll teach you to steal money that doesn't belong to you."

I turned my head around: "Mam," I called out, "get my lawyer on the blower, will you?"

"Clever, aren't you?" he said in a very unfriendly way, "but we won't rest until we clear all this up."

"Look," I pleaded, as if about to sob my socks off because he'd got me wrong, "it's all very well us talking like this, it's like a game almost, but I wish you'd tell me what it's all about, because honest-to-God I've just got out of bed and here you are at the door talking about me having pinched a lot of money, money that I don't know anything about."

He swung around now as it he'd trapped me, though I couldn't see why he might think so. "Who said anything about money? I didn't. What made you bring money into this little talk we're having?"

"It's you," I answered, thinking he was going barmy, and about to start foaming at the chops, "you've got money on the brain, like all policemen. Baker's shops as well."

He screwed his face up. "I want an answer from you: where's that money?"

But I was getting fed-up with all this. "I'll do a deal."

Judging by his flash-bulb face he thought he was suddenly on to a good thing. "What sort of a deal?"

So I told him: "I'll give you all the money I've got, one and fourpence ha'penny, if you stop this third-degree and let me go in and get my breakfast. Honest, I'm clambed to death. I ain't had a bite since yesterday. Can't you hear my guts rollin'?"

His jaw dropped, but on he went, pumping me for another half hour. A routine check-up, as they say on the pictures. But I knew I was winning on points.

Then he left, but came back in the afternoon to search the house. He didn't find a thing, not a French farthing. He asked me questions again and I didn't tell him anything except lies, lies, lies, because I can go on doing that forever without batting an eyelid. He'd got nothing on me and we both of us knew it, otherwise I'd have been down at the Guildhall in no time, but he kept on keeping on because I'd been in a Remand Home for a high-wall job before; and Mike was put through the same mill because all the local cops knew he was my best pal.

When it got dark me and Mike were in our parlour with a low light on and the telly off, Mike taking it easy in the rocking chair and me slouched out on the settee, both of us puffing a packet of Woods. With the door bolted and curtains drawn we talked about the dough we'd crammed up the drainpipe. Mike thought we should take it out and both of us do a bunk to Skegness or Cleethorpes for a good time in the arcades, living like lords in a boarding house near the pier, then at least we'd both have had a big beano before getting sent down.

"Listen, you daft bleeder," I said, "we aren't going to get caught at all, *and* we'll have a good time, later." We were so clever we didn't even go out to the pictures, though we wanted to.

In the morning old Hitler-face questioned me again, with one of his pals this time, and the next day they came, trying as hard as they could to get something out of me, but I didn't budge an inch. I know I'm showing off when I say this, but in me he'd met his match, and I'd never give in to questions no matter how long it was kept up. They searched the house a couple of time as well, which made me think they thought they really had something to go by, but I know now that they hadn't, and that it was all buckshee speculation. They turned the house upside down and inside out like an old sock, went from top to bottom and front to back but naturally didn't find a thing. The copper even poked his face up the front-room chimney (that hadn't been used or swept for years) and came down looking like Al Jolson so that he had to swill himself clean at the scullery sink. They kept tapping and pottering around the big aspidistra plant that grandma had left to mam, lifting it up from the table to look under the cloth, putting it aside so's they could move the table and get at the boards under the rug—but the big headed stupid ignorant bastards never once thought of emptying the soil out of the plant pot, where they'd have found the crumpled-up money-box that we'd buried the night we did the job. I suppose it's still there, now I think about it, and I suppose mam wonders now and again why the plant don't prosper like it used to—as if it could with a fistful of thick black tin lapped around its guts.

The last time he knocked at our door was one wet morning at five minutes to nine and I was sleep-logged in my crumby bed as usual. Mam had gone to work that day so I shouted for him to hold on a bit, and then went down to see who it was. There he stood, six-feet tall and sopping wet, and for the first time in my life I did a spiteful thing I'll never forgive myself for: I didn't ask him to come in out of the rain, because I wanted him to get double pneumonia and die. I suppose he could have pushed by me and come in if he'd wanted, but maybe he'd got used to asking questions on the doorstep and didn't want to be put off by changing his ground even though it was raining. Not that I don't like being spiteful because of any barmy principle I've got, but this bit of spite, as it turned out, did me no good at all. I should have treated him as a brother I hadn't seen for twenty years and dragged him in for a cup of tea and a fag, told him about the picture I hadn't seen the night before, asked him how his wife was after her operation and whether they'd shaved her moustache off to make it, and then sent him happy and satisfied out by the front door. But no, I thought, let's see what he's got to say for himself now.

He stood a little to the side of the door, either because it was less wet there, or because he wanted to see me from a different angle, perhaps having found it monotonous to watch a bloke's face always telling lies from the same side. "You've been identified," he said, twitching raindrops from his tash. "A woman saw you and your mate yesterday and she swears blind you are the same chaps she saw going into that bakery."

I was dead sure he was still bluffing, because Mike and I hadn't even seen each other the day before, but I looked worried. "She's a menace then to innocent people, whoever she is, because the only bakery I've been in lately is the one up our street to get some cut-bread on tick for mam."

He didn't bite on this. "So now I want to know where the money is"—as if I hadn't answered him at all.

"I think mam took it to work this morning to get herself some tea in the canteen." Rain was splashing down so hard I thought he'd get washed away if he didn't come inside. But I wasn't much bothered, and went on: "I remember I put it in the telly-vase last night—it was my only one-and-three and I was saving it for a packet of tips this morning—and I nearly had a jibbering black fit just now when I saw it had gone. I was reckoning on it for getting me through today because I don't think life's worth living without a fag, do you?"

I was getting into my stride and began to feel good, twigging that this would be my last pack of lies, and that if I kept it up for long enough this time I'd have the bastards beat: Mike and me would be off to the coast in a few weeks time having the fun of our lives, playing at penny football and latching on to a couple of tarts that would give us all they were good for. "And this weather's no good for picking-up fag-ends in the street," I said, "because they'd be sopping wet. Course, I know you could dry 'em out near the fire, but it don't taste the same you know, all said and done. Rainwater does summat to 'em that don't bear thinkin' about: it turns 'em back into hoss-tods without the taste though."

I began to wonder, at the back of my brainless eyes, why old copper-lugs didn't pull me up sharp and say he hadn't got time to listen to all this, but he wasn't looking at me anymore, and all my thoughts about Skegness went bursting to smithereens in my sludgy loaf. I could have dropped into the earth when I saw what he'd fixed his eyes on.

He was looking at *it*, an ever-loving fiver, and I could only jabber: "The one thing is to have some real fags because new hoss-tods is always better than stuff that's been rained on and dried, and I know how you feel about not being able to find money because one-and-three's one-and-three in anybody's pocket, and naturally if I see it knocking around I'll get you on the blower tomorrow straightaway and tell you where you can find it.

I thought I'd go down in a fit: three green-backs as well had been washed down by the water, and more were following, lying flat at first after their fall, then getting tilted at the corners by wind and rainspots as if they were alive and wanted to get back into the dry snug drainpipe out of the terrible weather, and you can't imagine how I wished they'd be able to. Old Hitler-face didn't know what to make of it but just kept staring down and down, and I thought I'd better keep on talking, though I knew it wasn't much good now.

"It's a fact, I know, that money's hard to come by and half-crowns don't get found on bus seats or in dustbins, and I didn't see any in bed last night because I'd 'ave known about it, wouldn't I? You can't sleep with things like that in the bed because they're too hard, and anyway at first they're. . . ." It took Hitler-boy a long time to catch one; they were beginning to spread over the yard a bit, reinforced by the third colour of a ten-bob note, before his hand clamped itself on to my shoulder.

III

The pop-eyed potbellied governor said to a pop-eyed potbellied Member of Parliament who sat next to his pop-eyed potbellied whore of a wife that I was his only hope for getting the Borstal Blue Ribbon

Prize Cup For Long Distance Cross Country Running (All England), which I was, and it set me laughing to myself inside, and I didn't say a word to any potbellied pop-eyed bastard that might give them real hope, though I knew the governor anyway took my quietness to mean he'd got that cup already stuck on the bookshelf in his office among the few other mildewed trophies.

"He might take up running in a sort of professional way when he gets out," and it wasn't until he'd said this and I'd heard it with my own flap-tabs that I realized it might be possible to do such a thing, run for money, trot for wages on piece work at a bob a puff rising bit by bit to a guinea a gasp and retiring through old age at thirty-two because of lace-curtain lungs, a football heart, and legs like varicose beanstalks. But I'd have a wife and car and get my grinning long-distance clock in the papers and have a smashing secretary to answer piles of letters sent by tarts who'd mob me when they saw who I was as I pushed my way into Woolworth's for a packet of razor blades and a cup of tea. It was something to think about all right, and sure enough the governor knew he'd got me when he said, turning to me as if I would at any rate have to be consulted about it all: "How does this matter strike you, then, Smith, my lad?"

A line of potbellied pop-eyes gleamed at me and a row of goldfish mouths opened and wiggled gold teeth at me, so I gave them the answer they wanted because I'd hold my trump card until later. "It'd suit me fine, sir," I said.

"Good lad. Good show. Right spirit. Splendid."

"Well," the governor said, "get that cup for us today and I'll do all I can for you. I'll get you trained so that you whack every man in the Free World." And I had a picture in my brain of me running and beating everybody in the world, leaving them all behind until only I was trot-trotting across a big wide moor alone, doing a marvellous speed as I ripped between boulders and reed-clumps, when suddenly: CRACK! CRACK!—bullets that can go faster than any man running, coming from a copper's rifle planted in a tree, winged me and split my gizzard in spite of my perfect running, and down I fell.

The potbellies expected me to say something else. "Thank you, sir," I said.

Told to go, I trotted down the pavilion steps, out on to the field because the big cross-country was about to begin and the two entries from Gunthorpe had fixed themselves early at the starting line and were ready to move off like white kangaroos. The sports ground looked a treat: with big tea-tents all round and flags flying and seats for families—empty because no mam or dad had known what opening day meant—and boys still running heats for the hundred yards, and lords and ladies walking from stall to stall, and the Borstal Boys Brass Band in blue uniforms; and up on the stands the brown jackets of Hucknall as well as our own grey blazers, and then the Gunthorpe lot with shirt sleeves rolled. The blue sky was full of sunshine and it couldn't have been a better day, and all of the big show was like something out of Ivanhoe that we'd seen on the pictures a few days before.

"Come on, Smith," Roach the sports master called to me, "we don't want you to be late for the big race, eh? Although I dare say you'd catch them up if you were." The others cat-called and grunted at this, but I took no notice and placed myself between Gunthorpe and one of the Aylesham trusties, dropped on my knees and plucked a few grass blades to suck on the way round. So the big race it was, for them, watching from the grandstand under a fluttering Union Jack, a race for the governor, that he had been waiting for, and I hoped he and all the rest of his pop-eyed gang were busy placing big bets on me, hundred to one to win, all the money they had in their pockets, all the wages they were going to get for the next five years, and the more they placed the happier I'd be. Because here was a dead cert going to die on the big name they'd built for him, going to go down dying with laughter whether it choked him or not. My knees felt the cool soil pressing into them, and out of my eye's corner I saw Roach lift his hand. The Gunthorpe boy twitched before the signal was given; somebody cheered too soon; Medway bent forward; then the gun went, and I was away.

We went once around the field and then along a half-mile drive of elms, being cheered all the way, and I seemed to feel I was in the lead as we went out by the gate and into the lane, though I wasn't interested enough to find out. The five-mile course was marked by splashes of whitewash gleaming on gateposts and trunks and stiles and stones, and a boy with a waterbottle and bandage-box stood every half-mile waiting for those that dropped out or fainted. Over the first stile, without trying, I was still nearly in the lead but one; and if any of you want tips about running, never be in a hurry, and never let any of the other runners know you are in a hurry even if you are. You can always overtake on long-distance running without letting the others smell the hurry in you; and when you've used your craft like this to reach the two or three up front then you can do a big dash later that puts everybody else's hurry in the shade because you've not had to make haste up till then. I ran to a steady jog-trot rhythm, and soon it was so smooth that I forgot I was running, and I was hardly able to know that my legs were lifting and falling and my arms going in and out, and my lungs didn't seem to be working at all, and my heart stopped that wicked thumping I always get at the beginning of a run. Because you see I never race at all; I just run, and somehow I know that if I forget I'm racing and only jog-trot along until I don't know I'm running I always win the race. For when my eyes recognize that I'm getting near the end of the course—by seeing a stile or cottage corner—I put on a spurt, and such a fast big spurt it is because I feel that up till then I haven't been running and that I've used up no energy at all. And I've been able to do this because I've been thinking; and I wonder if I'm the only one in the running business with this system of forgetting that I'm running because I'm too busy thinking; and I wonder if any of the other lads are on to the same lark, though I know for a fact that they aren't. Off like the wind along the cobbled footpath and rutted lane, smoother than the flat grass track on the field and better for thinking because it's not too smooth, and I was in my element that afternoon knowing that nobody could beat me at running but intending to beat myself before the day was over. For when the governor talked to me of being honest when I first came in he didn't know what the word meant or he wouldn't have had me here in this race, trotting along in shimmy and shorts and sunshine. He'd have had me where I'd have had him if I'd been in his place: in a quarry breaking rocks until he broke his back. At least old Hitler-face the plain-clothes dick was honester than the governor, because he at any rate had had it in for me and I for him, and when my case was coming up in court a copper knocked at our front door at four o'clock in the morning and got my mother out of bed when she was paralytic tired, reminding her she had to be in court at dead on half past nine. It was the finest bit of spite I've ever heard of, but I would call it honest, the same as my mam's words were honest when she really told that copper what she thought of him and called him all the dirty names she'd ever heard of, which took her half an hour and woke the terrace up.

I trotted on along the edge of a field bordered by the sunken lane, smelling green grass and honeysuckle, and I felt as though I came from a long line of whippets trained to run on two legs, only I couldn't see a toy rabbit in front and there wasn't a collier's cosh behind to make me keep up the pace. I passed the Gunthorpe runner whose shimmy was already black with sweat and I could just see the corner of the fenced-up copse in front where the only man I had to pass to win the race was going all out to gain the half-way mark. Then he turned into a tongue of trees and bushes where I couldn't see him anymore, and I couldn't see anybody and I knew what the loneliness of the long-distance runner running across country felt like, realizing that as far as I was concerned this feeling was the only honesty and realness there was in the world and I knowing it would be no different ever, no matter what I felt at odd times, and no matter what anybody else tried to tell me. The runner behind me must have been a long way off because it was so quiet, and there was even less noise and movement than there had been at five o'clock of a frosty winter morning. It was hard to understand, and all I knew was that you had to run, run, run, without knowing why you were running, but on you went through fields you didn't understand and into woods that made you afraid, over hills without knowing you'd been up and down, and shooting across streams that would have cut the heart out of you had you fallen into them. And the winning post was no end to it, even though crowds might be cheering you in, because on you had to go before you got your breath back, and the only time you stopped really was when you tripped over a tree trunk and broke your neck or fell into a disused well and stayed dead in the darkness forever. So I thought: they aren't going to get me on this racing lark, this running and trying to win, this jog-trotting for a bit of blue ribbon, because it's not the way to go on at all, though they swear blind that it is. You should think about nobody and go your own way, not on a course marked out for you by people holding mugs of water and bottles of iodine in case you fall and cut yourself so that they can pick you up—even if you want to stay where you are—and get you moving again.

On I went, out of the wood, passing the man leading without knowing I was going to do so. Flip-flap, flip-flap, jog-trot, jog-trot, crunchslap-crunchslap, across the middle of a broad field again, rhythmically running in my greyhound effortless fashion, knowing I had won the race though it wasn't half over, won it if I wanted it, could go on for ten or fifteen or twenty miles if I had to and drop dead at the finish of it, which would be the same, in the end, as living an honest life like the governor wanted me to. It amounted to: win the race and be honest, and on trot-trotting I went, having the time of my life, loving my progress because it did me good and set me thinking which by now I liked to do, but not caring at all when I remembered that I had to win this race as well as run it. One of the two, I had to win the race or run it, and I knew I could do both because my legs had carried me well in front—now coming to the short cut down the bramble bank and over the sunken road —and would carry me further because they seemed made of electric cable and easily alive to keep on slapping at those ruts and roots, but I'm not going to win because the only way I'd see I came in first would be if winning meant that I was going to escape the coppers after doing the biggest bank job of my life, but winning means the exact opposite, no matter how they try to kill or kid me, means running right into their white-gloved wall-barred hands and grinning mugs and staying there for the rest of my natural long life of stone-breaking anyway, but stone-breaking in the way I want to do it and not in the way they tell me.

Another honest thought that comes is that I could swing left at the next hedge of the field, and under its cover beat my slow retreat away from the sports ground winning post. I could do three or six or a dozen miles across the turf like this and cut a few main roads behind me so's they'd never know which one I'd taken; and maybe on the last one when it got dark I could thumb a lorry-lift and get a free ride north with somebody who might not give me away. But no, I said I wasn't daft didn't I? I won't pull out with only six months left and besides there's nothing I want to dodge and run away from; I only want a bit of my own back on the In-laws and Potbellies by letting them sit up there on their big posh seats and watch me lose this race, though as sure as God made me I know that when I do lose I'll get the dirtiest crap and kitchen jobs in the months to go before my time is up. I won't be worth a threpp'ny-bit to anybody here, which will be all the thanks I get for being honest in the only way I know. For when the governor told me to be honest it was meant to be in his way not mine, and if I kept on being honest in the way he wanted and won my race for him he'd see I got the cushiest six months still left to run; but in my own way, well, it's not allowed, and if I find a way of doing it such as I've got now then I'll get what-for in every mean trick he can set his mind to. And if you look at it in my way, who can blame him? For this is war—and ain't I said so?—and when I hit him in the only place he knows he'll be sure to get his own back on me for not collaring that cup when his heart's been set for ages on seeing himself standing up at the end of the afternoon to clap me on the back as I take the cup from Lord Earwig or some such chinless wonder with a name like that. And so I'll hit him where it hurts a lot, and he'll do all he can to get his own back, tit for tat, though I'll enjoy it most because I'm hitting first, and because I planned it longer. I don't know why I think these thoughts are better than any I've ever had, but I do, and I don't care why. I suppose it took me a long time to get going on all this because I've had no time and peace in all my bandit life, and now my thoughts are coming pat and the only trouble is I often can't stop, even when my brain feels as if it's got cramp, frostbite and creeping paralysis all rolled into one and I have to give it a rest by slap-dashing down through the brambles of the sunken lane. And all this is another upper-cut I'm getting in first at people like the governor, to show how—if I can—his races are never won even though some bloke always comes unknowingly in first, how in the end the governor is going to be doomed while blokes like me will take the pickings of his roasted bones and dance like maniacs around his Borstal's ruins. And so this story's like the race and once again I won't bring off a winner to suit the governor; no, I'm being honest like he told me to, without him knowing what he means, though I don't suppose he'll ever come in with a story of his own, even if he reads this one of mine and knows who I'm talking about.

I've just come up out of the sunken lane, kneed and elbowed, thumped and bramble-scratched, and the race is two-thirds over, and a voice is going like a wireless in my mind saying that when you've had enough of feeling good like the first man on earth of a frosty morning, and you've known how it is to be taken bad like the last man on earth on a summer's afternoon, then you get at last to being like the only man on earth and don't give a bogger about either good or bad, but just trot on with your slippers slapping the good dry soil that at least would never do you a bad turn. Now the words are like coming from a crystal-set that's broken down, and something's happening inside the shell-case of my guts that bothers me and I don't know why or what to blame it on, a grinding near my ticker as though a bag of rusty screws is loose inside me and I shake them up every time I trot forward. Now and again I break my rhythm to feel my left shoulder-blade by swinging a right hand across my chest as if to rub the knife away that has somehow got stuck there. But I know it's nothing to bother about, that more likely it's caused by too much thinking that now and again I take for worry. For sometimes I'm the greatest worrier in the world I think (as you twigged I'll bet from me having got this story out) which is funny anyway because my mam don't know the meaning of the word so I don't take after her; though dad had a hard time of worry all his life up to when he filled his bedroom with hot blood and kicked the bucket that morning when nobody was in the house. I'll never forget it, straight I won't, because I was the one that found him and I often wished I hadn't. Back from a session on the fruit-machines at the fish-and-chip shop, jingling my three-lemon loot to a nail-dead house, as soon as I got in I knew something was wrong, stood leaning my head against the cold mirror above the mantel-piece trying not to open my eyes and see my stone-cold clock —because I knew I'd gone as white as a piece of chalk since coming in as if I'd been got at by a Dracula-vampire and even my penny-pocket winnings kept quiet on purpose.

Gunthorpe nearly caught me up. Birds were singing from the briar hedge, and a couple of thrushies flew like lightning into some thorny bushes. Corn had grown high in the next field and would be cut down soon with scythes and mowers; but I never wanted to notice much while running in case it put me off my stroke, so by the haystack I decided to leave it all behind and put on such a spurt, in spite of nails in my guts, that before long I'd left both Gunthorpe and the birds a good way off; I wasn't far now from going into that last mile and a half like a knife through margarine, but the quietness I suddenly trotted into between two pickets was like opening my eyes underwater and looking at the pebbles on a stream bottom, reminding me again of going back that morning to the house in which my old man had croaked, which is funny because I hadn't thought about it at all since it happened and even then I didn't brood much on it. I wonder why? I suppose that since I started to think on these long-distance runs I'm liable to have anything crop up and pester at my tripes and innards, and now that I see my bloody dad behind each grass-blade in my barmy runner-brain I'm not so sure I like to think and that it's such a good thing after all. I choke my phlegm and keep on running anyway and curse the Borstal-builders and their athletics—flappity-flap, slop-slop, crunchslap-crunchslap-crunchslap—who've maybe got their own back on me from the bright beginning by sliding magic-lantern slides into my head that never stood a chance before. Only if I take whatever comes like this in my runner's stride can I keep on keeping on like my old self and beat them back; and now I've thought on this far I know I'll win, in the crunchslap end. So anyway after a bit I went upstairs one step at a time not thinking anything about how I should find dad and what I'd do when I did. But now I'm making up for it by going over the rotten life mam led him ever since I can remember, knocking-on with different men even when he was alive and fit and she not caring whether he knew it or not, and most of the time he wasn't so blind as she thought and cursed and roared and threatened to punch her tab, and I had to stand up to stop him even though I knew she deserved it. What a life for all of us. Well, I'm not grumbling, because if I did I might just as well win this bleeding race, which I'm not going to do, though if I don't lose speed I'll win it before I know where I am, and then where would I be?

Now I can hear the sportsground noise and music as I head back for the flags and the lead-in drive, the fresh new feel of underfoot gravel going against the iron muscles of my legs. I'm nowhere near puffed despite that bag of nails that rattles as much as ever, and I can still give a big last leap like gale-force wind if I want to, but everything is under control and I know now that there ain't another long-distance cross-country running runner in England to touch my speed and style. Our doddering bastard of a governor, our half-dead gangrened gaffer is hollow like an empty petrol drum, and he wants me and my running life to give him glory, to put in him blood and throbbing veins he never had, wants his potbellied pals to be his witnesses as I gasp and stagger up to his winning post so's he can say: "My Borstal gets that cup, you see. I win my bet, because it pays to be honest and try to gain the prizes I offer to my lads, and they know it, have known it all along. They'll always be honest now, because I made them so." And his pals will think: "He trains his lads to live right, after all; he deserves a medal but we'll get him made a Sir"—and at this very moment as the birds come back to whistling I can tell myself I'll never care a sod what any of the chinless spineless In-laws think or say. They've seen me and they're cheering now and loudspeakers set around the field like elephant's ears are spreading out the big news that I'm well in the lead, and can't do anything else but stay there. But I'm still thinking of the Out-law death my dad died, telling the doctors to scat from the house when they wanted him to finish up in hospital (like a bleeding guinea-pig, he raved at them). He got up in bed to throw them out and even followed them down the stairs in his shirt though he was no more than skin and stick. They tried to tell him he'd want some drugs but he didn't fall for it, and only took the pain-killer that mam and I got from a herb-seller in the next street. It's not till now that I know what guts he had, and when I went into the room that morning he was lying on his stomach with the clothes thrown back, looking like a skinned rabbit, his grey head resting just on the edge of the bed, and on the floor must have been all the blood he'd had in his body, right from his toe-nails up, for nearly all of the lino and carpet was covered in it, thin and pink.

And down the drive I went, carrying a heart blocked up like Boulder Dam across my arteries, the nail-bag clamped down tighter and tighter as though in a woodwork vice, yet with my feet like birdwings and arms like talons ready to fly across the field except that I didn't want to give anybody that much of a show, or win the race by accident. I smell the hot day now as I run towards the end, passing a mountain-heap of grass emptied from cans hooked on to the fronts of lawnmowers pushed by my pals; I rip a piece of tree-bark with my fingers and stuff it in my mouth, chewing wood and dust and maybe maggots as I run until I'm nearly sick, yet swallowing what I can of it just the same because a little birdie whistled to me that I've got to go on living for at least a bloody sight longer yet but that for six months I'm not going to smell that grass or taste that dusty bark or trot this lovely path. I hate to have to say this but something bloody-well made me cry, and crying is a thing I haven't bloody-well done since I was a kid of two or three. Because I'm slowing down now for Gunthorpe to catch me up, and I'm doing it in a place just where the drive turns in to the sportsfield—where they can see what I'm doing, especially the governor and his gang from the grandstand, and I'm going so slow I'm almost marking time. Those on the nearest seats haven't caught on yet to what's happening and are still cheering like mad ready for when I make that mark, and I keep on wondering when the bleeding hell Gunthorpe behind me is going to nip by on to the field because

I can't hold this up all day, and I think Oh Christ it's just my rotten luck that Gunthorpe's dropped out and that I'll be here for half an hour before the next bloke comes up, but even so, I say, I won't budge, I won't go for that last hundred yards if I have to sit down cross-legged on the grass and have the governor and his chinless wonders pick me up and carry me there, which is against their rules so you can bet they'd never do it because they're not clever enough to break the rules—like I would be in their place—even though they are their own. No, I'll show him what honesty means if it's the last thing I do, though I'm sure he'll never understand because if he and all them like him did it'd mean they'd be on my side which is impossible. By God I'll stick this out like my dad stuck out his pain and kicked them doctors down the stairs: if he had guts for that then I've got guts for this and here I stay waiting for Gunthorpe or Aylesham to bash that turf and go right slap-up against that bit of clothes-line stretched across the winning post. As for me, the only time I'll hit that clothes-line will be when I'm dead and a comfortable coffin's been got ready on the other side. Until then I'm a long-distance runner, crossing country all on my own no matter how bad it feels.

The Essex boys were shouting themselves blue in the face telling me to get a move on, waving their arms, standing up and making as if to run at that rope themselves because they were only a few yards to the side of it. You cranky lot, I thought, stuck at that winning post, and yet I knew they didn't mean what they were shouting, were really on my side and always would be, not able to keep their maulers to themselves, in and out of cop-shops and clink. And there they were now having the time of their lives letting themselves go in cheering me which made the governor think they were heart and soul on his side when he wouldn't have thought any such thing if he'd had a grain of sense. And I could hear the lords and ladies now from the grandstand, and could see them standing up to wave me in: "Run!" they were shouting in their posh voices. "Run!" But I was deaf, daft and blind, and stood where I was, still tasting the bark in my mouth and still blubbing like a baby, blubbing now out of gladness that I'd got them beat at last.

Because I heard a roar and saw the Gunthorpe gang throwing their coats up in the air and I felt the pat-pat of feet on the drive behind me getting closer and closer and suddenly a smell of sweat and a pair of lungs on their last gasp passed me by and went swinging on towards that rope, all shagged out and rocking from side to side, grunting like a Zulu that didn't know any better, like the ghost of me at ninety when I'm heading for that fat upholstered coffin. I could have cheered him myself: "Go on, go on, get cracking. Knot yourself up on that piece of tape." But he was already there, and so I went on, trot-trotting after him until I got to the rope, and collapsed, with a murderous sounding roar going up through my ears while I was still on the wrong side of it.

It's about time to stop; though don't think I'm not still running, because I am, one way or another. The governor at Borstal proved me right; he didn't respect my honesty at all; not that I expected him to, or tried to explain it to him, but if he's supposed to be educated then he should have more or less twigged it. He got his own back right enough, or thought he did, because he had me carting dustbins about every morning from the big full-working kitchen to the garden-bottoms where I had to empty them; and in the afternoon I spread out slops over spuds and carrots growing in the allotments. In the evenings I scrubbed floors, miles and miles of them. But it wasn't a bad life for six months, which was another thing he could never understand and would have made it grimmer if he could, and it was worth it when I look back on it, considering all the thinking I did, and the fact that the boys caught on to me losing the race on purpose and never had enough good words to say about me, or curses to throw out (to themselves) at the governor.

The work didn't break me; if anything it made me stronger in many ways, and the governor knew, when I left, that his spite had got him nowhere. For since leaving Borstal they tried to get me in the army, but I didn't pass the medical and I'll tell you why. No sooner was I out, after that final run and six-months hard, that I went down with pleurisy, which means as far as I'm concerned that I lost the governor's race all right, and won my own twice over, because I know for certain that if I hadn't raced my race I wouldn't have got this pleurisy, which keeps me out of khaki but doesn't stop me doing the sort of work my itchy fingers want to do.

I'm out now and the heat's switched on again, but the rats haven't got me for the last big thing I pulled. I counted six hundred and twenty-eight pounds and am still living off it because I did the job all on my own, and after it I had the peace to write all this, and it'll be money enough to keep me going until I finish my plans for doing an even bigger snatch, something up my sleeve I wouldn't tell to a living soul. I worked out my systems and hiding-places while pushing scrubbing-brushes around them Borstal floors, planned my outward life of innocence and honest work, yet at the same time grew perfect in the razor-edges of my craft for what I knew I had to do once free; and what I'll do again if netted by the poaching coppers.

In the meantime (as they say in one or two books I've read since, useless though because all of them ended on a winning post and didn't teach me a thing) I'm going to give this story to a pal of mine and tell him that if I do get captured again by the coppers he can try and get it put into a book or something, because I'd like to see the governor's face when he reads it, if he does, which I don't suppose he will; even if he did read it though I don't think he'd know what it was all about. And if I don't get caught the bloke I give this story to will never give me away; he'd lived in our terrace for as long as I can remember, and he's my pal. That I do know.

THOM GUNN

innocence

for TONY WHITE

He ran the course and as he ran he grew,
And smelt his fragrance in the field. Already,
Running he knew the most he ever knew,
The egotism of a healthy body.

Ran into manhood, ignorant of the past:
Culture of guilt and guilt's vague heritage,
Self-pity and the soul; what he possessed
Was rich, potential, like the bud's tipped rage.

The Corps developed, it was plain to see,
Courage, endurance, loyalty and skill
To a morale firm as morality,
Hardening him to an instrument, until

The finitude of virtues that were there
Bodied within the swarthy uniform
A compact innocence, child-like and clear,
No doubt could penetrate, no act could harm.

When he stood near the Russian partisan
Being burned alive, he therefore could behold
The ribs wear gently through the darkening skin
And sicken only at the Northern cold,

Could watch the fat burn with a violet flame
And feel disgusted only at the smell,
And judge that all pain finishes the same
As melting quietly by his boots it fell.

KENNETH REXROTH

the students take over

When the newspapers have got nothing else to talk about, they cut loose on the young. The young are always news. If they are up to something, that's news. If they aren't, that's news too. Things we did as kids and thought nothing of, the standard capers of all young animals, now make headlines, shake up police departments and rend the frail hearts of social workers. Partly this is due to the mythologies of modern civilization. Chesterton once pointed out that baby worship is to be expected of a society where the only immortality anybody really believes in is childhood. Partly it is due to the personal reactions of reporters, a class of men by and large prevented, occupationally, from ever growing up. Partly it is hope:

"We have failed, they may do better." Partly it is guilt: "We have failed them. Are they planning vengeance?"

In talking about the Revolt of Youth we should never forget that we are dealing with a new concept. For thousands of years nobody cared what youth were doing. They weren't news. They were minding.

They aren't minding now. That isn't news. They haven't been minding since the days of John Held, Jr., *College Humor* and F. Scott Fitzgerald. In those days they were cutting loose. In the Thirties they were joining up, giving one last try to the noble prescriptions of their elders. During the McCarthy Epoch and the Korean War they were turning their backs and walking away. Today they are striking back. That is news. Nobody else is striking back. Hardly a person over thirty in our mass societies believes it is possible to strike back, or would know how to go about it if he did. During the past couple of years, without caring about the consequences, making up their techniques as they went along, organizing spontaneously in the midst of action, young people all over the world have intervened in history.

As the University of California student said at the recent Un-American Activities Committee riot in San Francisco, "Chessman was the last straw. I'm fed up." It's about time somebody got fed up, because, to mix the metaphor, all the chickens are coming home to roost. It has become only too apparent that we can no longer afford the old catch-as-catch-can morality with which civilization has muddled through to 1960. Sloth, rascality, predatory dishonesty, evasion, bluster, no longer work. The machinery has become too delicate, too complicated, too world-encompassing. Maybe it was once true, a hundred and fifty years ago, that the sum total of the immoral actions of selfish men produced a social good. It is no longer true. Maybe once, societally speaking, if wolf ate wolf long enough and hard enough, you produced a race of intelligent dogs. Not now. Pretty soon we are just going to have a world populated by dead wolves.

Toward the end of his life H. G. Wells remarked that "something very queer was creeping over human affairs." He saw a kind of foolish dishonesty, a perverse lust for physical and moral violence, and a total lack of respect for the integrity of the personality invading every walk of life, all the relationships of men, individual and global. He seemed to be not only troubled, but puzzled. In his own *In the*

Days of the Comet the earth passes through the tail of a comet and a beneficent gas fills the atmosphere and makes all men good overnight. You feel that he suspected something very similar might have come upon us unawares out of outer space, but that in actuality the gas had turned out to be subtly and pervasively malignant. It is easy to see what he was getting at. Nobody sees it better today than the young student, his head filled with "the heritage of the ages," taught in school all the noblest aspirations of mankind, and brought face to face with the chaos of the world beyond the college gates. He's got to enter it, college will be over in a few months or years. He is entering it already fed up.

Think of the great disasters of our time. They have all been the result of a steadily growing immoralism. You could start indefinitely back—with Bismarck's telegram or the Opium War—but think of what those men alive have experienced: the First World War itself, a vast "counterrevolutionary" offensive; the Versailles Treaty; Fascism and Nazism with their institutionalization of every shoddy and crooked paranoia; the Moscow Trials; the betrayal of Spain; Munich; the Second World War with its noble utterances and its crooked deals; the horrible tale of fifteen years of peace and cold war; the Rosenbergs; the Hungarian Revolution; and, in the last few months, the rascality that has burst around our heads like exploding shrapnel—U-2, phony Summits, an orgy of irresponsibility and lies. This is the world outside the college gates. Millions of people are asked to enter it cheerfully each June, equipped with draft cards, social-security cards, ballots, job-application blanks countersigned by David Sarnoff, J. Edgar Hoover, Allen W. Dulles, the family physician and the pastor of the neighborhood church. Is it surprising that a lot of them should turn away at the door of this banquet hall, turn in their tickets and say, "Sorry, I'm already fed up"?

Marx believed that our civilization was born in the arms of its own executioner, twins who were enemies in the womb. Certainly ours is the only great culture which throughout its life has been accompanied by a creative minority which rejected all its values and claims. Almost all others have had a huge majority who shared in few, if any, of the benefits of civilization. Slaves and proletarians are nothing new, the words themselves are derived from another civilization. But a society which advances by means of an elite in permanent revolt and alienation is something new. In the last fifty years this elite itself has slowly gone under; it, too, has been overwhelmed by the society it both led and subverted. *L'Homme Révolté* has come to the end of his tether. One by one he has compromised and been compromised by all his thousand programs. Nobody believes him any more, so he has become a commercial stereotype, along with the cowboy and the Indian, the private detective, the war hero, and the bison and all other extinct animals. As the agent at MCA said to me three years back, "Revolt is the hottest commodity along The Street." The programs are used up and their promulgators are embarrassed. Youth is fed up with them too. And why not? Hitler fulfilled the entire emergency program of the Communist Manifesto, and in addition made May Day a legal holiday.

For the Bolsheviks, the good society would come automatically if the right power were applied to the right program. But power and program are not the question: what matters is the immediate realization of humane content, here, there, everywhere, in every fact and relationship of society. Today the brutal fact is that society cannot endure without this realization of humane content. The only way to realize it is directly, personally, in the immediate context. Anything else is not just too expensive; it is wrecking the machinery. Modern society is too complex and too delicate to afford social and political Darwinism any more. This means personal moral action. I suppose, if you wish to call it that, it means a spiritual revolution. Prophets and seers have been preaching the necessity for spiritual revolution for at least three thousand years and mankind has yet to come up with a bona fide one. But it is that kind of action and that kind of change that young people are demanding today.

Myself, past fifty, I cannot speak for the young. I am inclined to think they will fail. But that isn't the point. You might as well be a hero if society is going to destroy you anyway. There comes a time when courage and honesty become cheaper than anything else. And who knows, you might win. The nuclear explosion that you could not prevent doesn't care whether you were brave or not. Virtue, they say, in itself is intrinsically enjoyable. You can lose nothing, then, by striking back.

Furthermore, just because the machine is so vast, so complex, it is far more sensitive than ever before. Individual action does tell. Give a tiny poke at one of the insignificant gears down in its bowels and slowly it begins to shudder all over and suddenly belches out hot rivets. It is a question of qualitative change. Thousands of men built the pyramids. One punched card fed into a mechanical brain decides the gravest questions. A few punched cards operate whole factories. Modern society has passed the stage when it was a blind, mechanical monster. It is on the verge of becoming an infinitely responsive instrument.

So the first blows struck back were tiny, insignificant things. Not long after the last war Bayard Rustin got on a bus in Chicago and headed south. When they crossed the Mason-Dixon Line, he stayed where he was. The cops took him off. He "went limp." They beat him into unconsciousness. They took him to jail and finally to a hospital. When he got out, he got on another bus and continued south. So it went, for months—sometimes jail, sometimes the hospital, sometimes they just kicked him into the ditch. Eventually he got to New Orleans. Eventually Jim Crow was abolished on interstate carriers. Individual nonviolent direct action had invaded the South and won. The Southern Negro had been shown the only technique that had any possibility of winning.

Things simmered for a while and then, spontaneously, out of nowhere, the Montgomery bus boycott materialized. Every moment of the birth and growth of this historic action has been elaborately documented. Hour by hour we can study "the masses" acting by themselves. It is my modest, well-considered opinion that Martin Luther King, Jr., is the most remarkable man the South has produced since Thomas Jefferson—since, in other words, it became "the South." Now the most remarkable thing about Martin Luther King is that he is not remarkable at all. He is just an ordinary minister of the middle-class Negro church (or what Negroes call "middle class," which is pretty poor by white standards). There are thousands of men like him all over Negro America. When the voice called, he was ready. He was ready because he was himself part of that voice. Professional, white-baiting Negroes who thrill millionairesses in night clubs in the North would call him a square. He was a brave square. He is the best possible demonstration of the tremendous untapped potential of humanity that the white South has thrown away all these years. He helped to focus that potential and exert it. It won.

No outside organizers formed the Montgomery Improvement Association. They came around later, but they could never quite catch up with it. It is pretty hard to "catch up with," to institutionalize, a movement which is simply the form that a whole community has assumed in action. Although the force of such action is shaped by group loyalty, in the final analysis it must always be individual and direct. You can't delegate either boycott or non-violence. A committee can't act for you, you have to act yourself.

The Montgomery bus boycott not only won where Negro Zealotism, as well as Uncle Tomism, had always failed, but it demonstrated something that had always sounded like sheer sentimentality. It is better, braver, far more effective and far more pleasurable to act with love than with hate. When you have won, you have gained an unimpeachable victory. The material ends pass or are passed beyond. "Desegregated" buses seem natural in many Southern cities today. The guiltless moral victory remains, always as powerful as the day it was gained. Furthermore, each moral victory converts or neutralizes another block of the opponents' forces.

Before the Montgomery episode was over, Bayard Rustin and Martin Luther King had joined forces. Today they are world statesmen in a "shadow cabinet" that is slowly forming behind the wielders of power, and the advisers and auxiliary leaders in the councils of Negro Africa. At home in America the Montgomery achievement has become the source from which has flowed the moral awakening, first, of Negro, and following them, of white youth.

Everything seemed to be going along nicely. According to the papers and most of their professors, 99 and $^{44}/_{100}$ per cent of the nation's youth were cautiously preparing for the day when they could offer their young split-level brains to GM, IBM, Oak Ridge or the Voice of America. Madison Avenue had discovered its own pet minority of revolt and tamed it into an obedient mascot. According to *Time*, *Life*, MGM and the editors and publishers of a new, pseudo avant-garde, all the dear little rebels wanted to do was grow beards, dig jazz, take heroin and wreck other people's Cadillacs. While the exurbanite children sat with the baby sitter and thrilled to Wyatt Earp, their parents swooned in the aisles at *The Connection* or set up past bedtime reading switch-blade novelists. The psychological mechanisms were the same in both cases—sure-fire, time-tested and shopworn.

But as a matter of fact, anyone with any sense traveling about the country lecturing on college campuses during the past five years could tell that something very, very different was cooking. Time and again, hundreds of times, I have been asked, by some well-dressed, unassuming, beardless student, "I agree with you completely, but what shall we, my generation, *do*?" To this question I have been able to give only one answer: "I am fifty. You are twenty. It is for you to tell me what to do. The only thing I can say is, don't do the things my generation did. They didn't work." A head of steam was building up, the waters were rising behind the dam; the dam itself, the block to action, was the patent exhaustion of the old forms. What was accumulating was not any kind of programmatic "radicalization," it was a moral demand.

Parenthetically, I might say that a legend of the Red Thirties was growing up too. Let me say (and I was there): As far as practically every campus except CCNY and NYU was concerned, the Red Thirties are pure myth. At the height of the great upsurge in California labor, led in its own imagination by the Communist Party, neither the Young Communist League nor the Young Peoples Socialist League was able to keep a functioning student cadre in continuous operation on the University of California campus. At least every four years they had to start over again. And the leadership, the real bosses, were middle-aged party functionaries sent in from "The Center." One of them, bellowing with early senility, was to show up at the recent Un-American Activities Committee riot in San Francisco and scandalize the students.

The plain fact is that today students are incomparably better educated and more concerned than their elders. As the young do, they still tend to believe things written on paper. For the past five years, bull sessions have been discussing Kropotkin, Daniel De Leon, Trotsky, Gandhi, St. Simon, Plato—an incongruous mixture of the world's cat bellers—looking for the answer. The gap between the generations has been closing up. Teaching them is a new group of young professors, too young to have been compromised by their actual role in the splendid Thirties, themselves realistic-minded products of the GI Bill; and neither ex-dupes nor ex-fellow travelers, but serious scholars of the radical past. It is only just recently that they have come up, only just recently that the creative minority of students has stopped assuming that just because a man stood at a podium he was *ipso facto* a fraud. So the head of steam built up, the waters mounted behind the dike.

And then one day four children walked into a dime store in a small Southern city and pulled out the plug. Four children picked up the massive chain of the Social Lie and snapped it at its weakest link. Everything broke loose.

Children had won at Little Rock, but they had not initiated the action, they had been caught in the middle in a conflict of equally dishonest political forces, and they had won only a token victory. All the world had marveled at those brave young faces, beautiful under the taunts and spittle. If they had not stood fast, the battle would have been lost; it was their bravery alone that won it. But it was a battle officered by their elders, and like all the quarrels among their elders nowadays, it ended in a morally meaningless compromise.

From the first sit-ins the young have kept the command in their own hands. No "regularly constituted outside authority" has been able to catch up with them. The sit-ins swept the South so rapidly that it was impossible to catch up with them physically, but it was even harder for routinized bureaucrats with vested interests in race relations and civil liberties to catch up with them ideologically. The whole spring went by before the professional leaders began to get even a glimmering of what was happening. In the meantime the old leadership was being pushed aside. Young ministers just out of the seminary, maverick young teachers in Jim Crow colleges, choir mistresses and schoolmarms and Sunday-school teachers in all the small cities of the South pitched in and helped—and let the students lead *them,* without bothering to "clear it with Roy." In a couple of months the NAACP found itself with a whole new cadre sprung up from the grass roots.

The only organization which understood what was going on was CORE, the Committee on Racial Equality, organized years ago in an evacuated Japanese flat, "Sakai House" in San Francisco, by Bayard Rustin, Caleb Foote and a few others, as a direct-action, race-relations offshoot of the Fellowship of Reconciliation (the FOR) and the Friends Service Committee. CORE was still a small group of intellectual enthusiasts and there simply weren't enough people to go around. To this day most Negroes know little more of CORE than its name, which they have seen in the Negro press, and the bare fact that its program is direct, nonviolent action. This didn't deter the high-school and college students in the Jim Crow high schools and colleges in Raleigh and Durham. They set up their own direct nonviolent-action organization and in imitation of CORE gave it a name whose initials spelled a word, COST. Soon there were

COST "cells" in remote hill-country high schools, complete with codes, hand signals, couriers, all the apparatus of youthful enthusiasm. Needless to say, the very words frightened the older Negro leadership out of its wits.

The police hosed and clubbed the sit-inners, the Uncle Tom presidents of the captive Jim Crow colleges expelled them in droves, white students came South and insisted on being arrested along with the Negroes, sympathy picket lines were thrown in front of almost every chain variety store in almost every college town in the North. Even some stores with no branches in the South and no lunch counters anywhere found themselves picketed until they cleared themselves of any implication of Jim Crow.

The effect on the civilized white minority in the South was extraordinary. All but a few had gone on accepting the old stereotypes. There were good Negroes, to be sure, but they didn't want to mix. The majority were ignorant, violent, bitter, half-civilized, incapable of planned, organized action, happy in Jim Crow. "It would take another two hundred years." In a matter of weeks, in thousands of white brains, the old stereotypes exploded. Here were the Negro children of servants, sharecroppers and garbagemen—"their" servants and sharecroppers and garbagemen, who had always been content with their place—directly engaged in the greatest controlled moral action the South had ever seen. They were quiet, courteous, full of good will to those who abused them; and they sang, softly, all together, under the clubs and firehoses, "We will not be moved." Long protest walks of silent Negroes, two abreast, filed through the provincial capitals. A major historical moral issue looked into the eyes of thousands of white spectators in Southern towns which were so locked in "our way of life" that they were unaware they lived in a great world. The end of Jim Crow suddenly seemed both near and inevitable. It is a profoundly disturbing thing to find yourself suddenly thrust upon the stage of history.

I was at the first Louisiana sit-in with a girl from the local paper who had interviewed me that morning. She was typical, full of dying prejudices, misinformation and superstitious fears. But she knew it. She was trying to change. Well, the sit-in did a good job of changing her. It was terrific. A group of well-bred, sweet-faced kids from Southern University filed into the dime store, hand in hand, fellows and girls in couples, and sat down quietly. Their faces were transfused with quiet, innocent dedication. They looked like the choir coming into a fine Negro church. They weren't served. They sat quietly, talking together. Nobody, spectators or participants, raised his voice. In fact, most of the bystanders didn't even stare rudely. When the police came, the youngsters spoke softly and politely, and once again, fellows and girls hand in hand, they filed out, singing a hymn, and got in the paddy wagon.

The newspaper girl was shaken to her shoes. Possibly it was the first time in her life she had ever faced what it meant to be a human being. She came to the faculty party for me at Louisiana State that night. Her flesh was still shaking and she couldn't stop talking. She had come up against one of the big things of life and she was going to be always a little different afterward.

The response on the campuses of the white colleges of the South was immediate. There had always been interracial committees and clubs around, but they had been limited to a handful of eccentrics. These increased tremendously and involved large numbers of quite normal students. Manifestations of sympathy with the sit-ins and joint activities with nearby Negro schools even came to involve student-government and student-union bodies. Editorials in college papers, with almost no exceptions, gave enthusiastic support. Believe me, it is quite an experience to eat dinner with a fraternity at a fashionable Southern school and see a can to collect money for CORE at the end of the table.

More important than sympathy actions for and with the Negroes, the sit-ins stimulated a similar burst, a runaway brush fire, of activity for all sorts of other aims. They not only stimulated the activity, they provided the form and in a sense the ideology, Nonviolent direct action popped up everywhere—so fast that even the press wire services could no longer keep track of it, although they certainly played it up as the hottest domestic news of the day. The actions dealt with a few things: compulsory ROTC, peace, race relations, civil liberties, capital punishment—all, in the final analysis, moral issues. In no case were they concerned with politics in the ordinary sense of the word.

Here the ROTC marched out to troop the colors and found a line of students sitting down across the parade ground. In another school a protest march paraded around and through and between the ranks of the marching ROTC, apparently to everybody's amusement. In other schools the faculty and even the administration and, in one place, the governor joined in protest rallies against ROTC.

There were so many peace and disarmament meetings and marches it is impossible to form a clear picture—they seem to have taken place everywhere and, for the first time, to have brought out large numbers. Off campus, as it were, the lonely pacifists who had been sitting out the civil-defense propaganda stunt in New York called their annual "sit out" and were dumbfounded at the turnout. For the first time, too, the courts and even the police weakened. Few were arrested, and fewer sentenced.

The Chessman execution provoked demonstrations, meetings, telegrams, on campuses all over the country. In Northern California the "mass base" of all forms of protest was among the students and the younger teachers. They provided the cadre, circulated petitions, sent wires, interviewed the Governor, and kept up a continuous vigil at the gates of San Quentin. All this activity was unquestionably spontaneous. At no time did the American Civil Liberties Union or the regular anti-capital-punishment organizations initiate, or even take part in, any mass action, whatever else they may have done. Chessman, of course, had a tremendous appeal to youth; he was young, he was an intellectual, even an artist of sorts; before his arrest he had been the kind of person they could recognize, if not approve of, among themselves. He was not very different from the hero of *On the Road*, who happened to be locked up in San Quentin along with him. As his life drew to a close, he showed a beautiful magnanimity in all he did or said. On all the campuses of the country—of the world, for that matter—he seemed an almost typical example of the alienated and outraged youthful "delinquent" of the post-World War II era—the product of a delinquent society. To the young who refused to be demoralized by society, it appeared that that society was killing him only to sweep its own guilt under the rug. I think almost everyone (Chessman's supporters included) over thirty-five seriously underestimates the psychological effect of the Chessman case on the young.

At all points the brutal reactionary tendencies in American life were being challenged, not on a political basis, Left versus Right, but because of their patent dishonesty and moral violence. The most spectacular challenge was the riot at the hearing of the Un-American Activities Committee in San Francisco. There is no question but that this was a completely spontaneous demonstration. The idea that Communist agitators provoked it is ludicrous. True, all that were left of the local Bolsheviks turned out, some thirty of them—Stalinists and the two groups of Trotskyites. Even the "youth leader" who, twenty-eight years before, at the age of thirty, had been assigned to lead the YCL, showed up and roared and stomped incoherently, and provided comic relief. Certainly no one took him seriously. There was one aspect about the whole thing that was not spontaneous. That was the work of the committee. They planned it that way. Over the protests and warnings of the city administration they deliberately framed up a riot. When the riot came, it was the cops who lost their nerve and rioted, if rioting means uncontrolled mob violence. The kids sat on the floor with their hands in their pockets and sang "We shall not be moved."

Spectacular as it was, there are actions more important than the San Francisco riot. Here and there about the country, lonely, single individuals have popped up out of nowhere and struck their blows. It is almost impossible to get information about draft resisters, nonregistrants, conscientious objectors, but here and there one pops up in the local press or, more likely, in the student press.

Even more important are the individual actions of high school students whom only a hopeless paranoiac could believe anybody had organized. A sixteen-year-old boy in Queens, and then three in the Bronx, refused to sign loyalty oaths to get their diplomas. As kudos are distributed in a New York suburban high school, a boy gets up and rejects an award from the American Legion. Everybody is horrified at his bad manners. A couple of days later two of his prizes are offered to the two runners-up, who reject them in turn. This is spontaneous direct action if ever there was. And the important thing about it is that in all these cases, these high-school kids have made it clear that they do not object to either loyalty oaths or the American Legion because they are "reactionary," but because they are morally contemptible.

The Negro faculties and presidents of the Jim Crow colleges, who not only opposed the sit-ins but expelled dozens of the sit-inners, now found themselves faced with deserted campuses. They were overtaken by a tremendous ground-swell of approval of their youngsters' actions from Negro parents, and were dumbfounded by the sympathy shown by a broad stratum of the white South. One by one they swung around, until Uncle Toms who had expelled students taking part in sit-ins during their Easter vacations in other states, went on public record as saying, "If your son or daughter telephones you and says he or she has been arrested in a sit-in, get down on your knees and thank God."

Not only did the New Revolt of Youth become the hottest domestic copy in years, but it reached the ears of all the retired and semiretired and comfortably fixed pie-card artists of every lost and every long-since-won cause of the labor and radical movements. Everybody shouted, "Myself when young!" and pitched in with application blanks. The AFL-CIO sent out a well-known leader of the Esperanto movement who reported that the kids were muddled and confused and little interested in the trade-union movement which they, mistakenly in his opinion, thought of as morally compromised. YPSL chapters of the Thomasite Socialists rose from the graves of twenty years. Youth experts with theories about what their grandchildren were talking about went on cross-country tours. *Dissent* had a subscription drive. The Trotskyites came up with programs. Everybody got in the act—except, curiously, the Communists. As a matter of fact, back in the dusty office in New York, they were grimly deadlocked in their last factional fight. Although the movement was a spontaneous outburst of direct nonviolent action, it didn't quite please the libertarians and pacifists. They went about straightening everybody out, and *Liberation* came out with an article defining the correct Line and pointing out the errors of the ideologically immature.

As the kids go back to school this fall, this is going to be the greatest danger they will face—all these eager helpers from the other side of the age barrier, all these cooks, each with a time-tested recipe for the broth. All over the world this kind of ferment is stewing on college campuses. In Korea and Japan and Turkey the students have marched and brought down governments, and they have humbled the President of the greatest power in history. So far the movement is still formless, a world-wide upheaval of disgust. Even in Japan the Zengakuren, which does have a sort of ideology—the Left communism against which Lenin wrote his famous pamphlet—has only been able to act as a cheerleader. It has failed to impose its leadership, its organization or its principles on the still chaotic upsurge. In France the official Neo-Gandhian Movement, in alliance with certain sections of the Catholic Left, does seem to have given some sort of shape and leadership. I am inclined to think that this is due to the almost total ignorance of French youth of this generation—they had to go to the official sources for information and guidance, they just didn't have enough, themselves, to get started.

Is this in fact a "political" upsurge? It isn't now—it is a great moral rejection, a kind of mass vomit. Everybody in the world knows that we are on the verge of extinction and nobody does anything about it. The kids are fed up. The great problems of the world today are immediate world-wide peace, immediate race equality and immediate massive assistance to the former colonial peoples. All of them could be started toward solution by a few decisive acts of moral courage among the boys at the top of the heap. Instead, the leaders of the two ruling nations abuse each other like little boys caught out behind the barn. Their apologists stage elaborate military and ideological defenses of Marxian socialism and laissez-faire capitalism, neither of which has ever existed on the earth or ever will exist. While the Zengakuren howls in the streets, Khrushchev delivers a speech on the anniversary of Lenin's "Leftism, an Infantile Disorder" and uses it to attack—Mao! Meanwhile a boy gets up in a New York suburban school and contemptuously hands back his "patriotic" prize. He is fed up.

PAUL GOODMAN

youth in the organized society— growing up in america

It's hard to grow up when there isn't enough man's work. There is "nearly full employment" (with highly significant exceptions), but there get to be fewer jobs that are necessary or unquestionably useful; that require energy and draw on some of one's best capacities; and that can be done keeping one's honor and dignity. In explaining the widespread troubles of adolescents and young men, this simple objective factor is not much mentioned. Let us here insist on it.

By man's work I mean a very simple idea, so simple that it is clearer to ingenuous boys than to most adults. To produce necessary food and shelter is man's work. During most of economic history most men have done this drudging work, secure that it was justified and worthy of a man to do it, though often feeling that the social conditions under which they did it were *not* worthy of a man, thinking, "It's better to die than to live so hard"—but they worked on. When the environment has been forbidding, as in wresting a living in the Swiss Alps or the Aran Islands, we regard such work with poetic awe. In emergencies it is heroic, as when the bakers of Paris maintained the supply of bread during the French Revolution, or the milkman did not miss a day's delivery when the bombs recently tore up London.

At present there is little such subsistence work. Let us guess that one-twentieth of our economy is devoted to it. Production of food is actively discouraged. Farmers are not wanted and the young men go elsewhere. (The farm population is now less than 20 per cent.) Building, on the contrary, is immensely needed. One would think that ambitious boys would flock to this work. Here we find that building, too, is discouraged. In the great city of New York now for twenty years hundreds of thousands are ill-housed, yet we do not see that science, industry, and labor are enthusiastically enlisted for the quick solution of this definite problem. The promoters are interested in long-term investments, the real estate men in speculation, the city-planners in votes and graft. The building craftsmen cannily see to it that their own numbers remain few, their methods antiquated, and their rewards high. Nobody is much interested in providing shelter, and nobody is at all interested in providing new manly jobs.

Once we turn away from the absolutely necessary subsistence jobs, however, we find that an enormous proportion of our production is not even unquestionably useful. Everybody knows and also feels this, and there has recently been a flood of books about our surfeit of honey, our insolent chariots, and the follies of ex-urban ranch houses; our hucksters and our synthetic demand. Many acute things are said about this useless production and advertising, but not much about the workmen producing it and their frame of mind; and nothing at all, so far as I have noticed, about the plight of a young fellow looking for a manly occupation. The eloquent critics of the American way of life have themselves been so seduced by it that they think only in terms of selling commodities and point out that the goods are valueless; but they fail to see that people are being wasted and their skills insulted. (To give an analogy, in the many gleeful onslaughts on the Popular Culture that have appeared in recent years, there has been little thought of the plight of the honest artist cut off from his audience and some times, as in public arts like theater and architecture, from his medium.)

What is strange about it? American society has tried so hard and so ably to defend the practice and theory of production for profit and not primarily for use, that now it has succeeded in making its jobs and products profitable and useless.

Consider a likely useful job. A youth who is alert and willing but not "verbally intelligent"—perhaps he has quit high school at the eleventh grade (the median), as soon as he legally could—chooses for auto mechanic. That's a good job, familiar to him, he often watched them as a kid. It's careful and dirty at the same time. In a small garage it's sociable; one can talk to the customers (girls). You please people in trouble by fixing their cars, and a man is proud to see rolling out on its own the car that limped in behind the tow truck. The pay is as good as the next fellow's, who is respected.

So our young man takes this first-rate job. But what when he then learns that the cars have a built-in obsolescence, that the manufacturers do not want them to be repaired or repairable? They have lobbied a law that requires them to provide spare parts for only five years (it used to be ten). Repairing the new cars is a matter of cosmetics not mechanics; and the repairs are pointlessly expensive—a tail fin might cost $150. The insurance rates therefore double and treble on old and new cars both. Gone are the days of keeping jalopies in good shape, the artist-work of a proud mechanic. But everybody is paying for foolishness, for in fact the new models are only trivially superior; the whole thing is a sell.

It is hard for the young man now to maintain his feelings of justification, sociability, serviceability. It is not surprising if he quickly becomes cynical and time-serving, interested in a fast buck. And so, on the notorious *Reader's Digest* test—the car with a disconnected coil wire—the investigators found 63 per cent of mechanics charged for repairs they didn't make, and lucky if they didn't also take out the new fuel pump and replace it with a used one. (65 per cent of radio repair shops, but only 49 per cent of watch repairmen "lied, overcharged, or gave false diagnoses.")

There is an hypothesis that an important predisposition to juvenile delinquency is the combination of low verbal intelligence with high manual intelligence, delinquency giving a way of self-expression where other avenues are blocked by lack of schooling. A lad so endowed might well apply himself to the useful trade of mechanic.

Most manual jobs do not lend themselves so readily to knowing the facts and fraudulently taking advantage. In factory jobs the workman is likely to be ignorant of what goes on, since he performs a small operation on a big machine that he does not understand. Even so there is evidence that he has the same disbelief in the enterprise as a whole, with a resulting attitude of profound indifference.

Semi-skilled factory operatives are the largest category of workmen. (I am leafing through the U.S. Department of Labor's *Occupational Outlook Handbook, 1957.*) Big companies have tried the devices of applied anthropology to enhance the loyalty of the men to the firm, but apparently the effort is hopeless, for it is found that a thumping majority of the men don't care about the job or the firm; they couldn't care less and you can't make them care more. But this is *not* because of wages, hours, or working conditions, or management. On the contrary, the tests of Robert Dubin that show the men's indifferences to the company, show also their (unaware) admiration for the way the company has designed and manages the plant; it is their very model of style, efficiency, and correct behavior. Maybe if they understood more, they would admire less. The union and the grievance committee take care of wages, hours, and conditions; these are the things the workmen themselves fought for and won. (Something was missing in that victory, and we have inherited the failure as well as the success.) The conclusion must be that workmen are indifferent to the job because of its intrinsic nature: the work does not enlist a man's worthwhile capacities, it is not "interesting"; it is not his, he is not "in" on it; the product is not unquestionably useful; and he doesn't care about the enterprise. And research directly on this subject, by Frederick Herzberg, shows that it is defects in the intrinsic aspects of the job that make workmen "unhappy." (A survey of the literature, in Herzberg's *Job Attitudes,* shows that interest is second in importance only to security, whereas wages, conditions, hours, ease, and benefits are far less important. But foremen, significantly enough, think that the most important thing to the workman is his wages.)

"Security" is always first; but in normal conditions a large part of security comes from knowing your contribution is useful, and the rest from knowing it's uniquely yours: they need you.

What a remarkable thing such studies tell us! That men want to do good work and work that is somehow theirs. But they are thwarted. Is not this the "waste of our human resources" that is talked about?

The case is that by the "sole prerogative" clause in union contracts the employer has the sole right to determine what is to be produced, how it is to be produced, what plants are to be built and where, what kinds of machinery are to be installed, when workers are to be hired and when laid off, and how production operations are to be rationalized (Frank Marquart). Under these circumstances, it is not surprising if the factory operatives' actual code has absolutely nothing to do with useful service or increasing production, but is devoted to "interpersonal relations": (1) don't turn out too much work; (2) don't turn out too little work; (3) don't squeal on a fellow worker; (4) don't act like a big-shot (Elton Mayo; these are not Mayo's principles). This is how to belong.

II

Let us go on to the occupational outlook of those who are verbally bright. Among this group, just because they cannot help asking more general questions, the problem of finding man's work is harder and their disillusion more poignant. The more intelligent worker's "indifference" is likely to appear more nakedly as profound resignation, and his cynicism may sharpen to outright racketeering.

"Teaching," says the *Handbook*, "is the largest of the professions." So suppose our now verbally bright young man chooses for teacher, in the high school system or, by exception, in the elementary schools if he understands that these are the vitally important grades and require the most ability to teach well (and of course have less prestige). Teaching is necessary and useful work; it is real and creative, for it directly confronts an important subject matter, the children themselves; it is obviously self-justifying; and it is ennobled by the arts and sciences. Those who practice teaching do not for the most part succumb to cynicism or indifference—the children are too immediate and real for the teachers to become callous—but they certainly come to suffer first despair and then deep resignation. Resignation occurs psychologically as follows: frustrated in essential action, they nevertheless cannot quit in anger, because the task is necessary; so the anger turns inward and is felt as resignation.

For the job is carried on in impossible conditions of overcrowding and saving public money. *Not* that there is not enough social wealth, but first things are not put first. Also, the school system has spurious aims. It soon becomes clear that the underlying aims are to relieve the home and keep the kids quiet; or, suddenly, the aim is to produce physicists. Timid supervisors, bigoted clerics, and ignorant school boards forbid real teaching. The emotional release and sexual expression of the children are taboo. A commercially debauched popular culture makes learning disesteemed. The academic curriculum is mangled by the demands of reactionaries, liberals, and demented warriors. Progressive methods are emasculated. Attention to each case is out of the question, and all the children, the bright, the average, and the dull are systematically retarded one way or another, while the teacher's hands are tied. Naturally the pay is low—for the work is hard, useful, and of public concern, all three of which categories tend to get lower pay. It is alleged that the low pay is why there is a shortage of teachers and why the best do not choose the profession. My guess is that the best avoid it because of the certainty of mis-educating. Nor are the best *wanted* by the system, for they are not safe. Bertrand Russell was rejected by New York's City College and would not have been accepted in a New York grade school.

Next, what happens to the verbally bright who have no zeal for a serviceable profession and who have no particular scientific or artistic bent? For the most part they make up the tribes of salesmanship, entertainment, business management, Madison Avenue. Here of course there is no question of utility or honor to begin with, so an ingenuous boy will not look here for a manly career. Nevertheless, though we can pass by the sufferings of these well-paid callings, much publicized by their own writers, they are important to our theme because of the model they present to the growing boy.

Consider the men and women in TV advertisements, demonstrating the product and singing the jingle. They are clowns and mannequins, in grimace, speech, and action. And again, what I want to call attention to in this advertising is not the economic problem of synthetic demand, and not the cultural problem of Popular Culture, but the human problem that these are human beings working as clowns; that the writers and designers of it are human beings thinking like idiots; and the broadcasters and underwriters know and abet what goes on: *"Fruitily, bubbily, Hoffman's is dubbily good as good can be!"* Alternately, they are liars, confidence men, smooth talkers, obsequious, insolent, etc., etc.

The popular-cultural content of the advertisements is somewhat neutralized by *Mad* magazine, the bible of the twelve-year-olds who can read. But far more influential and hard to counteract is the *fact* that the workmen and the patrons of this enterprise are human beings. (Highly approved too.) They are not good models toward looking for manly jobs that are useful and necessary, requiring human energy and capacity, and that can be done with honor and dignity. They are a good sign that not many such jobs will be available.

The rigged quiz shows, which created a scandal last year, were a remarkably pure distillate of our American cookery. We start with the brute facts that (a) in our abundant expanding economy it is necessary to give money away to increase spending, production, and profits; and (b) that this money must not be used for useful public goods in taxes, but must be ploughed back as "business expenses," even when there is a shameful shortage of schools, housing, etc. Yet when the TV people at first tried simply to give the money away for nothing, there was a great Calvinistic outcry that this was demoralizing—just as we may gamble on the horses only to improve the breed. So they hit on the notion of a contest with prizes. But then, of course, they could not resist making the show itself profit-making and competitive in the (also rigged) ratings with other shows, so the experts in the entertainment-commodity manufactured phony contests. And to cap the climax of fraudulence, the hero of the phony contests proceeded to persuade himself, so he says, that his behavior was educational!

The behavior of the networks was correspondingly typical. These business organizations claim the loyalty of their employees, but at the first breath of trouble they were ruthless and disloyal to their employees. (Even McCarthy was loyal to his gang.) They want to maximize profits and yet be absolutely safe from any risk. Consider their claim that they knew nothing about the fraud. (In my opinion this was a plain lie.) If they watched the shows that they were broadcasting, they could not possibly, as professionals, not have known the facts, for there were obvious type-casting, acting, plot, etc. If they are not professionals, they are incompetent. But if they don't watch what they broadcast, then they are utterly irresponsible, and on what grounds do they have the franchises to the channels? We may offer them the choice: that they are liars or incompetent or irresponsible.

The new direction of the investigation seems to me more important, the inquiry into the bribed disc-jockeying; for this deals directly with our crucial economic problem of synthesized demand, made taste, debauching the public and preventing the emergence and formation of natural taste. In such circumstances there cannot possibly be an American culture, we are doomed to nausea and barbarism. And *then* these baboons have the effrontery to declare that they give the people what the people demand, and are not responsible for the level of the movies, the music, the plays, the books!

Finally, in leafing through the *Occupational Outlook Handbook,* we notice that Armed Forces employ a large number. Here our young man can become involved in a world-wide demented enterprise with personnel and activities corresponding.

III

Thus, on the simple criteria of unquestioned utility, employing human capacities, and honor, there are not enough worthy jobs in our economy for average boys and adolescents to grow up toward. There are of course thousands of jobs that are worthy and self-justifying, and thousands that can be made so by stubborn integrity. Extraordinary intelligence or special talent, also, can often carve out a place for itself—conversely, their usual corruption and waste are all the more sickening. But by and large our economic society is *not* geared for the cultivation of its young or the attainment of important goals that they can work toward.

This is evident from the usual kind of vocational guidance, which consists in measuring the boy and finding some place in the economy where he can be fitted; chopping him down to make him fit; or neglecting him if they can't find his slot. Personnel directors do not much try to scrutinize the economy in order to find some activity which is a real opportunity for the boy, and creating an opportunity if they can't find one. To do this would be a horrendous task; I am not sure if it could be done if we wanted to. But the question is whether anything less makes sense if we mean to speak seriously about the troubles of young men.

Surely by now, however, many readers are objecting that this entire argument is pointless because people in *fact* don't think of their jobs in this way at all. *Nobody* asks if a job is useful or honorable (within the limits of business ethics). A man gets a job that pays well, or well enough, that has prestige, and good conditions, or at least tolerable conditions. I agree with these objections as to the fact. (I hope we are wrong.) *But the question is what it means to grow up into such a fact:* "During my productive years I will spend eight hours a day doing what is no good."

Yet economically and vocationally, a very large proportion of the young people are in a more drastic plight than anything so far mentioned. In our society as it is, there are not enough worthy jobs. But if our society, being as it is, were run more efficiently and soberly, for a majority there would soon not be any jobs at all. There is at present nearly full employment and there may be for some years, yet a vast number of young people are rationally unemployable, useless. This paradox is essential to explain their present temper.

Our society, which is not geared to the cultivation of its young, *is* geared to a profitable expanding production, a so-called high standard of living of mediocre value, and the maintenance of nearly full employment. Politically, the chief of these is full employment. In a crisis, when profitable production is temporarily curtailed, government spending increases and jobs are manufactured. In "normalcy"—a condition of slow boom—the easy credit, installment buying, and artificially induced demand for useless goods, create jobs for all and good profits for some.

Now back in the 30's when the New Deal attempted by hook or crook to put people back to work and give them money to revive the shattered economy, there was an outcry of moral indignation from the conservatives that many of the jobs were "boondoggling," useless made work. It was insisted, and rightly, that such work was demoralizing to the workers themselves. It is a question of a word, but a candid critic might certainly say that many of the jobs in our present "normal" production are useless made work. The tailfins and built-in obsolescence might be called boondoggling. The $64,000

Question and the busy hum of Madison Avenue might certainly be called boondoggling. Certain tax-dodge foundations are boondoggling. What of business lunches and expense accounts? fringe benefits? the comic categories of occupation in the building trades? the extra stagehands and musicians of the theater crafts? These jolly devices to put money back to work no doubt have a demoralizing effect on somebody or other (certainly on me, they make me green with envy), but where is the moral indignation from Top Management?

Suppose we would cut out the boondoggling and gear our society to a more sensible abundance, with efficient production of quality goods, distribution in a natural market, counter-inflation, and sober credit. At once the work week would be cut to, say, twenty hours instead of forty. (Important People have already mentioned the figure thirty.) Or alternately, half the labor force would be unemployed. Suppose too—and how can we not suppose it?—that the automatic machines are put to general use, instead of just getting rid of badly organized unskilled labor. The unemployment will be still more drastic.

To give the most striking example: in steel, the annual increase in productivity is 4 per cent, the plants work at 50 per cent of capacity, and the companies can break even working at *less than 30 per cent* of capacity. These are the conditions that forced the steel strike, as desperate self-protection. (Estes Kefauver, quoting Gardiner Means and Fred Gardner.)

Everybody knows this, nobody wants to talk about it much, for we don't know how to cope with it. The effect is that we are living a kind of lie. Long ago, labor used to fight for the shorter work week, but now they don't, because they are pretty sure they don't want it. Indeed, when hours are reduced, the tendency is to get a second, part-time, job and raise the standard of living, *because* the job is meaningless and one must have something; but the standard of living is pretty meaningless too. Nor is this strange atmosphere a new thing. For at least a generation the maximum sensible use of our productivity could have thrown a vast population out of work, or relieved everybody of a lot of useless work, depending on how you take it. (Consider with how little cutback of useful civilian production the economy produced the war goods and maintained an army of unemployed.) The plain truth is that at present very many of us are useless, not needed, rationally unemployable. It is in this paradoxical atmosphere that young persons grow up. It looks busy and expansive, but it is rationally at a stalemate.

These considerations apply to all ages and classes; but it is of course among poor youth (and the aged) that they show up first and worst. These are the most unemployable. Our society has not been geared to the cultivation of the young for a long time. At present 42 per cent have graduated high school (predicted Census, 1960); less than 8 per cent have graduated college. The high school trend for at least the near future is not much different, there will be a high proportion of drop-outs; but *markedly more* of the rest are going on to college, that is, the stratification is deepening between those who have prospects and those who have none. Now the schooling in neither the high schools nor the colleges is much good—if it were better more kids would stick to it; yet at present, if we made a list we should find that a large proportion of the dwindling number of unquestionably useful or self-justifying jobs, in the humane professions and the arts and sciences, require education; and in the future, there is no doubt that the more educated will have the jobs in running an efficient highly technical economy and an administrative and verbal society.

> *Between 1947 and 1957, professional and technical workers increased 61 per cent, clerical workers 23 per cent, but factory operatives only 4½ per cent and laborers 4 per cent* CENSUS

For the uneducated there will be no jobs at all. This is humanly most unfortunate, for presumably those who have learned something in schools, and have the knack to survive the boredom of those schools, could also make something of idleness; whereas the uneducated are useless at leisure too. It takes application, a fine sense of value, and a powerful community spirit for a people to have serious leisure, and this has not been the genius of the Americans.

From this point of view we can sympathetically understand the pathos of our American school policy, which otherwise seems so inexplicable; at great expense compelling kids to go to school who do not want to and who will not profit by it. There are of course unpedagogic motives, like relieving the home, controlling delinquency, and keeping kids from competing for jobs. But there is also this desperately earnest pedagogic motive, of preparing the kids to take *some* part in a democratic society that does not need them. Otherwise, what will become of them, if they don't know anything?

Compulsory public education spread universally during the 19th century to provide the reading, writing, and arithmetic necessary to build a modern industrial economy. Now with the over-maturity of the economy, the teachers are struggling to preserve the elementary system when the economy no longer requires it and is stingy about paying for it. The demand is for scientists and technicians, the 15 per cent of the "academically talented." "For a vast majority [in the high schools]," says Dr. James Conant in *The Child, the Parent, and the State,* "the vocational courses are the vital core of the program. They represent something related directly to the ambitions of the boys and girls." But somehow, more than 50 per cent quit.

(Let me make a comment on Dr. Conant's vastly publicized report on the high schools. The important question that he fails to ask is why there are only 15 per cent who are "academically talented" enough to take hard subjects. Does he think that the general dullness of the high school population has occurred in a void? And why do large percentages even of the brightest—from 25 per cent to 50 per cent, depending on the region—shirk the hard courses or quit school? What is lacking in their motivation? If he were concerned, as he claims, about conserving human resources, his zeal would be to find why most are so inept and to invent techniques to unblock them and increase the pool of talent. But there is nothing of this in Dr. Conant's report.)

Let us sum up again. The majority of young people are faced with the following alternative: either society is a benevolently frivolous racket in which they'll manage to boondoggle, though less profitably, than the more privileged; or society is serious (and they hope still benevolent enough to support them), but they are useless and hopelessly out. Such thoughts do not encourage productive life. Naturally young people are more sanguine and look for man's work, but few find it. Some settle for a "good job"; most settle for a lousy job; a few, but an increasing number, don't settle.

I often ask, "What do you want to work at? If you have the chance. When you get out of school, college, the service, etc."

Some answer right off and tell their definite plans and projects. I'm pleased for them, but it's a bit boring, because they are such squares.

Quite a few will, with prompting, come out with astounding stereotyped conceited fantasies like being a movie actor when they are "discovered"—like "Marlon Brando, but in my own way."

Very rarely somebody will, maybe defiantly and defensively, maybe diffidently but proudly, make you know that he knows very well what he is going to do, is indeed already doing it, which is the real test.

The usual answer, perhaps the normal answer, is "I don't know," meaning, "I'm looking; I haven't found the right thing; it's discouraging but not hopeless."

But the terrible answer is, "Nothing." The young man doesn't want to do anything.

I remember talking to half a dozen young fellows at Van Wagner's Beach outside of Hamilton, Ontario; and all of them had this one thing to say, "Nothing." They didn't believe that what to work at was the kind of thing one *wanted*. They rather expected that two or three of them would work for the electric company in town, but they couldn't care less. I turned away from the conversation abruptly, because of the uncontrollable burning tears in my eyes and pain in my breast. Not feeling sorry for them, but tears of frank dismay for the waste of our humanity (they were nice kids). And it is out of that incident that many years later I am writing this report.

IV

The simple job plight of these adolescents could not be remedied without a social revolution. Therefore is it not astonishing if the most well-intentioned public spokesmen do not mention it at all. But it is hard to grow up in a society where one's important problems are treated as nonexistent. It is impossible to belong to it, it is hard to fight to change it. The effect must be rather to feel disaffected, and all the more restive if one is smothered by well-meaning social workers and PAL's who don't seem to understand the real irk. The boys cannot articulate the real irk themselves, for they haven't learned to say it.

For instance, what public spokesman could discuss the jobs? The ideal of a real job that you risk your soul in and make good or be damned, belongs to the heroic age of capitalist enterprise, imbued with self-righteous beliefs about hard work, thrift, and public morals. Such an ideal might still have been mentioned in public fifty years ago; in our era of risk-insured semi-monopolies and advertised vices, it would be met with a ghastly stillness. Or alternately, to want a job that exercises a man's capacities in an enterprise useful to society, is utopian anarcho-syndicalism, it is labor invading the domain of management. No labor leader has entertained such a thought in our generation. Management has the "sole prerogative" to determine the products and the machines. Again, to speak of the likelihood or the desirability of unemployment, like Norbert Wiener or J. K. Galbraith, is to be politically non-professional.

During, let us say, 1890–1936, on Marxist grounds, the fight for working conditions, for security, wages, hours, the union, the dignity of labor, *was* mentioned, and it gave the worker or the youth something worthwhile. But because of their historical theory of the "alienation of labor" (that the worker *must* become less and less in control of the work of his hands), the Marxist parties never fought for the man-worthy job itself. What is surprising now if workmen accept their alienation, and are indifferent also to Marxist politics?

When the objective factors cannot be mentioned, however, other things are said instead, and let us now examine their style, as applied, for instance to juvenile delinquency, on which there is a good deal of oratory.

In our times the usual principle of such speech is that the others, the delinquent boys, are not taken seriously as existing, as having real aims in a real world like oneself. They are not condemned, they are not accepted. Instead they are a "youth problem" and the emphasis is on their "background conditions" that one can manipulate, and they are said to be subject to "tensions" that one can alleviate. The aim is not to give human beings real goals that warrant belief, and tasks to share in, but to reestablish "belonging," although this kind of speech and thought is precisely calculated to avoid contact and so makes belonging impossible. When such efforts don't work, one finally takes some of the boys seriously as existing and uses force to make them not exist.

Let me give a childish but important illustration how this works out. A boy has a few great sexual adventures, but then he has had the bad luck to get caught and get in trouble. They try to persuade him by punishment and other explanations that some different behavior is much better, but he knows by the evidence of his senses that nothing could be better. If he gives in, he lives on in a profound disbelief, a disbelief in their candor and a disbelief even in his own body feelings. But if he persists and proves incorrigible, then the evidence of his senses is attached to what is socially punished, explained away, and put away. The basic trouble here is that they do not really believe he has had the sexual experience. The objective factor is inconvenient for them; therefore it cannot exist. Instead, there is *merely* a case of insecure affection at home, slum housing, comic books, and naughty companions—tensions and conditions. My hunch is that this kind of early sexual adventure and misadventure is fairly common in delinquency. It is called precocious, abnormal, artificially stimulated, etc., an index of future delinquency. In my opinion that's rubbish, but be that as it may; what is important in the particular case is that there is a stubborn new fact. Attempting to nullify it makes further growth impossible (and *creates* the future delinquency). The sensible course would be to accept it is a valuable part of future growth. But if this were done, they fear that the approved little hero would be a rotten apple to his peers who would now suddenly *all* have become precocious, abnormal, artificially stimulated, and prone to delinquency.

The sexual plight of these children is officially not mentioned. The revolutionary attack on hypocrisy of Ibsen, Ellis, Dreiser, etc., etc., did not succeed this far. Is it an eccentric opinion that an important part of the kid's restiveness in school from the onset of puberty has to do with puberty? (In his school, Bertrand Russell thought it was better if they had the sex, so they could give their undivided attention to mathematics, which was the main thing.) But since this objective factor does not *exist* in our schools, the school itself begins to be irrelevant. The question here is not whether the sexuality should be discouraged or encouraged. That is an important issue, but far more important is that it is hard to grow up when existing things are treated as though they did not exist. For then there is no dialogue, it is impossible to be taken seriously, to be understood, to make a bridge between oneself and society.

In American society we have perfected a remarkable form of censorship: to allow every one his political right to say what he believes, but to swamp his little boat with literally thousands of millions of newspapers, mass-circulation magazines, best-selling books, broadcasts, and public pronouncements that disregard what he says and give the official way of looking at things. Usually there is no conspiracy to do this; it is simply that what he says is not what people are talking about, it is not newsworthy.

(There is no conspiracy, but it is *not* undeliberate. "If you mean to tell me," said an editor to me, "that our magazine tries to have articles on important issues and treat them in such a way that nothing can come of it—who can deny it?" Try, also, to get a letter printed in the New York *Times* if your view on this issue calls attention to an essential factor that is not being mentioned.)

Naturally, the more simply true a statement is in any issue where everybody is quite confused, the less newsworthy it will be, the less it will be what everybody is talking about. When the child in the story said, "But the Emperor has no clothes on!" the newspapers and broadcasts surely devoted many columns to describing the beautiful new clothes and also mentioned the interesting psychological incident of the child. Instead of being proud of him, his parents were ashamed; but on the other hand they received $10,000 in sympathetic contributions toward his rehabilitation, for he was a newsworthy case. But he had a block in reading.

Where there is official censorship it is a sign that speech is serious. Where there is none, it is pretty sure that the official spokesmen have all the loud-speakers.

But let us return to our theme of vocation and develop it a step further. Perhaps the young fellows *really* want to do something, that is, something worthwhile, for only a worthwhile achievement finishes a doing. A person rests when he has finished a real job. If the object is important, it gives structure to many a day's action and dreaming—one might even continue in school. Unfortunately our great society balks us, for it simply does not take seriously the fact, or the possibility, that people want this; nor the philosophic truth that except in worthwhile activity there is no way to be happy. For instance, in a standard questionnaire of a delinquent by Milton Barron, in a hundred headings there does not occur the question, "What do you want to be? What do you want to work at? What do you want to achieve?" (But Donald Taft's *Criminology*, which Barron is adapting, here has the sentence: "Absence of vocational interest at the age when it is normal . . . is telltale of a starved life.")

In despair, the fifteen-year-olds hang around and do nothing at all, neither work nor play. Without a worthwhile prospect, without a sense of justification, the made play of the Police Athletic League is not interesting, it is not their own. They do not do their school work, for they are waiting to quit, and it is harder than it used to be for them to get part-time jobs. Indeed, the young fellows, and not only delinquents, spend a vast amount of time doing nothing. They hang around together, but don't talk about anything, nor even, if you watch their faces, do they passively take in the scene. Conversely, at the movies where the real scene is by-passed, they watch with absorbed fantasy, and afterward sometimes mimic what they saw.

If there is nothing worthwhile, it is hard to do anything at all. When one does nothing, one is threatened by the question whether one *is* nothing. To this insulting doubt, however, there is a lively response: it is a system of values centering around threatened grownup-ness and defensive conceit. This is the so-called "threatened masculinity," not in the sense of being called a girl, but of being called, precisely, "boy," the Negro term of insult. With this, there is an endless compulsion to prove potency and demand esteem. They don't talk about much of interest, but there is a vast amount of hot rhetoric to assert that oneself is as "good as anybody else," no more useless, stupid, nor cowardly. For instance, if they play a game, the interest in the game is weak; they are looking elsewhere when the ball is served, there are lapses in attention, they smoke cigarettes even while playing handball. The interest in victory is surprisingly weak: there is not much glow of self-esteem. But the need for proof is overwhelming: "I won you, didn' I? I won you last week too, didn' I?"

During childhood, they played games with fierce intensity, giving themselves as a sacrifice to the game, for play was the chief business of growth, finding-and-making themselves in the world. Now when they are too old merely to play, to what shall they give themselves with fierce intensity? They cannot play for recreation, since they have not been used up.

The proving behavior is endless. Since each activity is not

interesting to begin with, its value does not deepen and it does not bear much repetition. Its value as proof rapidly diminishes. In these circumstances, the inevitable tendency is to raise the ante of the compulsive activity that proves one is potent and not useless. (This analysis applies equally to these juveniles and to status-seeking junior executives in business firms and on Madison Avenue.)

It is not surprising, then, that, as Frederic Thrasher says in *The Gang*, "Other things being equal, the imaginative boy has an excellent chance to become the leader of the gang. He has the power to make things interesting for them. He 'thinks up things for us to do.'" At this point let us intervene and say what the Official Spokesmen say.

V

Last summer, after a disastrous week when there were several juvenile murders, Governor Rockefeller of New York made the statement (New York *Times*, September 2, 1959):

> *We have to constantly devise new ways to bring about a challenge to these young folks and to provide an outlet for their energies and give them a sense of belonging.*

The statement is on the highest level of current statesmanship—that is why I have chosen it. It has been coached by sociologists and psychologists. It has the proper therapeutic and not moralistic attitude, and it does not mention the police. (The direct appeal to force came a couple of weeks later, when there were other incidents.)

The gist of it is that the Governor of New York is to play the role that Thrasher assigns to the teen-age gang leader. He is to think up new "challenges." (The word could not have been more unfortunate.) But it is the word "constantly" that is the clue. A challenge can hardly be worthwhile, meaningful, or therapeutic if another must constantly and obsessively be devised to siphon off a new threat of "energy." Is not this raising the ante? Solidly meeting a real need does not have this character.

("The leader," says Thrasher, "sometimes controls the gang by means of summation, i.e., by progressively urging the members from one deed to another, until finally an extreme of some sort is reached.")

My guess is that in playing games the Governor will not have so lively an imagination as the lad he wants to displace as leader; unlike the grownups, the gang will never select him. One of the objective factors that make it hard to grow up is that governors are likely to be men of mediocre humane gifts.

The psychology of the Governor's statement is puzzling. There are no such undifferentiated energies as he speaks of. There are energies of specific functions with specific real objects. In the case here they might be partly as follows: In adolescents a strong energy would be sexual reaching. As with other adolescents, it is thwarted or imperfectly gratified, but these have probably not learned so well as others to cushion the suffering and be patient; so that another strong energy of the delinquents would be diffuse rage of frustration, perhaps directed at a scapegoat. If they have been kept from constructive activity making them feel worthwhile, a part of their energy might be envious and malicious destructiveness of property. As they are powerless, it is spite; and as they are humiliated, it is vengeance. As they feel rejected and misunderstood, as by governors, their energy is woe; but they react to this with cold pride, and all the more fierce gang loyalty to their peers. For which of these specific energies does the Governor of New York seriously plan to devise an outlet? Their own imaginative gang-leader presumably does devise challenges that fit the bill enough to let off steam for a few hours.

What is the sociology of "belonging" here? In the great society they are certainly uprooted. But in the gang their conformity is sickeningly absolute; they have uniform jackets and uniform morals. They speak a jargon and no one has a different idea that might brand him as queer. Since they have shared forbidden behavior, they are all in the same mutually-blackmailing boat and correspondingly guilty and suspicious toward the outsider. It is a poor kind of community they have; friendship, affection, personal helpfulness are remarkably lacking in it; they are "cool," afraid to display feeling; yet does the Governor seriously think that he can offer a good community that warrants equal loyalty?

Our society has evolved a social plan, a city plan, an economy and physical plant, in which this delinquent youth is an organic part. The problem is *not* to get them to belong to society, for they belong a priori by being the next generation. The burden of proof and performance is quite the other way: for the system of society to accommodate itself to all its constituent members. But can it be denied that by and large the official practice is to write these boys off as useless and unwanted, and to try to cajole or baffle them into harmlessness?

Suppose we look at it the other way. Like any other constitutional group they exert an annoying pressure, but they are inarticulate. In some dumb way they are surely right, but what the devil do they want? Has much effort been made to ask them and help them find words? We can guess that they want two broad classes of things: changes in the insulting and depriving circumstances that have made them ornery, spiteful, vengeful, conceited, ignorant, and callous—unable to grow; and objective opportunities in which to grow.

Let us go back to the Governor. On the same occasion, he issued to the press the following formal statement:

> *The problem of juvenile delinquency has no easy remedy. There is no quick or overnight solution. It is compounded of neglect by parents, broken homes, poor living conditions, unhealthy background, economic deprivation, mental disturbance, and lack of religious training.*

This is not a bad list of background conditions; it satisfies every popular and scientific theory of etiology. The question is, does the Governor seriously not understand how organic these conditions are in our society? They cannot be remedied by gimmicks or social work. He speaks of broken homes; has he some plan to improve the institution of modern marriage, especially among folk for whom it is hardly an institution? The present day urban poor are largely Negro and Spanish, they are excluded from many unions, they often earn less than the minimum wage, they are unschooled; naturally there is economic deprivation, poor living conditions. How is their religion relevant if it is irrelevant to the basic community functions of vocation and war, and wrong on sex? There is no community and not even a community plan; naturally there is unhealthy background.

What great concerted effort is being led by the Governor to remedy these conditions, not overnight, but in the next five, ten, or twenty years?

Indeed, *official* policy has often worked to increase delinquency, rather than remedy it. For instance, in a characteristically earnest analysis, Charles Abrams has shown how the public housing policy has had this effect. Slums have been torn down wholesale, disrupting established community life. By not building on vacant land and by neglecting master planning, our officials have created insoluble problems of relocation and vastly increased the number of one-room flats, making decent family life impossible. (Suppose you were fifteen years old and returned home at 11 P.M., as the Mayor urges, to a room with mama and papa in one bed and two little brothers in your bed and a baby yowling; you might well stay out until four in the morning.) Again, families are ousted from public housing when their incomes increase, so eliminating and penalizing the better models; and on the other hand, other families are expelled on irrelevant moral criteria without thought of what becomes of them. And income segregation in large blocks was itself bound to increase tension, like any segregation. All this has been *official* policy. The picture gets even grimmer if we turn to the quasi-official graft in Title I that for two- and three-year stretches has stalled either demolition or construction, while families pay rent in limbo.

Now finally (January 1960), the Governor's practical anti-delinquency youth program is offered for legislation. Let me summarize its chief points: (1) Reduce the age of felonies to fifteen. (2) Space for 390 more in the forest camps (added to the 110 now there). (3) Admit a few older to these camps. (4) Establish "Youth Opportunity Centers"—residences for youths "on the verge of delinquency." (5) Provide "halfway houses" for those in transition from institutions to freedom. (6) Certify boardinghouses to which the court can direct the youngsters. (7) Ease compulsory continuation school. (8) Permit after-school work from fourteen to sixteen. (9) Encourage work-and-study programs "to keep potential dropouts in school long enough to prepare for employment." (10) Centralize probation services. (11) Increase probation staff.

Of these eleven points, eight seem to be aimed primarily at punishment or control: the boys are really unwanted, the problem is to render them harmless. Only two (8 and 9) envisage, very unimpressively, a substantive change. What on earth has happened to devising "new ways, constant challenges"? But let me call attention to the forest work camps (2 and 3). There is good evidence that these are excellent and have provided a rewarding experience. But then certainly they should be made available not for convicted delinquents as such, but for all kids who want to work there a year. Naturally, however, there is no money—not even for more than five hundred delinquent boys altogether. The question is whether or not such a program of camps for many thousand boys is less important than one of the Park Commissioner's new highways to Westchester. Until they will face that question, our public officials are not serious.

Positively, the delinquent behavior seems to speak clearly enough. It asks for manly opportunities to work, make a little money, and have self-esteem; to have some space to bang around in that is not always somebody's property; to have better schools to open for them horizons of interest; to have more and better sex without fear or shame; to share somehow in the symbolic goods (like the cars) that are made so much of; to have a community and a country to be loyal to; to claim attention and have a voice. These are not outlandish demands. Certainly they cannot be satisfied directly in our present system, they are baffling. That is why the problem is baffling, and the final recourse is to a curfew, to ordinances against carrying knives, to threatening the parents, to reformatories with newfangled names, and to eleven hundred more police on the streets.

PHILIP LARKIN

church going

Once I am sure there's nothing going on
I step inside, letting the door thud shut.
Another church: matting, seats, and stone,
And little books; sprawlings of flowers, cut
For Sunday, brownish now; some brass and stuff
Up at the holy end; the small neat organ;
And a tense, musty, unignorable silence,
Brewed God knows how long. Hatless, I take off
My cycle-clips in awkward reverence,

Move forward, run my hand around the font.
From where I stand, the roof looks almost new—
Cleaned, or restored? Someone would know: I don't.
Mounting the lectern, I peruse a few

Hectoring large-scale verses, and pronounce
'Here endeth' much more loudly than I'd meant.
The echoes snigger briefly. Back at the door
I sign the book, donate an Irish sixpence,
Reflect the place was not worth stopping for.

Yet stop I did: in fact I often do,
And always end much at a loss like this,
Wondering what to look for; wondering, too,
When churches fall completely out of use
What we shall turn them into, if we shall keep
A few cathedrals chronically on show,
Their parchment, plate and pyx in locked cases,
And let the rest rent-free to rain and sheep.
Shall we avoid them as unlucky places?

Or, after dark, will dubious women come
To make their children touch a particular stone;
Pick simples for a cancer; or on some
Advised night see walking a dead one?
Power of some sort or other will go on
In games, in riddles, seemingly at random;
But supersition, like belief, must die,
And what remains when disbelief has gone?
Grass, weedy pavement, brambles, buttress, sky,

A shape less recognizable each week,
A purpose more obscure. I wonder who
Will be the last, the very last, to seek
This place for what it was; one of the crew
That tap and jot and know what rood-lofts were?
Some ruin-bibber, randy for antique,
Or Christmas-addict, counting on a whiff
Of gown-and-bands and organ-pipes and myrrh?
Or will he be my representative,

Bored, uninformed, knowing the ghostly silt
Dispersed, yet tending to this cross of ground
Through suburb scrub because it held unspilt
So long and equably what since is found

Only in separation—marriage, and birth,
And death, and thoughts of these—for whom was built
This special shell? For, though I've no idea
What this accoutred frowsty barn is worth,
It pleases me to stand in silence here;

A serious house on serious earth it is,
In whose blent air all our compulsions meet,
Are recognized, and robed as destinies.
And that much never can be obsolete,
Since someone will forever be surprising
A hunger in himself to be more serious,
And gravitating with it to this ground,
Which, he once heard, was proper to grow wise in,
If only that so many dead lie round.

S. S. GARDONS

the mouse

ON MY SISTER'S DEATH

I remember one evening—we were small—
Playing outdoors, we found a mouse,
A dusty little gray one, lying
By the side steps. Afraid he might be dead,
We carried him all around the house
On a piece of tinfoil, crying.

Ridiculous children; we could bawl
Our eyes out about nothing. Still,
How much violence had we seen?
They teach you—quick—you have to be well-bred
In all events: We can't all win;
Don't whine to get your will.

We live with some things, after all,
Bitterer than dying, cold as hate:
The old insatiable loves,
The vague desire that keeps watch overhead,
Polite, wakeful as a cat,
To tease us with our lives;

That pats at you, wants to see you crawl
Some, then picks you back alive;
That needs you just a little hurt.
The mind goes blank, then the eyes. Weak with dread,
In shock, the breath comes short;
We go about our lives.

And then the little animal
Plays out: the dulled heart year by year
Turns from its own needs, forgets its grief.
Asthmatic, timid, twenty-five, unwed—
The day we left you by your grave,
I wouldn't spare one tear.

S. S. GARDONS

fourth of july

The drifting smoke is gone, today,
From the mill chimneys; the laborers from the great
Iron foundries are on strike. They celebrate
Their Independence her own way.

She stopped a year ago today.
Firecrackers mark the occasion down the street;
I thumb through magazines and keep my seat.
What can anybody say?

In her room, nights, we lie awake
By racks of unworn party dresses, shoes,
Her bedside asthma pipe, the glasses whose
Correction no one else will take.

Stuffed dogs look at us from the shelf
When we sit down together at the table.
You put a face on things the best you're able
And keep your comments to yourself.

It is a hideous mistake.
My young wife, unforgivably alive,
Takes a deep breath and blows out twenty-five
Candles on her birthday cake.

It is agreed she'll get her wish.
The candles smell; smoke settles through the room
Like a cheap stage set for Juliet's tomb.
I leave my meal cold on the dish.

We take the children to the park
To watch the fireworks and the marching band.
For hours a drill team pivots at command.
For hours we sit in the dark

Hearing some politician fume;
Someone leads out a blond schoolgirl to crown
Queen of this war-contract factory town;
Skyrockets and the last guns boom.

I keep my seat and wonder where,
Into what ingrown nation has she gone
Among a people silent and withdrawn;
I wonder in the stifling air

Of what deprived and smoke-filled town
They brush together and do not feel lust,
Hope, rage, love; within what senseless dust
Is she at home to settle down;

Where do they know her, and the dead
Meet in a vacancy of shared disgrace,
Keep an old holiday of blame and place
Their tinsel wreath on her dark head?

We tramp home through the sulfurous smoke
That is my father's world. Now we must
Enter my mother's house of lint and dust
She could not breathe; I wheeze and choke.

It is an evil, stupid joke:
My wife is pregnant; my sister's in her grave.
We live in the home of the free and of the brave.
No one would hear me, even if I spoke.

S. S. GARDONS

the survivors

We wondered what might change
Once you were not here;
Tried to guess how they would rearrange
Their life, now you were dead. Oh, it was strange
Coming back this year—

To find the lawn unkept
And the rock gardens dense
With bindweed; the tangling rosebushes crept
And squandered over everything except
The trash thrown by the fence;

The rose trellises blown
Down and still sprawled there;
Broken odd ends of porch furniture thrown
Around the yard; everything overgrown
Or down in disrepair.

On the tree they still protect
From the ungoverned gang
Of neighbor boys,—eaten with worms, bird-pecked,
But otherwise uncared-for and unpicked,
The bitter cherries hang,

Brown and soft and botched.
The ground is thick with flies.
Around in front, two white stone lions are crouched
By the front steps; someone has patched
Cement across their eyes.

The Venetian blinds are drawn;
Inside, it is dark and still.
Always upon some errand, one by one,
They go from room to room, vaguely, in the wan
Half-light, deprived of will.

Mostly they hunt for some-
thing they've misplaced; otherwise
They turn the pages of magazines and hum
Tunelessly. At any time they come
To pass, they drop their eyes.

Only at night they meet.
By voiceless summoning
They come to the livingroom; each repeats
Some words he has memorized; each takes his seat
In the hushed, expectant ring

By the television set.
No one can draw his eyes
From that unnatural, cold light. They wait.
The screen goes dim and they hunch closer yet,
As the image dies.

In the cellar where the sewers
Rise, unseen, the pale white
Ants grow in decaying stacks of old newspapers.
Outside, street lamps appear; old friends of yours
Call children in for the night.

And you have been dead one year.
Nothing is different here.

AFTERWORD

the young! the wonderful!

I was awakened one Saturday night out of an unusually sound sleep; my oldest son was prodding me apologetically: "You're wanted on the phone, long distance." As I padded slipperless and cold to the phone I wondered which of my drunken friends was going to touch me for a loan.

"Hello," I said, as best I could.

"These kids are wonderful," was the answer.

"What kids? My kids?"

"No, these kids. Course your kids are wonderful, too." And my friend went on to explain that he had just been released from jail in San Francisco for participating in a sit-in in the lobby of an elegant hotel. It had taken him hours to get home because the police had released him without his car keys or his money. "I know what you're thinking," he said, "these kids will be betrayed by their leaders the way everyone else has been betrayed. No, not these kids. You've got to see them to believe them." And it seemed that there was nothing else he could tell me to convince me that the kids were wonderful, although I was willing enough to believe him, willing enough to believe anything just so long as I could get back to bed, and to the dreamless sleep of those whose lives have taken the shapes of machines.

My friend hung up still elated although he must have suspected he had not made my evening, as the expression goes. I assured my waiting son that things were all right out there in big America, and went back to sleep, and dreamed nothing, and awakened with a dim remembrance that cleared that day and the next, and as it cleared it took on a heightened, almost sinister meaning: My friend had joined for that evening the ranks of the young. Just a short sleep ago, we, he and I, were the young, but now we were no longer wonderful, at least not so for more than an evening. We were no longer capable of risking betrayal in the service of an idea or of changing much of anything except the way we combed our hair. My friend had the courage to be America's oldest practicing teen-ager, but I didn't, and from now on I could expect to be awakened in the middle of the night and told the truth: that I had joined the ranks of the elders who make things happen as they do. I had taken out no application papers, I had made no vows, but there I was, slipperless, defenseless, sinister, in my own house with my own family. I can expect the young any day to ring themselves around me or my house or my car or my classroom. I shall have to step over their bodies to carry on business as usual, and of course I will, even though I know they are wonderful.

If it comes at all it comes in subtle ways, this knowledge that you are no longer young, no longer wonderful, this knowledge that you are old and responsible; not responsible in any significant moral or psychological way, simply accountable for things as they are, that you have made your uneasy peace with things as they are, that is, with ownership. You earn and spend and wouldn't have it otherwise, you accept war, unnecessary death, discrimination, poverty, and the rest of the public evils of our time. One is tempted to say the knowledge comes and one is sickened by it, but that is not true, for if one were sickened one might still be of their party. One accepts it with the most characteristic of expressions, a shrug, and is no more touched than one would be if informed that a minor character out of childhood had succumbed, Herbert Hoover or Rin Tin Tin. One has learned that the self has its frontiers, its boundaries, and they may be no further away than the ends of one's fingers or the recesses of one's billfold; one has learned that "being part is an exertion that declines."

2

One is frequently telling others or being told by others of the ills of today's young. Their central problem, so I am told or am telling, is their need to conform, which is another way of saying that their failure is a failure to conform to another generation's expectations. I sometimes wonder if my chief complaint isn't that they're not making the mistakes I made. I have heard myself say in all seriousness, "They take no real interest in politics." When I say such things do I sound like one of those men who claim that nothing new has happened since the Greeks, that is, do I make it clear I'm suffering from some strange sexual malady?

It may be true that they are less interested in politics than my generation was, that generation which came of age roughly around the Second World War. I haven't heard talk of a third party since Pogo got election fever during the Eisenhower era, and I've taken this to mean that the young are spiritless, indifferent, crass, goods-seeking, and entering adulthood without an essential adolescent experience.

I wonder. As I look back on my own political activity, I remember dimly a succession of dreary afternoon meetings which I then knew would terminate in some significant action: the end of poverty, the end of discrimination, the end of armed conflict. I remember one packed meeting in the basement of the student union; a young Republican and a young Marxist were debating before a huge and awkward map of the world, and when the map finally fell to the floor and the little colored pins scattered about, one of the speakers said to the other, "Thus your argument collapses." But I can't remember who said it to whom, though I do remember that the class Trotskyite remarked that the comment was irrelevant. I also remember that all of these political meetings culminated for me in a political rally in the grand manner held in an ice hockey arena. It cost a dollar to get in, and the place was jammed. The preliminaries included a folk singer from South Dakota, a famous lady playwright, a scarred Negro film actor whose anger was frightening and personal, and a huge bruised old hero of the United Auto Workers who was rumored to be a Jew and a Red but was probably neither. The lights went out and a rented high school band struck up the national anthem, off key in the darkness, and when the lights came back on they were on Henry Wallace. After that my brother and I went to one political meeting looking for those fabled dialectical girls who took on all downtrodden young men, but we never found them and we never went back.

Sixteen years later when Barry Goldwater and Allen Dulles came to speak on our campus, both on the same day, the student body packed the basketball arena first at twelve and then at two. Later that day a group of my better students confessed to me that it had been a way of getting out of class. "Once we'd decided to use the excuse not to go to class we thought we might as well hear them; there wasn't anything else to do." "Yeah," his buddy added, "we don't have a car." Goldwater hadn't been too bad, one girl commented, "he made a joke." They were all a little sorry to discover that Goldwater didn't have any ideas or attitudes now that he was running in earnest. They'd hoped for some fireworks; they knew of some Poly Sci majors who'd come prepared to ask him some brutal questions on income tax and segregation, but everything was so polite they'd lost heart. It occurred to me that Goldwater had recently discovered what these kids always knew: third parties don't win.

It is also quite possible that these kids know what Goldwater will never know; that questions aren't answered and problems aren't solved through politics, if at all. I am continually amazed by their decency toward one another and their gentleness; I cannot imagine one of my students killing another one because of an ideal. While it can be argued that they lack a passionately held set of goals, it can also be argued that they are free of a powerful bar to the recognition of each other's humanity. What I am suggesting is that it's a very good thing that they do not resemble the young of my own decade and hence are continually frustrating their fathers and teachers.

I am merely suggesting because I do not understand them. As I sit observing them before class chatting with each other and with me, I know I do not know them. From the lofty eminence of a raised desk and an assistant professorship, I look down into their unused eyes and wonder why they have come to me to learn how to write poems and how from behind such clear complexions they produce such intense, passionate utterances of loneliness and need. What must it cost to live with the young decade after decade as Paul Goodman, Kenneth Rexroth, and my midnight caller have done? The next time I saw my caller he said to me with the courage of those who are willing to be fools, "These kids are crying out to this country to use them, to take their courage, their energy, their compassion and put them to some decent, honorable use." And I reminded him of the television advertisement we'd both seen that depicted a package of Wisconsin cheese that sat all night in the freezer crying to be eaten. "Eat me, Eat me," it cried, "and make me happy." We both laughed because he is such a good-natured man and because I knew the joke was on me.

PHILIP LEVINE

3

on seeing things

GEORGE ORWELL

politics and the english language

Most people who bother with the matter at all would admit that the English language is in a bad way, but it is generally assumed that we cannot by conscious action do anything about it. Our civilization is decadent and our language—so the argument runs—must inevitably share in the general collapse. It follows that any struggle against the abuse of language is a sentimental archaism, like preferring candles to electric light or hansom cabs to aeroplanes. Underneath this lies the half-conscious belief that language is a natural growth and not an instrument which we shape for our own purposes.

Now, it is clear that the decline of a language must ultimately have political and economic causes: it is not due simply to the bad influence of this or that individual writer. But an effect can become a cause, reinforcing the original cause and producing the same effect in an intensified form, and so on indefinitely. A man may take to drink because he feels himself to be a failure, and then fail all the more completely because he drinks. It is rather the same thing that is happening to the English language. It becomes ugly and inaccurate because our thoughts are foolish, but the slovenliness of our language makes it easier for us to have foolish thoughts. The point is that the process is reversible. Modern English, especially written English, is full of bad habits which spread by imitation and which can be avoided if one is willing to take the necessary trouble. If one gets rid of these habits one can think more clearly, and to think clearly is a necessary first step towards political regeneration: so that the fight against bad English is not frivolous and is not the exclusive concern of professional writers. I will come back to this presently, and I hope that by that time the meaning of what I have said here will have become clearer. Meanwhile, here are five specimens of the English language as it is now habitually written.

These five passages have not been picked out because they are especially bad—I could have quoted far worse if I had chosen—but because they illustrate various of the mental vices from which we now suffer. They are a little below the average, but are fairly representative samples. I number them so that I can refer back to them when necessary:

> (1) *I am not, indeed, sure whether it is not true to say that the Milton who once seemed not unlike a seventeenth-century Shelley had not become, out of an experience ever more bitter in each year, more alien* [sic] *to the founder of that Jesuit sect which nothing could induce him to tolerate.* PROFESSOR HAROLD LASKI
> ESSAY IN *Freedom of Expression*

> (2) *Above all, we cannot play ducks and drakes with a native battery of idioms which prescribes such egregious collocations of vocables as the Basic* put up with *for* tolerate *or* put at a loss *for* bewilder. PROFESSOR LANCELOT HOGBEN (*Interglossa*)

> (3) *On the one side we have the free personality: by definition it is not neurotic, for it has neither conflict nor dream. Its desires, such as they are, are transparent, for they are just what institutional approval keeps in the forefront of consciousness; another institutional pattern would alter their number and intensity; there is little in them that is natural, irreducible, or culturally dangerous. But* on the other side, *the social bond itself is nothing but the mutual reflection of these self-secure integrities. Recall the definition of love. Is not this the very picture of a small academic? Where is there a place in this hall of mirrors for either personality or fraternity?* ESSAY ON PSYCHOLOGY IN POLITICS (*New York*)

> (4) *All the "best people" from the gentlemen's clubs, and all the frantic fascist captains, united in common hatred of Socialism and bestial horror of the rising tide of the mass revolutionary movement, have turned to acts of provocation, to foul incendiarism, to medieval legends of poisoned wells, to legalize their own destruction of proletarian organizations, and rouse the agitated petty-bourgeoisie to chauvinistic fervor on behalf of the fight against the revolutionary way out of the crisis.* COMMUNIST PAMPHLET

> (5) *If a new spirit is to be infused into this old country, there is one thorny and contentious reform which must be tackled, and that is the humanization and galvanization of the B.B.C. Timidity here will bespeak canker and atrophy of the soul. The heart of Britain may be sound and of strong beat, for instance, but the*

> *British lion's roar at present is like that of Bottom in Shakespeare's* Midsummer Night's Dream—*as gentle as any sucking dove. A virile new Britain cannot continue indefinitely to be traduced in the eyes, or rather ears, of the world by the effete languors of Longham Place, brazenly masquerading as "standard English." When the Voice of Britain is heard at nine o'clock, better far and infinitely less ludicrous to hear aitches honestly dropped than the present priggish, inflated, inhibited, school-ma'amish arch braying of blameless bashful mewing maidens!* LETTER IN *Tribune*

Each of these passages has faults of its own, but, quite apart from avoidable ugliness, two qualities are common to all of them. The first is staleness of imagery; the other is lack of precision. The writer either has a meaning and cannot express it, or he inadvertently says something else, or he is almost indifferent as to whether his words mean anything or not. This mixture of vagueness and sheer incompetence is the most marked characteristic of modern English prose, and especially of any kind of political writing. As soon as certain topics are raised, the concrete melts into the abstract and no one seems able to think of turns of speech that are not hackneyed: prose consists less and less of *words* chosen for the sake of their meaning, and more and more of *phrases* tacked together like the sections of a prefabricated hen-house. I list below, with notes and examples, various of the tricks by means of which the work of prose-construction is habitually dodged:

DYING METAPHORS A newly invented metaphor assists thought by evoking a visual image, while on the other hand a metaphor which is technically "dead" (e.g. *iron resolution*) has in effect reverted to being an ordinary word and can generally be used without loss of vividness. But in between these two classes there is a huge dump of worn-out metaphors which have lost all evocative power and are merely used because they save people the trouble of inventing phrases for themselves. Examples are: *Ring the changes on, take up the cudgels for, toe the line, ride roughshod over, stand shoulder to shoulder with, play into the hands of, no axe to grind, grist to the mill, fishing in troubled waters, on the order of the day, Achilles' heel, swan song, hotbed.* Many of these are used without knowledge of their meaning (what is a "rift," for instance?), and incompatible metaphors are frequently mixed, a sure sign that the writer is not interested in what he is saying. Some metaphors now current have been twisted out of their original meaning without those who use them even being aware of the fact. For example, *toe the line* is sometimes written *tow the line*. Another example is *the hammer and the anvil*, now always used with the implication that the anvil gets the worst of it. In real life it is always the anvil that breaks the hammer, never the other way about: a writer who stopped to think what he was saying would be aware of this, and would avoid perverting the original phrase.

OPERATORS OR VERBAL FALSE LIMBS These save the trouble of picking out appropriate verbs and nouns, and at the same time pad each sentence with extra syllables which give it an appearance of symmetry. Characteristic phrases are *render inoperative, militate against, make contact with, be subjected to, give rise to, give grounds for, have the effect of, play a leading part* (*role*) *in, make itself felt, take effect, exhibit a tendency to, serve the purpose of, etc., etc.* The keynote is the elimination of simple verbs. Instead of being a single word, such as *break, stop, spoil, mend, kill*, a verb becomes a *phrase*, made up of a noun or adjective tacked on to some general-purposes verb such as *prove, serve, form, play, render*. In addition, the passive voice is wherever possible used in preference to the active, and noun constructions are used instead of gerunds (*by examination of* instead of *by examining*). The range of verbs is further cut down by means of the *-ize* and *de-* formations, and the banal statements are given an appearance of profundity by means of the *not un-* formation. Simple conjunctions and prepositions are replaced by such phrases as *with respect to, having regard to, the fact that, by dint of, in view of, in the interests of, on the hypothesis that*; and the ends of sentences are saved by anticlimax by such resounding common-places as *greatly to be desired, cannot be left out of account, a development to be expected in the near future, deserving of serious consideration, brought to a satisfactory conclusion*, and so on and so forth.

PRETENTIOUS DICTION Words like *phenomenon, element, individual* (as noun), *objective, categorical, effective, virtual, basic, primary, promote, constitute, exhibit, exploit, utilize, eliminate, liquidate*, are used to dress up simple statement and give an air of scientific impartiality to biased judgments. Adjectives like *epoch-making, epic, historic, unforgettable, triumphant, age-old, inevitable, inexorable, veritable*, are used to dignify the sordid processes of international politics, while writing that aims at glorifying war usually takes on an archaic color, its characteristic words being: *realm, throne, chariot, mailed fist, trident, sword, shield, buckler, banner, jackboot, clarion.* Foreign words and expressions such as *cul de sac, ancien régime, deus ex machina, mutatis mutandis, status quo, gleichschaltung, weltanschauung,* are used to give an air of culture and elegance. Except for the useful abbreviations *i.e., e.g.,* and *etc.,* there is no real need for any of the hundreds of foreign phrases now current in English. Bad writers, and especially scientific, political and sociological writers, are nearly always haunted by the notion that Latin or Greek words are grander than Saxon ones, and unnecessary words like *expedite, ameliorate, predict, extraneous, deracinated, clandestine, subaqueous* and hundreds of others constantly gain ground from their Anglo-Saxon opposite numbers.* The jargon peculiar to Marxist writing (*hyena, hangman, cannibal, petty bourgeois, these gentry, lacquey, flunkey, mad dog, White Guard,* etc.) consists largely of words and phrases translated from Russian, German or French; but the normal way of coining a new word is to use a Latin or Greek root with the appropriate affix and, where necessary, the size formation. It is often easier to make up words of this kind (*deregionalize, impermissible, extramarital, nonfragmentary* and so forth) than to think up the English words that will cover one's meaning. The result, in general, is an increase in slovenliness and vagueness.

MEANINGLESS WORDS In certain kinds of writing, particularly in art criticism and literary criticism, it is normal to come across long passages which are almost completely lacking in meaning.† Words like *romantic, plastic, values, human, dead, sentimental, natural,*

* An interesting illustration of this is the way in which the English flower names which were in use till very recently are being ousted by Greek ones, *snapdragon* becoming *antirrhinum, forget-me-not* becoming *myosotis,* etc. It is hard to see any practical reason for this change of fashion: it is probably due to an instinctive turning-away from the more homely word and a vague feeling that the Greek word is scientific.

† Example: "Comfort's catholicity of perception and image, strangely Whitmanesque in range, almost the exact opposite in aesthetic compulsion, continues to evoke that trembling atmospheric accumulative hinting at a cruel, an inexorably serene timelessness. . . . Wrey Gardiner scores by aiming at simple bull's-eyes with precision. Only they are not so simple, and through this contented sadness runs more than the surface bitter-sweet of resignation." *Poetry Quarterly*

vitality, as used in art criticism, are strictly meaningless, in the sense that they not only do not point to any discoverable object, but are hardly ever expected to do so by the reader. When one critic writes, "The outstanding feature of Mr. X's work is its living quality," while another writes, "The immediately striking thing about Mr. X's work is its peculiar deadness," the reader accepts this as a simple difference of opinion. If words like *black* and *white* were involved, instead of the jargon words *dead* and *living,* he would see at once that language was being used in an improper way. Many political words are similarly abused. The word *Fascism* has now no meaning except in so far as it signifies "something not desirable." The words *democracy, socialism, freedom, patriotic, realistic, justice,* have each of them several different meanings which cannot be reconciled with one another. In the case of a word like *democracy,* not only is there no agreed definition, but the attempt to make one is resisted from all sides. It is almost universally felt that when we call a country democratic we are praising it: consequently the defenders of every kind of régime claim that it is a democracy, and fear that they might have to stop using the word if it were tied down to any one meaning. Words of this kind are often used in a consciously dishonest way. That is, the person who uses them has his own private definition, but allows his hearer to think he means something quite different. Statements like *Marshal Pétain was a true patriot. The Soviet Press is the freest in the world, The Catholic Church is opposed to persecution,* are almost always made with intent to deceive. Other words used in variable meanings, in most cases more or less dishonestly, are: *class, totalitarian, science, progressive, reactionary, bourgeois, equality.*

Now that I have made this catalogue of swindles and perversions, let me give another example of the kind of writing that they lead to. This time it must of its nature be an imaginary one. I am going to translate a passage of good English into modern English of the worst sort. Here is a well-known verse from *Ecclesiastes:*

> *I returned and saw under the sun, that the race is not to the swift, nor the battle to the strong, neither yet bread to the wise, nor yet riches to men of understanding, nor yet favour to men of skill; but time and chance happeneth to them all.*

Here it is in modern English: "Objective consideration of contemporary phenomena compels the conclusion that success or failure in competitive activities exhibits no tendency to be commensurate with innate capacity, but that a considerable element of the unpredictable must invariably be taken into account."

This is a parody, but not a very gross one. Exhibit 3, above, for instance, contains several patches of the same kind of English. It will be seen that I have not made a full translation. The beginning and ending of the sentence follow the original meaning fairly closely, but in the middle the concrete illustrations—race, battle, bread—dissolve into the vague phrase "success or failure in competitive activities." This had to be so, because no modern writer of the kind I am discussing—no one capable of using phrases like "objective consideration of contemporary phenomena"—would ever tabulate his thoughts in that precise and detailed way. The whole tendency of modern prose is away from concreteness. Now analyse these two sentences a little more closely. The first contains forty-nine words but only sixty syllables, and all its words are those of everyday life. The second contains thirty-eight words of ninety syllables: eighteen of its words are from Latin roots, and one from Greek. The first sentence contains six vivid images, and only one phrase ("time and chance") that could be called vague. The second contains not a single fresh, arresting phrase, and in spite of its ninety syllables it gives only a shortened version of the meaning contained in the first. Yet without a doubt it is the second kind of sentence that is gaining ground in modern English. I do not want to exaggerate. This kind of writing is not yet universal, and outcrops of simplicity will occur here and there in the worst-written page. Still, if you or I were told to write a few lines on the uncertainty of human fortunes, we should probably come much nearer to my imaginary sentence than to the one from *Ecclesiastes*.

As I have tried to show, modern writing at its worst does not consist in picking out words for the sake of their meaning and inventing images in order to make the meaning clearer. It consists in gumming together long strips of words which have already been set in order by someone else, and making the results presentable by sheer humbug. The attraction of this way of writing is that it is easy. It is easier—even quicker, once you have the habit—to say *In my opinion it is not an unjustifiable assumption that* than to say *I think*. If you use ready-made phrases, you not only don't have to hunt about for words; you also don't have to bother with the rhythms of your sentences, since these phrases are generally so arranged as to be more or less euphonious. When you are composing in a hurry—when you are dictating to a stenographer, for instance, or making a public speech—it is natural to fall into a pretentious, Latinized style. Tags like *a consideration which we should do well to bear in mind* or *a conclusion to which all of us would readily assent* will save many a sentence from coming down with a bump. By using stale metaphors, similes and idioms, you save much mental effort, at the cost of leaving your meaning vague, not only for your reader but for yourself. This is the significance of mixed metaphors. The sole aim of a metaphor is to call up a visual image. When these images clash—as in *The Fascist octopus has sung its swan song, the jackboot is thrown into the melting pot*—it can be taken as certain that the writer is not seeing a mental image of the objects he is naming; in other words he is not really thinking. Look again at the examples I gave at the beginning of this essay. Professor Laski (1) uses five negatives in fifty-three words. One of these is superfluous, making nonsense of the whole passage, and in addition there is the slip *alien* for akin, making further nonsense, and several avoidable pieces of clumsiness which increase the general vagueness. Professor Hogben (2) plays ducks and drakes with a battery which is able to write prescriptions, and, while disapproving of the everyday phrase *put up with,* is unwilling to look *egregious* up in the dictionary and see what it means; (3), if one takes an uncharitable attitude towards it, is simply meaningless: probably one could work out its intended meaning by reading the whole of the article in which it occurs. In (4), the writer knows more or less what he wants to say, but an accumulation of stale phrases chokes him like tea leaves blocking a sink. In (5), words and meaning have almost parted company. People who write in this manner usually have a general emotional meaning—they dislike one thing and want to express solidarity with another—but they are not interested in the detail of what they are saying. A scrupulous writer, in every sentence that he writes, will ask himself at least four questions, thus: What am I trying to say? What words will express it? What image or idiom will make it clearer? Is this image fresh enough to have an effect? And he will probably ask himself two more: Could I put it more shortly? Have I said anything that is avoidably ugly? But you are not obliged to go to all this trouble. You can shirk it by simply throwing your mind open and letting the ready-made phrases come crowding in. They will construct your sentences for you—even think your thoughts for you, to a certain extent—and at need they will perform the important service of partially concealing your meaning even from yourself. It is at this point that the special connection between politics and the debasement of language becomes clear.

In our time it is broadly true that political writing is bad writing. Where it is not true, it will generally be found that the writer is some kind of rebel, expressing his private opinions and not a "party line." Orthodoxy, of whatever color, seems to demand a lifeless, imitative style. The political dialects to be found in pamphlets, leading articles, manifestos, White Papers and the speeches of under-secretaries do, of course, vary from party to party, but they are all alike in that one almost never finds in them a fresh, vivid, home-made turn of speech. When one watches some tired hack on the platform mechanically repeating the familiar phrases—*bestial atrocities, iron heel, bloodstained tyranny, free peoples of the world, stand shoulder to shoulder*—one often has a curious feeling that one is not watching a live human being but some kind of dummy: a feeling which suddenly becomes stronger at moments when the light catches the speaker's spectacles and turns them into blank discs which seem to have no eyes behind them. And this is not altogether fanciful. A speaker who uses that kind of phraseology has gone some distance towards turning himself into a machine. The appropriate noises are coming out of his larynx, but his brain is not involved as it would be if he were choosing his words for himself. If the speech he is making is one that he is accustomed to make over and over again, he may be almost unconscious of what he is saying, as one is when one utters the responses in church. And this reduced state of consciousness, if not indispensable, is at any rate favorable to political conformity.

In our time, political speech and writing are largely the defence of the indefensible. Things like the continuance of British rule in India, the Russian purges and deportations, the dropping of the atom bombs on Japan, can indeed be defended, but only by arguments which are too brutal for most people to face, and which do not square with the professed aims of political parties. Thus political language has to consist largely of euphemism, question-begging and sheer cloudy vagueness. Defenceless villages are bombarded from the air, the inhabitants driven out into the countryside, the cattle machine-gunned, the huts set on fire with incendiary bullets: this is called *pacification*. Millions of peasants are robbed of their farms and sent trudging along the roads with no more than they can carry: this is called *transfer of population* or *rectification of frontiers.* People are imprisoned for years without trial, or shot in the back of the neck or sent to die of scurvy in Arctic lumber camps: this is called *elimination of unreliable elements.* Such phraseology is needed if one wants to name things without calling up mental pictures of them. Consider for instance some comfortable English professor defending Russian totalitarianism. He cannot say outright, "I believe in killing off your opponents when you can get good results by doing so." Probably, therefore, he will say something like this: "While freely conceding that the Soviet régime exhibits certain features which the humanitarian may be inclined to deplore, we must, I think, agree that a certain curtailment of the right to political opposition is an unavoidable concomitant of transitional periods, and that the rigors which the Russian people have been called upon to undergo have been amply justified in the sphere of concrete achievement."

The inflated style is itself a kind of euphemism. A mass of Latin words falls upon the facts like soft snow, blurring the outlines and covering up all the details. The great enemy of clear language is insincerity. When there is a gap between one's real and one's declared aims, one turns as it were instinctively to long words and exhausted idioms, like a cuttlefish squirting out ink. In our age there is no such thing as "keeping out of politics." All issues are political issues, and politics itself is a mass of lies, evasions, folly, hatred and schizophrenia. When the general atmosphere is bad, language must suffer. I should expect to find—this is a guess which I have not sufficient knowledge to verify—that the German, Russian and Italian languages have all deteriorated in the last ten or fifteen years, as a result of dictatorship.

But if thought corrupts language, language can also corrupt thought. A bad usage can spread by tradition and imitation, even among people who should and do know better. The debased language that I have been discussing is in some ways very convenient. Phrases like *a not unjustifiable assumption, leaves much to be desired, would serve no good purpose, a consideration which we should do well to bear in mind,* are a continuous temptation, a packet of aspirins always at one's elbow. Look back through this essay, and for certain you will find that I have again and again committed the very faults I am protesting against. By this morning's post I have received a pamphlet dealing with conditions in Germany. The author tells me that he "felt impelled" to write it. I open it at random, and here is almost the first sentence that I see: "[The Allies] have an opportunity not only of achieving a radical transformation of Germany's social and political structure in such a way as to avoid a nationalistic reaction in Germany itself, but at the same time of laying the foundations of a co-operative and unified Europe." You see, he "feels impelled" to write—feels, presumably, that he has something new to say—and yet his words, like cavalry horses answering the bugle, group themselves automatically into the familiar dreary pattern. This invasion of one's mind by ready-made phrases (*lay the foundations, achieve a radical transformation*) can only be prevented if one is constantly on guard against them, and every such phrase anaesthetizes a portion of one's brain.

I said earlier that the decadence of our language is probably curable. Those who deny this would argue, if they produced an argument at all, that language merely reflects social conditions, and that we cannot influence its development by any direct tinkering with words and constructions. So far as the general tone or spirit of a language goes, this may be true, but it is not true in detail. Silly words and expressions have often disappeared, not through any evolutionary process but owing to the conscious action of a minority. Two recent examples were *explore every avenue* and *leave no stone unturned*, which were killed by the jeers of a few journalists. There is a long list of flyblown metaphors which could similarly be got rid of if enough people would interest themselves in the job; and it should also be possible to laugh the *not un-* formation out of existence,* to reduce the amount of Latin and Greek in the average sentence, to drive out foreign phrases and strayed scientific words, and, in general, to make pretentiousness unfashionable. But all these are minor points. The defence of the English language implies more than this, and perhaps it is best to start by saying what it does *not* imply.

To begin with it has nothing to do with archaism, with the salvaging of obsolete words and turns of speech, or with the setting up of a "standard English" which must never be departed from. On the contrary, it is especially concerned with the scrapping of

* One can cure oneself of the *not un-* formation by memorizing this sentence: *A not unblack dog was chasing a not unsmall rabbit across a not ungreen field.*

every word or idiom which has outworn its usefulness. It has nothing to do with correct grammar and syntax, which are of no importance so long as one makes one's meaning clear, or with the avoidance of Americanisms, or with having what is called a "good prose style." On the other hand it is not concerned with fake simplicity and the attempt to make written English colloquial. Nor does it even imply in every case preferring the Saxon word to the Latin one, though it does imply using the fewest and shortest words that will cover one's meaning. What is above all needed is to let the meaning choose the word, and not the other way about. In prose, the worst thing one can do with words is to surrender to them. When you think of a concrete object, you think wordlessly, and then, if you want to describe the thing you have been visualizing you probably hunt about till you find the exact words that seem to fit it. When you think of something abstract you are more inclined to use words from the start, and unless you make a conscious effort to prevent it, the existing dialect will come rushing in and do the job for you, at the expense of blurring or even changing your meaning. Probably it is better to put off using words as long as possible and get one's meaning as clear as one can through pictures or sensations. Afterwards one can choose—not simply *accept*—the phrases that will best cover the meaning, and then switch round and decide what impression one's words are likely to make on another person. This last effort of the mind cuts out all stale or mixed images, all prefabricated phrases, needless repetitions, and humbug and vagueness generally. But one can often be in doubt about the effect of a word or a phrase, and one needs rules that one can rely on when instinct fails. I think the following rules will cover most cases:

(i) Never use a metaphor, simile or other figure of speech which you are used to seeing in print.

(ii) Never use a long word where a short one will do.

(iii) If it is possible to cut a word out, always cut it out.

(iv) Never use the passive where you can use the active.

(v) Never use a foreign phrase, a scientific word or a jargon word if you can think of an everyday English equivalent.

(vi) Break any of these rules sooner than say anything outright barbarous.

These rules sound elementary, and so they are, but they demand a deep change of attitude in anyone who has grown used to writing in the style now fashionable. One could keep all of them and still write bad English, but one could not write the kind of stuff that I quoted in those five specimens at the beginning of this article.

I have not here been considering the literary use of language, but merely language as an instrument for expressing and not for concealing or preventing thought. Stuart Chase and others have come near to claiming that all abstract words are meaningless, and have used this as a pretext for advocating a kind of political quietism. Since you don't know what Fascism is, how can you struggle against Fascism? One need not swallow such absurdities as this, but one ought to recognize that the present political chaos is connected with the decay of language, and that one can probably bring about some improvement by starting at the verbal end. If you simplify your English, you are freed from the worst follies of orthodoxy. You cannot speak any of the necessary dialects, and when you make a stupid remark its stupidity will be obvious, even to yourself. Political language—and with variations this is true of all political parties, from Conservatives to Anarchists—is designed to make lies sound truthful and murder respectable, and to give an appearance of solidity to pure wind. One cannot change this all in a moment, but one can at least change one's own habits, and from time to time one can even, if one jeers loudly enough, send some worn-out and useless phrase—some *jackboot, Achilles' heel, hotbed, melting pot, acid test, veritable inferno* or other lump of verbal refuse—into the dustbin where it belongs.

[*1946*]

HENRY MILLER

*of art and the future**

To most men the past is never yesterday, or five minutes ago, but distant, misty epochs some of which are glorious and others abominable. Each one reconstructs the past according to his temperament

* Written expressly for Cyril Connolly.

and experience. We read history to corroborate our own views, not to learn what scholars think to be true. About the future there is as little agreement as about the past, I've noticed. We stand in relation to the past very much like the cow in the meadow—endlessly chewing the cud. It is not something finished and done with, as we sometimes fondly imagine, but something alive, constantly changing, and perpetually with us. But the future too is with us perpetually, and alive and constantly changing. The difference between the two, a thoroughly fictive one, incidentally, is that the future we create whereas the past can only be recreated. As for that constantly vanishing point called the present, that fulcrum which melts simultaneously into past and future, only those who deal with the eternal know and live in it, acknowledging it to be all.

At this moment, when almost the entire world is engaged in war, the plight of a few artists—for we never have more than a handful, it seems—appears to be a matter of the utmost unimportance. At the outbreak of the war art was by universal agreement at a perilously low ebb. So was life, one might say. The artist, always in advance of his time, could register nothing but death and destruction. The normal ones, i.e., the unfeeling, unthinking ones, regarded the art products of their time as morbid, perverse and meaningless. Just because the political picture was so black they demanded of their hirelings that they paint something bright and pleasing. Now all are bogged down, those who saw and those who did not, and what the future contains is dependent on that very creative quality which unfortunately seems vital only in times of destruction. Now every one is exhorted to be creative—with gun in hand.

To every man fighting to bring the war to a victorious end the result of the conflict calls up a different picture. To resume life where one left off is undoubtedly the deepest wish of those now participating in the holocaust. It is here that the greatest disillusionment will occur. To think of it descriptively we have to think of a man jumping off a precipice, escaping miraculously from certain death and then, as he starts to climb back, suddenly discovering that the whole mountain side has collapsed. The world we knew before September 1939 is collapsing hour by hour. It had been collapsing long before that, but we were not so aware of it, most of us. Paris, Berlin, Prague, Amsterdam, Rome, London, New York —they may still be standing when peace is declared, but it will be as though they did not exist. The cultural world in which we swam, not very gracefully, to be sure, is fast disappearing. The cultural era of Europe, and that includes America, is finished. The next era belongs to the technician; the day of the mind machine is dawning. God pity us!

Taking a rough, uncritical view of history we realize at a glance that in every stage of civilization the condition of the common man has been anything but a civilized one. He has lived like a rat —through good epochs and bad ones. History was never written for the common man but for those in power. The history of the world is the history of a privileged few. Even in its grandeur it stinks.

We are not suddenly going to turn a new page with the cessation of this fratricidal war. Another wretched peace will be made, never fear, and there will be another breathing spell of ten or twenty years and then we shall go to war again. And the next war will also be regarded as a just and holy war, as is this one now. But whatever the reason for or nature of the coming war, it will no more resemble this one than this one resembles the previous one which, significantly enough, we speak of as "World War No. 1." In the future we shall have only "world wars"—that much is already clear.

With total wars a new element creeps into the picture. From now on every one is involved, without exception. What Napoleon began with the sword, and Balzac boasted he would finish with the pen, is actually going to be carried through by the collaboration of the whole wide world, including the primitive races whom we study and exploit shamelessly and ruthlessly. As war spreads wider and wider so will peace sink deeper and deeper into the hearts of men. If we must fight more whole-heartedly we shall also be obliged to live more whole-heartedly. If the new kind of warfare demands that everybody and everything under the sun be taken cognizance of, so will the new kind of peace. Not to be able to be of service will be unthinkable. It will constitute the highest treason, probably punishable by death. Or perhaps a more ignominious end awaits the unfit and unserviceable: in lieu of becoming cannon fodder they may become just fodder.

The first world war ushered in the idea of a league of nations, an international court of arbitration. It failed because there was no real solidarity among the so-called nations, most of them being only cats' paws. This war will bring about the realization that the nations of the earth are made up of individuals, not masses. The common man will be the new factor in the world-wide collective mania which will sweep the earth.

The date most commonly agreed upon (by professional prophets) for the end of this war is the Fall of 1947. But by 1944 it is quite possible that the war will assume its true aspect, that of world-wide revolution. It will get out of the control of those now leading "the masses" to slaughter. The masses will slaughter in their own fashion for a while. The collapse of German and Italy will precipitate the débâcle, thereby creating a rift between the British and American peoples, for England (her men of power) is still more fearful of a Russian victory than of a German defeat. France has still to play her true role. Fired by the success of the Soviets, she will overleap all bounds, and, just as in the French Revolution, amaze the world by her spirit and vitality. There will be more blood shed in France than in any other part of Europe, before a quietus is established.

An era of chaos and confusion, beginning in 1944, will continue until almost 1960. All boundaries will be broken down, class lines obliterated, and money become worthless. It will be a caricature of the Marxian Utopia. The world will be enthralled by the ever-unfolding prospects seeming to offer nothing but good. Then suddenly it will be like the end of a debauch. A protracted state of *Katzenjammer* will set in. Then commences the real work of consolidation, when Europe gets set to meet the Asiatic invasion, due about the turn of the century. For, with the culmination of this war, China and India will play a most prominent and important part in world affairs. We have roused them from their lethargy and we shall pay for having awakened them. The East and the West *will* meet one day—in a series of death-like embraces.* After that the barriers between peoples and races will break down and the melting-pot (which America only pretends to be) will become an actuality. Then, and only then, will the embryonic man of the new order appear, the man who has no feeling of class, caste, color or country, the man who has no need of possessions, no use for money, no archaic prejudices about the sanctity of the home or

* The present strife with Japan is more a clash of rivals than of genuine antagonists. But it serves to damage irreparably our unwarranted prestige in the East.

of marriage with its accompanying tread-mill of divorce. A totally new conception of individuality will be born, one in which the collective life is the dominant note. In short, for the first time since the dawn of history, men will serve one another, first out of an enlightened self-interest, and finally out of a greater conception of love.

The distinctive feature of this "epoch of the threshold", so to speak, will be its visionary-realistic quality. It will be an era of realization, accomplishment and vision. It will create deeper, more insoluble problems than ever existed before. Immense horizons will open up, dazzling and frightening ones. The ensuing conflicts will assume more and more the character of clashes between wizards, making our wars appear puny and trifling by comparison. The white and the black forces will come out in the open. Antagonisms will be conscious and deliberate, engaged in joyously and triumphantly, and to the bitter end. The schisms will occur not between blocs of nations or peoples but between two divergent elements, both clear-cut and highly aware of their goals, and the line between them will be as wavering as the flow of the zodiacal signs about the ecliptic. The problem for the next few thousand years will be one of power, power in the abstract and ultimate. Men will be drunk with power, having unlocked the forces of the earth in ways now only dimly apprehended. The consolidation of the new individuality, rooted in the collective (man no longer worshipping the Father but acknowledging sources of power greater than the Sun) will dissolve the haunting problem of power. A dynamic equilibrium, based upon the recognition of a new creative center, will establish itself, permitting the free play of all the fluid, potent forces locked within the human corpus. Then it may be possible to look forward to the dawn of what has already been described as "The Age of Plentitude".*

Before the present conflict is terminated it is altogether likely that we shall see unleashed the deadly secret weapon so often hinted at on all sides. At the very beginning of the war I described (in an unpublished book on America) the ironic possibilities which the discovery and use of a deadly "human flit" would entail. The ambivalent attitude of dread and ridicule which this idea generally elicits is significant. It means that the inconceivable and un-

* Title of Dane Rudhyar's new and as yet unpublished book.

conscionable has already become a dire possibility. That the men of science will be coerced into yielding up the secret now in their possession I have no doubt. If the Japanese can unblushingly carry on their program of systematically doping their victims it is not at all unthinkable that we on our side will come forth with an even more effective, certainly a more drastic and immediate, weapon of destruction. All the rules of warfare which have hitherto obtained are destined to be smashed and relegated to the scrap-heap. This is merely a corollary to the dissolution of the Hague Tribunal, the Maginot Line and all our fond conceptions of peace, justice and security. It is not that we have become more brutal and cynical, more ruthless and immoral—it is that ever since the last war we are consciously or unconsciously (probably both) making war upon war. The present methods of making war are too ineffectual, too protracted, too costly in every sense. All that impedes us thus far is the lack of imaginative leaders. The common people are far more logical, ruthless and totalitarian in spirit than the military and political cliques. Hitler, for all that has been said against him, is hardly the brilliant imaginative demon we credit him with being. He merely served to unleash the dark forces which we tried to pretend did not exist. With Hitler Pluto came out into the open. In England and America we have far more realistic, far more ruthless, types. All that deters them is fear of consequences: they are obsessed by the image of the boomerang. It is their habit to act obliquely, shamefacedly, with guilty consciences. But this conscience is now being broken down, giving way to something vastly different, to what it was originally, what the Greeks called syneidesis. Once a deep vision of the future opens up these types will proceed with the directness and remorselessness of monomaniacs.

The problem of power, what to do with it, how to use it, who shall wield it or not wield it, will assume proportions heretofore unthinkable. We are moving into the realm of incalculables and imponderables in our every-day life just as for the last few generations we have been accustoming ourselves to this realm through the play of thought. Everything is coming to fruition, and the harvest will be brilliant and terrifying. To those who look upon such predictions as fantastic I have merely to point out, ask them to imagine, what would happen should we ever unlock the secret patents now hidden in the vaults of our unscrupulous exploiters. Once the present crazy system of exploitation crumbles, and it is crumbling hourly, the powers of the imagination, heretofore stifled and fettered, will run riot. The face of the earth can be changed utterly overnight once we have the courage to concretize the dreams of our inventive geniuses. Never was there such a plenitude of inventors as in this age of destruction. And there is one thing to bear in mind about the man of genius—even the inventor—usually he is on the side of humanity, not the devil. It has been the crowning shame of this age to have exploited the man of genius for sinister ends. But such a procedure always acts as a boomerang: ultimately the man of genius always has his revenge.

Within the next fifteen years, when the grand clean-up goes into effect, the man of genius will do more to liberate the fettered sleeping giants than was ever done in the whole history of man. There will be strange new offices, strange new powers, strange new rules. It will seem for a while as though everything were topsy-turvy, and so it *will* be, regarded from to-day's vantage point. What is now at the bottom will come to the top, and vice versa. The world has literally been standing on its head for thousands of years. So great has been the pressure from above that a hole has been bored through the very stuff of consciousness. Into the empty vessel of life the waters are now pouring. The predatory few, who sought to arrange life in their own vulpine terms, will be the first to be drowned. "The few," I say, but in all truth they are legion. The floods of destruction sweep high and low; we are all part and parcel of the same mould; we have all been abetting the crime of man against man. The type of man we represent will be drowned out utterly. A new type will arise, out of the dregs of the old. That is why the stirring of sleepy Asia is fraught with such fateful consequences for the man of Europe, or shall I say, the man of the Western world. All this muck, these lees and dregs of humanity, the coolies and Untouchables, will have to be absorbed in our blood-stream. The clash of East and West will be like a marriage of the waters; when the new dry land eventually appears the old and the new will be indistinguishable.

The human fundament is in the East. We have talked breathlessly about equality and democracy without ever facing the reality of it. We shall have to take these despised and neglected ones to our bosom, melt into them, absorb their anguish and misery. We cannot have a real brotherhood so long as we cherish the illusion of racial superiority, so long as we fear the touch of yellow, brown, black or red skins. We in America will have to begin by embracing the Negro, the Indian, the Mexican, the Filipino, all those Untouchables whom we so blithely dismiss from our consciousness by pointing to our Bills of Rights. We have not even begun to put the Emancipation Proclamation into effect. The same is true of course for England, for imperialist Holland, and colonial France. Russia took the first genuine steps in this direction, and Russia, nobody will dispute, has certainly not been weakened by carrying out her resolution to the letter.

And now, what about Art? What is the place and the future of art in all this turmoil? Well, in the first place, it seems to me that what we have hitherto known as art will be non-existent. Oh yes, we will continue to have novels and paintings and symphonies and statues, we will even have verse, no doubt about it. But all this will be as a hangover from other days, a continuation of a bad dream which ends only with a full awakening. The cultural era is past. The new civilization, which may take centuries or a few thousand years to usher in, will not be another civilization—it will be the open stretch of realization which all the past civilizations have pointed to. The city, which was the birth-place of civilization, such as we know it to be, will exist no more. There will be nuclei of course, but they will be mobile and fluid. The peoples of the earth will no longer be shut off from one another within states but will flow freely over the surface of the earth and intermingle. There will be no fixed constellations of human aggregates. Governments will give way to management, using the word in a broad sense. The politician will become as superannuated as the dodo bird. The machine will never be dominated, as some imagine; it will be scrapped, eventually, but not before men have understood the nature of the mystery which binds them to their creation. The worship, investigation and subjugation of the machine will give way to the lure of all that is truly occult. This problem is bound up with the larger one of power—and of possession. Man will be forced to realize that power must be kept open, fluid and free. His aim will be not to possess power but to radiate it.

At the root of the art instinct is this desire for power—vicarious power. The artist is situated hierarchically between the hero and the saint. These three types rule the world, and it is difficult to say which wields the greatest power. But none of them are what might be called adepts. The adept is the power behind the powers, so to speak. He remains anonymous, the secret force from which the suns derive their power and glory.

To put it quite simply, art is only a stepping-stone to reality; it is the vestibule in which we undergo the rites of initiation. Man's task is to make of himself a work of art. The creations which man makes manifest have no validity in themselves; they serve to awaken, that is all. And that, of course, is a great deal. But it is not the all. Once awakened, everything will reveal itself to man as creation. Once the blinders have been removed and the fetters unshackled, man will have no need to recreate through the elect cult of genius. Genius will be the norm.

Throughout history the artist has been the martyr, immolating himself in his work. The very phrase, "a work of art", gives off a perfume of sweat and agony. Divine creation, on the other hand, bears no such connotation. We do not think of sweat and tears in connection with the creation of the universe; we think of joy and light, and above all of play. The agony of a Christ on Calvary, on the other hand, illustrates superbly the ordeal which even a Master must undergo in the creation of a perfect life.

In a few hundred years or less books will be a thing of the past. There was a time when poets communicated with the world without the medium of print; the time will come when they will communicate silently, not as poets merely, but as seers. What we have overlooked, in our frenzy to invent more dazzling ways and means of communication, is to communicate. The artist lumbers along with crude implements. He is only a notch above his predecessor, the cave man. Even the film art, requiring the services of veritable armies of technicians, is only giving us shadow plays, old almost as man himself.

No, the advance will not come through the aid of subtler mechanical devices, nor will it come through the spread of education. The advance will come in the form of a break through. New forms of communication will be established. New forms presuppose new desires. The great desire of the world to-day is to break the bonds which lock us in. It is not yet a conscious desire. Men do not yet realize what they are fighting for. This is the beginning of a long fight, a fight from within outwards. It may be that the present war will be fought entirely in the dark. It may be that the revolution ensuing will envelop us in even greater darkness. But even in the blackest night it will be a joy and a boon to know that we are touching hands around the world. That has never happened before. We can touch and speak and pray in utter darkness. And we can wait for the dawn—no matter how long—provided we all wait together.

The years immediately ahead of us will be a false dawn, that is my belief. We cannot demolish our educational, legal and economic pediments overnight, nor even our phony religious superstructures. Until these are completely overthrown there is not much hope of a new order. From birth we live in a web of chaos in which all is illusion and delusion. The leaders who now and then arise, by what miracle no one knows, these leaders who come forward expressly to lead us out of the wilderness, are nearly always crucified. This happens on both sides of the fence, not just in the domain of Axis tyrants. It can happen in Soviet Russia too, as we know. And it happens in a less spectacular but all the more poisonous, insidious way in the United States, "home of the brave and land of the free." It is idle to blame individuals, or even classes of society. Given the educational, legal, economic and religious background of the cultural nations of this day, the results are inevitable. The savagery of a Céline is like the prattle of a child to those who can look into the heart of things with naked eye. Often, when I listen to the radio, to a speech by one of our politicians, to a sermon by one of our religious maniacs, to a discourse by one of our eminent scholars, to an appeal by one of our men of good will, to the propaganda dinned into us night and day by the advertising fiends, I wonder what the men of the coming century would think could they listen in for just one evening.

I do not believe that this repetitious cycle of insanity which is called history will continue forever. I believe there will be a great break through—within the next few centuries. I think that what we are heralding as the Age of Technic will be nothing more than a transition period, as was the Renaissance. We will need, to be sure, all our technical knowledge and skill to settle once and for all the problem of securing to every man, woman and child the fundamental necessities. We will make a drastic revision, it also goes without saying, of our notion of necessities, which is an altogether crude and primitive one. With the concomitant emancipation of woman, entailed by this great change, the awakening of the love instinct will transform every domain of life. The era of neuters is drawing to a close. With the establishment of a new and vital polarity we shall witness the birth of male-and-female in every individual. What then portends in the realm of art is truly unthinkable. Our art has been masculine through and through, that is to say, lop-sided. It has been vitiated by the unacknowledged feminine principle. This is as true of ancient as of modern art. The tyrannical, subterranean power of the female must come to an end. Men have paid a heavy tribute for their seeming subjugation of the female.

If we dare to imagine a solution of these seemingly fixed problems, dare to imagine an end of perhaps ten thousand years of pseudo-civilization, dare to imagine a change as radical as from the Stone Age to the Age of Electricity, let us say, for in the future we will not advance slowly step by step as in the past but with the rush of the whirlwind, then who can say what forms of expression art will assume? Myself I cannot see the persistence of the artist type. I see no need for the individual man of genius in such an order. I see no need for martyrs. I see no need for vicarious atonement. I see no need for the fierce preservation of beauty on the part of a few. Beauty and Truth do not need defenders, nor even expounders. No one will ever have a lien on Beauty or Truth; they are creations in which all participate. They need only to be apprehended; they exist eternally. Certainly, when we think of the conflicts and schisms which occur in the realm of art, we know that they do not proceed out of love of Beauty or Truth. Ego worship is the one and only cause of dissension, in art as in other realms. The artist is never defending art, but simply his own petty conception of art. Art is as deep and high and wide as the universe. There is nothing but art, if you look at it properly. It is almost banal to say so yet it needs to be stressed continually: all is creation, all is change, all is flux, all is metamorphosis. But how many deeply and sincerely believe that? Are we not devotees of the static? Are we not always on the defensive? Are we not always trying to circumscribe, erect barriers, set up tabus? Are we not always preparing for war? Are we not always in the grip of "fear and trembling"? Are we not always sanctifying, idolizing, martyrizing, proselytizing? What a pitiful, ignominious spiritual shambles, these last ten thousand years! *Civilized,* we say. What a horrible word! What bedeviled idiocy skulks behind that arrogant mark! Oh, I am not thinking of this war, nor of the last one, nor of any or all the wars men have waged in the name of *Civilization.* I am thinking of the periods in between, the rotten, stagnant eras of peace, the lapses and relapses, the lizard-like sloth, the creepy mole-like burrowing in, the fungus growths, the barnacles, the stink-weeds; I am thinking of the constant fanatical dervish dance that goes on in the name of all that is unreal, unholy and unattainable, thinking of the sadistic-masochistic tug of war, now one getting the upper hand, now the other. In the name of humanity when will we cry *Enough!*

There are limits to everything, and so I believe there is a limit to human stupidity and cruelty. But we are not yet there. We have not yet drained the bitter cup. Perhaps only when we have become full-fledged monsters will we recognize the angel in man. Then, when the ambivalence is clear, may we look forward with confidence to the emergence of a new type of man, a man as different from the man of to-day as we are from the *pithecanthropus erectus*. Nor is this too much to hope for, even at this remote distance. There have been precursors. Men have walked this earth who, for all they resemble us, may well have come from another planet. They have appeared singly and far apart. But to-morrow they may come in clusters, and the day after in hordes. The birth of Man follows closely the birth of the heavens. A new star never makes its appearance alone. With the birth of a new type of man a current is set in motion which later enables us to perceive that he was merely the foam on the crest of a mighty wave.

I have a strange feeling that the next great impersonation of the future will be a woman. If it is a greater reality we are veering towards then it must be woman who points the way. The masculine hegemony is over. Men have lost touch with the earth; they are clinging to the window-panes of their unreal superstructures like blind bats lashed by the storms of oceanic depths. Their world of abstractions spells babble.

When men are at last united in darkness woman will once again illumine the way—by revealing the beauties and mysteries which enfold us. We have tried to hide from our sight the womb of night, and now we are engulfed in it. We have pretended to be single when we were dual, and now we are frustrate and impotent. We shall come forth from the womb united, or not at all. Come forth not in brotherhood, but in brotherhood and sisterhood, as man and wife, as male and female. Failing, we shall perish and rot in the bowels of the earth, and time pass us by ceaselessly and remorselessly.

D. H. LAWRENCE

reflections on the death of a porcupine

There are many bare places on the little pine trees, towards the top, where the porcupines have gnawed the bark away and left the white flesh showing. And some trees are dying from the top.

Everyone says, porcupines should be killed; the Indians, Mexicans, Americans all say the same.

At full moon a month ago, when I went down the long clearing in the brilliant moonlight, through the poor dry herbage a big porcupine began to waddle away from me, towards the trees and the darkness. The animal had raised all its hairs and bristles, so that by the light of the moon it seemed to have a tall, swaying, moonlit aureole arching its back as it went. That seemed curiously fearsome, as if the animal were emitting itself demon-like on the air.

It waddled very slowly, with its white spiky spoon-tail steering flat, behind the round bear-like mound of its back. It had a lumbering, beetle's, squalid motion, unpleasant. I followed it into the darkness of the timber, and there, squat like a great tick, it began scrapily to creep up a pine-trunk. It was very like a great aureoled tick, a bug, struggling up.

I stood near and watched, disliking the presence of the creature. It is a duty to kill the things. But the dislike of killing him was greater than the dislike of him. So I watched him climb.

And he watched me. When he had got nearly the height of a man, all his long hairs swaying with a bristling gleam like an aureole, he hesitated, and slithered down. Evidently he had decided, either that I was harmless, or else that it was risky to go up any further, when I could knock him off so easily with a pole. So he slithered podgily down again, and waddled away with the same bestial, stupid motion of that white-spiky repulsive spoon-tail. He was as big as a middle-sized pig: or more like a bear.

I let him go. He was repugnant. He made a certain squalor in the moonlight of the Rocky Mountains. As all savagery has a touch of squalor, that makes one a little sick at the stomach. And anyhow, it seemed almost more squalid to pick up a pine bough and push him over, hit him and kill him.

A few days later, on a hot, motionless morning when the pine trees put out their bristles in stealthy, hard assertion; and I was not in a good temper, because Black-eyed Susan, the cow, had disappeared into the timber, and I had had to ride hunting her, so it was nearly nine o'clock before she was milked: Madame came in suddenly out of the sunlight, saying: "I got such a shock! There are two strange dogs, and one of them has got the most awful beard, all round his nose."

She was frightened, like a child, at something unnatural.

"Beard! Porcupine quills, probably! He's been after a porcupine."

"Ah!" she cried in relief. "Very likely! Very likely!"—then with a change of tone: "Poor thing, will they hurt him?"

"They will. I wonder when he came."

"I heard dogs bark in the night."

"Did you? Why didn't you say so? I should have known Susan was hiding—"

The ranch is lonely, there is no sound in the night, save the innumerable noises of the night, that you can't put your finger on; cosmic noises in the far deeps of the sky, and of the earth.

I went out. And in the full blaze of sunlight in the field, stood two dogs, a black-and-white, and a big, bushy, rather handsome sandy-red dog, of the collie type. And sure enough, this latter did look queer and a bit horrifying, his whole muzzle set round with white spines, like some ghastly growth; like an unnatural beard.

The black-and-white dog made off as I went through the fence. But the red dog whimpered and hesitated, and moved on hot bricks. He was fat and in good condition. I thought he might belong to some shepherds herding sheep in the forest ranges, among the mountains.

He waited while I went up to him, wagging his tail and whimpering, and ducking his head, and dancing. He daren't rub his nose with his paws any more: it hurt too much. I patted his head and looked at his nose, and he whimpered loudly.

He must have had thirty quills, or more, sticking out of his nose, all the way round: the white, ugly ends of the quills protruding an inch, sometimes more, sometimes less, from his already swollen blood-puffed muzzle.

The porcupines here have quills only two or three inches long.

But they are devilish; and a dog will die if he does not get them pulled out. Because they work further and further in, and will sometimes emerge through the skin away in some unexpected place.

Then the fun began. I got him in the yard: and he drank up the whole half-gallon of the chickens' sour milk. Then I started pulling out the quills. He was a big, bushy, handsome dog, but his nerve was gone, and every time I got a quill out, he gave a yelp. Some long quills were fairly easy. But the shorter ones, near his lips, were deep in, and hard to get hold of, and hard to pull out when you did get hold of them. And with every one that came out, came a little spurt of blood and another yelp and writhe.

The dog wanted the quills out: but his nerve was gone. Every time he saw my hand coming to his nose, he jerked his head away. I quieted him, and stealthily managed to jerk out another quill, with the blood all over my fingers. But with every one that came out, he grew more tiresome. I tried and tried and tried to get hold of another quill, and he jerked and jerked, and writhed and whimpered, and ran under the porch floor.

It was a curiously unpleasant, nerve-trying job. The day was blazing hot. The dog came out and I struggled with him again for an hour or more. Then we blindfolded him. But either he smelled my hand approaching his nose, or some weird instinct told him. He jerked his head, this way, that way, up, down, sideways, roundwise, as one's fingers came slowly, slowly, to seize a quill.

The quills on his lips and chin were deep in, only about a quarter of an inch of white stub protruding from the swollen, blood-oozed, festering black skin. It was very difficult to jerk them out.

We let him lie for an interval, hidden in the quiet cool place under the porch floor. After half an hour, he crept out again. We got a rope round his nose, behind the bristles, and one held while the other got the stubs with the pliers. But it was too trying. If a quill came out, the dog's yelp startled every nerve. And he was frightened of the pain, it was impossible to hold his head still any longer.

After struggling for two hours, and extracting some twenty quills, I gave up. It was impossible to quiet the creature, and I had had enough. His nose on the top was clear: a punctured, puffy, blood-darkened mess; and his lips were clear. But just on his round little chin, where the few white hairs are, was still a bunch of white quills, eight or nine, deep in.

We let him go, and he dived under the porch, and there he lay invisible: save for the end of his bushy, foxy tail, which moved when we came near. Towards noon he emerged, ate up the chicken-food, and stood with that doggish look of dejection, and fear, and friendliness, and greediness, wagging his tail.

But I had had enough.

"Go home!" I said. "Go home! Go home to your master, and let him finish for you."

He would not go. So I led him across the blazing hot clearing, in the way I thought he should go. He followed a hundred yards, then stood motionless in the blazing sun. He was not going to leave the place.

And I! I simply did not want him.

So I picked up a stone. He dropped his tail, and swerved towards the house. I knew what he was going to do. He was going to dive under the porch, and there stick, haunting the place.

I dropped my stone, and found a good stick under the cedar tree. Already in the heat was that sting-like biting of electricity, the thunder gathering in the sheer sunshine, without a cloud, and making one's whole body feel dislocated.

I could not bear to have that dog around any more. Going quietly to him, I suddenly gave him one hard hit with the stick, crying: "Go home!" He turned quickly, and the end of the stick caught him on his sore nose. With a fierce yelp, he went off like a wolf, downhill, like a flash, gone. And I stood in the field full of pangs of regret, at having hit him, unintentionally, on his sore nose.

But he was gone.

And then the present moon came, and again the night was clear. But in the interval there had been heavy thunder-rains, the ditch was running with bright water across the field, and the night, so fair, had not the terrific, mirror-like brilliancy, touched with terror, so startling bright, of the moon in the last days of June.

We were alone on the ranch. Madame went out into the clear night, just before retiring. The stream ran in a cord of silver across the field, in the straight line where I had taken the irrigation ditch. The pine tree in front of the house threw a black shadow. The mountain slope came down to the fence, wild and alert.

"Come!" said she excitedly. "There is a big porcupine drinking at the ditch. I thought at first it was a bear."

When I got out he had gone. But among the grasses and the coming wild sunflowers, under the moon, I saw his greyish halo, like a pallid living bush, moving over the field, in the distance, in the moonlit *clair-obscur*.

We got through the fence, and following, soon caught him up. There he lumbered, with his white spoon-tail spiked with bristles, steering behind almost as if he were moving backwards, and this was his head. His long, long hairs above the quills quivering with a dim grey gleam, like a bush.

And again I disliked him.

"Should one kill him?"

She hesitated. Then with a sort of disgust:

"Yes!"

I went back to the house, and got the little twenty-two rifle. Now never in my life had I shot at any live thing: I never wanted to. I always felt guns very repugnant: sinister, mean. With difficulty I had fired once or twice at a target: but resented doing even so much. Other people could shoot if they wanted to. Myself, individually, it was repugnant to me even to try.

But something slowly hardens in a man's soul. And I knew now, it had hardened in mine. I found the gun, and with rather trembling hands, got it loaded. Then I pulled back the trigger and followed the porcupine. It was still lumbering through the grass. Coming near, I aimed.

The trigger stuck. I pressed the little catch with a safety-pin I found in my pocket, and released the trigger. Then we followed the porcupine. He was still lumbering towards the trees. I went sideways on, stood quite near to him, and fired, in the clear-dark of the moonlight.

And as usual I aimed too high. He turned, went scuttling back whence he had come.

I got another shell in place, and followed. This time I fired full into the mound of his round back, below the glistening grey halo. He seemed to stumble on to his hidden nose, and struggled a few strides, ducking his head under like a hedgehog.

"He's not dead yet! Oh, fire again!" cried Madame.

I fired, but the gun was empty.

So I ran quickly, for a cedar pole. The porcupine was lying

still, with subsiding halo. He stirred faintly. So I turned him and hit him hard over the nose; or where, in the dark, his nose should have been. And it was done. He was dead.

And in the moonlight, I looked down on the first creature I had ever shot.

"Does it seem mean?" I asked aloud, doubtful.

Again Madame hesitated. Then: "No!" she said resentfully.

And I felt she was right. Things like the porcupine, one must be able to shoot them, if they get in one's way.

One must be able to shoot. I, myself, must be able to shoot, and to kill.

For me, this is a *volte-face*. I have always preferred to walk round my porcupine, rather than kill it.

Now, I know it's no good walking round. One must kill.

I buried him in the adobe hole. But some animal dug down and ate him; for two days later there lay the spines and bones spread out, with the long skeletons of the porcupine-hands.

The only nice thing about him—or her, for I believe it was a female, by the dugs on her belly—were the feet. They were like longish, alert black hands, paw-hands. That is why a porcupine's tracks in the snow look almost as if a child had gone by, leaving naked little human foot-prints, like a little boy.

So, he is gone: or she is gone. But there is another one, bigger and blacker-looking, among the west timber. That too is to be shot. It is part of the business of ranching: even when it's only a little half-abandoned ranch like this one.

Whenever man establishes himself, upon the earth, he has to fight for his place, against the lower orders of life. Food, the basis of existence, has to be fought for even by the most idyllic of farmers. You plant, and you protect your growing crop with a gun. Food, food, how strangely it relates man with the animal and vegetable world! How important it is! And how fierce is the fight that goes on around it.

The same when one skins a rabbit, and takes out the inside, one realizes what an enormous part of the animal, comparatively, is intestinal, what a big part of him is just for food-apparatus; for *living on* other organisms.

And when one watches the horses in the big field, their noses to the ground, bite-bite-biting at the grass, and stepping absorbedly on, and bite-bite-biting without ever lifting their noses, cropping off the grass, the young shoots of alfalfa, the dandelions, with a blind, relentless, unwearied persistence, one's whole life pauses. One suddenly realizes again how all creatures devour, and *must* devour the lower forms of life.

So Susan, swinging across the field, snatches off the tops of the little wild sunflowers as if she were mowing. And down they go, down her black throat. And when she stands in her cowly oblivion chewing her cud, with her lower jaw swinging peacefully, and I am milking her, suddenly the camomiley smell of her breath, as she glances round with glaring, smoke-blue eyes, makes me realize it is the sunflowers that are her ball of cud. Sunflowers! And they will go to making her glistening black hide, and the thick cream on her milk.

And the chickens, when they see a great black beetle, that the Mexicans call a *toro*, floating past, they are after it in a rush. And if it settles, instantly the brown hen stabs it with her beak. It is a great beetle two or three inches long: but in a second it is in the crop of the chicken. Gone!

And Timsy, the cat, as she spies on the chipmunks, crouches in another sort of oblivion, soft, and still. The chipmunks come to drink the milk from the chickens' bowl. Two of them met at the bowl. They were little squirrely things with stripes down their backs. They sat up in front of one another, lifting their inquisitive little noses and humping their backs. Then each put its two little hands on the other's shoulders, they reared up, gazing into each other's faces; and finally they put their two little noses together, in a sort of kiss.

But Miss Timsy can't stand this. In a soft, white-and-yellow leap she is after them. They skip with the darting jerk of chipmunks, to the wood-heap, and with one soft, high-leaping sideways bound Timsy goes through the air. Her snow-flake of a paw comes down on one of the chipmunks. She looks at it for a second. It squirms. Swiftly and triumphantly she puts her two flowery little white paws on it, legs straight out in front of her, back arched, gazing concentratedly yet whimsically. Chipmunk does not stir. She takes it softly in her mouth, where it dangles softly, like a lady's tippet. And with a proud, prancing motion the Timsy sets off towards the house, her white little feet hardly touching the ground.

But she gets shooed away. We refuse to loan her the sitting-room any more, for her gladiatorial displays. If the chippy must be "butchered to make a Timsy holiday," it shall be outside. Disappointed, but still high-stepping, the Timsy sets off towards the clay oven by the shed.

There she lays the chippy gently down, and soft as a little white cloud lays one small paw on its striped back. Chippy does not move. Soft as thistle-down she raises her paw a tiny, tiny bit, to release him.

And all of a sudden, with an elastic jerk, he darts from under the white release of her paw. And instantly, she is up in the air and down she comes on him, with the forward-thrusting bolts of her white paws. Both creatures are motionless.

Then she takes him softly in her mouth again, and looks round, to see if she can slip into the house. She cannot. So she trots towards the wood-pile.

It is a game, and it is pretty. Chippy escapes into the wood-pile, and she softly, softly reconnoitres among the faggots.

Of all the animals, there is no denying it, the Timsy is the most pretty, the most fine. It is not her mere *corpus* that is beautiful; it is her bloom of aliveness. Her "infinite variety"; the soft, snow-flakey lightness of her, and at the same time her lean, heavy ferocity. I had never realized the latter, till I was lying in bed one day moving my toe, unconsciously, under the bedclothes. Suddenly a terrific blow struck my foot. The Timsy had sprung out of nowhere, with a hurling, steely force, thud upon the bedclothes where the toe was moving. It was as if someone had aimed a sudden blow, vindictive and unerring.

"Timsy!"

She looked at me with the vacant, feline glare of her hunting eyes. It is not even ferocity. It is the dilation of the strange, vacant arrogance of power. The power is in her.

And so it is. Life moves in circles of power and of vividness, and each circle of life only maintains its orbit upon the subjection of some lower circle. If the lower cycles of life are not *mastered*, there can be no higher cycle.

In nature, one creature devours another, and this is an essential part of all existence and of all being. It is not something to lament over, nor something to try to reform. The Buddhist who refuses to take life is really ridiculous, since if he eats only two grains of rice per day, it is two grains of life. We did not make creation, *we* are not the authors of the universe. And if we see that the whole of creation is established upon the fact that one life devours another life, one cycle of existence can only come into existence through the subjugating of another cycle of existence, then what is the good of trying to pretend that it is not so? The only thing to do is to realize what is higher, and what is lower, in the cycles of existence.

It is nonsense to declare that there *is* no higher and lower. We know full well that the dandelion belongs to a higher cycle of existence than the hartstongue fern, that the ant's is a higher form of existence than the dandelion's, that the thrush is higher than the ant, that Timsy, the cat, is higher than the thrush, and that I, a man, am higher than Timsy.

What do we mean by higher? Strictly, we mean more alive. More vividly alive. The ant is more vividly alive than the pine tree. We know it, there is no trying to refute it. It is all very well saying that they are both alive in two different ways, and therefore they are incomparable, incommensurable. This is also true.

But one truth does not displace another. Even apparently contradictory truths do not displace one another. Logic is far too coarse to make the subtle distinctions life demands.

Truly, it is futile to compare an ant with a great pine tree, in the absolute. Yet as far as *existence* is concerned, they are not only placed in comparison to one another, they are occasionally pitted against one another. And if it comes to a contest, the little ant will devour the life of the huge tree. If it comes to a contest.

And, in the cycles of *existence*, this is the test. From the lowest form of existence, to the highest, the test question is: *Can thy neighbour finally overcome thee?*

If he can, then he belongs to a higher cycle of existence.

This is the truth behind the survival of the fittest. Every cycle of existence is established upon the overcoming of the lower cycles of existence. The real question is, wherein does *fitness* lie? Fitness for what? Fit merely to survive? That which is only fit to survive will survive only to supply food or contribute in some way to the existence of a higher form of life, which is able to do more than survive, which can really *vive*, live.

Life is more vivid in the dandelion than in the green fern, or than in a palm tree.

Life is more vivid in a snake than in a butterfly.

Life is more vivid in a wren than in an alligator.

Life is more vivid in a cat than in an ostrich.

Life is more vivid in the Mexican who drives the wagon, than in the two horses in the wagon.

Life is more vivid in me, than in the Mexican who drives the wagon for me.

We are speaking in terms of *existence:* that is, in the terms of species, race, or type.

The dandelion can take hold of the land, the palm tree is driven into a corner, with the fern.

The snake can devour the fiercest insect.

The fierce bird can destroy the greatest reptile.

The great cat can destroy the greatest bird.

The man can destroy the horse, or any animal.

One race of man can subjugate and rule another race.

All this in terms of *existence*. As far as existence goes, that life-species is the highest which can devour, or destroy, or subjugate every other life-species against which it is pitted in contest.

This is a law. There is no escaping this law. Anyone, or any race, trying to escape it, will fall a victim: will fall into subjugation.

But let us insist and insist again, we are talking now of existence, of species, of types, of races, of nations, not of single individuals, nor of *beings*. The dandelion in full flower, a little sun bristling with sun-rays on the green earth, is a nonpareil, a non-such. Foolish, foolish, foolish to compare it to anything else on earth. It is itself incomparable and unique.

But that is the fourth dimension, of *being*. It is in the fourth dimension, nowhere else.

Because, in the time-space dimension, any man may tread on the yellow sun-mirror, and it is gone. Any cow may swallow it. Any bunch of ants may annihilate it.

This brings us to the inexorable law of life.

1. Any creature that attains to its own fullness of being, its own *living* self, becomes unique, a nonpareil. It has its place in the fourth dimension, the heaven of existence, and there it is perfect, it is beyond comparison.

2. At the same time, every creature exists in time and space. And in time and space it exists relatively to all other existence, and can never be absolved. Its existence impinges on other existences, and is itself impinged upon. And in the struggle for existence, if an effort on the part of any one type or species or order of life

can finally destroy the other species, then the destroyer is of a more vital cycle of existence than the one destroyed. (When speaking of existence we always speak in types, species, not individuals. Species exist. But even an individual dandelion has *being.*)

3. The force which we call *vitality,* and which is the determining factor in the struggle for existence, is, however, derived also from the fourth dimension. That is to say, the ultimate source of all vitality is in that other dimension, or region, where the dandelion blooms, and which men have called heaven, and which now they call the fourth dimension: which is only a way of saying that it is not to be reckoned in terms of space and time.

4. The primary way, in our existence, to get vitality, is to absorb it from living creatures lower than ourselves. It is thus transformed into a new and higher creation. (There are many ways of absorbing: devouring food is one way, love is often another. The best way is a pure relationship, which includes the *being* on each side, and which allows the transfer to take place in a living flow, enhancing the life in both beings.)

5. No creature is fully itself till it is, like the dandelion, opened in the bloom of pure relationship to the sun, the entire living cosmos.

So we still find ourselves in the tangle of existence and being, a tangle which man has never been able to get out of, except by sacrificing the one to the other.

Sacrifice is useless.

The clue to all existence is being. But you can't have being without existence, any more than you can have the dandelion flower without the leaves and the long tap root.

Being is *not* ideal, as Plato would have it: nor spiritual. It is a transcendent form of existence, and as much material as existence is. Only the matter suddenly enters the fourth dimension.

All existence is dual, and surging towards a consummation into being. In the seed of the dandelion, as it floats with its little umbrella of hairs, sits the Holy Ghost in tiny compass. The Holy Ghost is that which holds the light and the dark, the day and the night, the wet and the sunny, united in one little clue. There it sits, in the seed of the dandelion.

The seed falls to earth. The Holy Ghost rouses, saying: "*Come!*" And out of the sky come the rays of the sun, and out of earth comes dampness and dark and the death-stuff. They are called in, like those bidden to a feast. The sun sits down at the hearth, inside the seed; and the dark, damp death-returner sits on the opposite side, with the host between. And the host says to them: "*Come! Be merry together!*" So the sun looks with desirous curiosity on the dark face of the earth, and the dark damp one looks with wonder on the bright face of the other, who comes from the sun. And the host says: "*Here you are at home! Lift me up, between you, that I may cease to be a Ghost. For it longs me to look out, it longs me to dance with the dancers.*"

So the sun in the seed, and the earthy one in the seed take hands, and laugh, and begin to dance. And their dancing is like a fire kindled, a bonfire with leaping flame. And the treading of their feet is like the running of little streams, down into the earth. So from the dance of the sun-in-the-seed with the earthy death-returner, green little flames of leaves shoot up, and hard little trickles of roots strike down. And the host laughs, and says: "*I am being lifted up! Dance harder! Oh wrestle, you two, like wonderful wrestlers, neither of which can win.*" So sun-in-the-seed and the death-returner, who is earthy, dance faster and faster and the leaves rising greener begin to dance in a ring above-ground, fiercely overwhelming any outsider, in a whirl of swords and lions' teeth. And the earthy one wrestles, wrestles with the sun-in-the-seed, so the long roots reach down like arms of a fighter gripping the power of earth, and strangle all intruders, strangling any intruder mercilessly. Till the two fall in one strange embrace, and from the centre the long flower-stem lifts like a phallus, budded with a bud. And out of the bud the voice of the Holy Ghost is heard crying: "*I am lifted up! Lo! I am lifted up! I am here!*" So the bud opens, and there is the flower poised in the very middle of the universe, with a ring of green swords below, to guard it, and the octopus, arms deep in earth, drinking and threatening. So the Holy Ghost, being a dandelion flower, looks round, and says: "*Lo! I am yellow! I believe the sun has lent me his body! Lo! I am sappy with golden, bitter blood! I believe death out of the damp black earth has lent me his blood! I am incarnate! I like my incarnation! But this is not all. I will keep this incarnation. It is good! But oh! if I can win to another incarnation, who knows how wonderful it will be! This one will have to give place. This one can help to create the next.*"

So the Holy Ghost leaves the clue of himself behind, in the seed, and wanders forth in the comparative chaos of our universe, seeking another incarnation.

And this will go on forever. Man, as yet, is less than half grown. Even his flower-stem has not appeared yet. He is all leaves and roots, without any clue put forth. No sign of bud anywhere.

Either he will have to start budding, or he will be forsaken of the Holy Ghost: abandoned as a failure in creation, as the ichthyosaurus was abandoned. Being abandoned means losing his vitality. The sun and the earth-dark will cease rushing together in him. Already it is ceasing. To men, the sun is becoming stale, and the earth sterile. But the sun itself will never become stale, nor the earth barren. It is only that the *clue* is missing inside men. They are like flowerless, seedless fat cabbages, nothing inside.

Vitality depends upon the clue of the Holy Ghost inside a creature, a man, a nation, a race. When the clue goes, the vitality goes. And the Holy Ghost seeks forever a new incarnation, and subordinates the old to the new. You will know that any creature or race is still alive with the Holy Ghost, when it can subordinate the lower creatures or races, and assimilate them into a new incarnation.

No man, or creature, or race can have vivid vitality unless it be moving towards a blossoming: and the most powerful is that which moves towards the as-yet-unknown blossom.

Blossoming means the establishing of a pure, *new* relationship with all the cosmos. This is the state of heaven. And it is the state of a flower, a cobra, a jenny-wren in spring, a man when he knows himself royal and crowned with the sun, with his feet gripping the core of the earth.

This too is the fourth dimension: this state, this mysterious other reality of things in a perfected relationship. It is into this perfected relationship that every straight line curves, as if to some core, passing out of the time-space dimension.

But any man, creature, or race moving towards blossoming will have to draw immense supplies of vitality from men, or creatures below, passionate strength. And he will have to accomplish a perfected relation with all things.

There will be conquest, always. But the aim of conquest is a perfect relation of conquerors with conquered, for a new blossoming. Freedom is illusory. Sacrifice is illusory. Almightyness is illusory. Freedom, sacrifice, almightyness, these are all human side-tracks, cul-de-sacs, bunk. All that is real is the overwhelmingness of a new inspirational command, a new relationship with all things.

Heaven is always there. No achieved consummation is lost. Procreation goes on forever, to support the achieved revelation. But the torch of revelation itself is handed on. And this is all important.

Everything living wants to procreate more living things.

But more important than this is the fact that every revelation is a torch held out, to kindle new revelations. As the dandelion holds out the sun to me, saying: "*Can you take it!*"

Every gleam of heaven that is shown—like a dandelion flower, or a green beetle—quivers with strange passion to kindle a new gleam, never yet beheld. This is not self-sacrifice: it is self-contribution: in which the highest happiness lies.

The torch of existence is handed on, in the womb of procreation.

And the torch of revelation is handed on, by every living thing, from the protococcus to a brave man or a beautiful woman, handed to whosoever can take it. He who can take it, has power beyond all the rest.

The cycle of procreation exists purely for the keeping alight of the torch of perfection, in any species: the torch being the dandelion in blossom, the tree in full leaf, the peacock in all his plumage, the cobra in all his colour, the frog at full leap, woman in all the mystery of her fathomless desirableness, man in the fullness of his power: every creature become its pure self.

One cycle of perfection urges to kindle another cycle, as yet unknown.

And with the kindling from the torch of revelation comes the inrush of vitality, and the need to consume and *consummate* the lower cycles of existence, into a new thing. This consuming and this consummating means conquest, and fearless mastery. Freedom lies in the honourable yielding towards the new flame, and the honourable mastery of that which shall be new, over that which must yield. As I must master my horses, which are in a lower cycle of existence. And they, they are relieved and *happy* to serve. If I turn them loose into the mountain ranges, to run wild till they die, the thrill of real happiness is gone out of their lives.

Every lower order seeks in some measure to serve a higher order: and rebels against being conquered.

It is always conquest, and it always will be conquest. If the conquered be an old, declining race, they will have handed on their torch to the conqueror: who will burn his fingers badly, if he is too flippant. And if the conquered be a barbaric race, they will consume the fire of the conqueror, and leave him flameless, unless he watch it. But it is always conquest, conquered and conqueror, forever. The kingdom of heaven is the kingdom of conquerors, who can serve the conquest forever, after their own conquest is made.

In heaven, in the perfected relation, is peace: in the fourth dimension. But there is getting there. And that, forever, is the process of conquest.

When the rose blossomed, then the great Conquest was made by the vegetable kingdom. But even this conqueror of conquerors, the rose, had to lend himself towards the caterpillar and the butterfly of a later conquest. A conqueror, but tributary to the later conquest.

There is no such thing as equality. In the kingdom of heaven, in the fourth dimension, each soul that achieves a perfect relationship with the cosmos, from its own centre, is perfect, and incomparable. It has no superior. It is a conqueror, and incomparable.

But every man, in the struggle of conquest towards his own consummation, must master the inferior cycles of life, and never relinquish his mastery. Also, if there be men beyond him, moving on to a newer consummation than his own, he must yield to their greater demand, and serve their greater mastery, and so be faithful to the kingdom of heaven which is within him, which is gained by conquest and by loyal service.

Any man who achieves his own being will, like the dandelion or the butterfly, pass into that other dimension which we call the fourth, and the old people called heaven. It is the state of perfected relationship. And here a man will have his peace forever: whether he serve or command, in the process of living.

But even this entails his faithful allegiance to the kingdom of heaven, which must be forever and forever extended, as creation conquers chaos. So that my perfection will but serve a perfection which still lies ahead, unrevealed and unconceived, and beyond my own.

We have tried to build walls round the kingdom of heaven: but it's no good. It's only the cabbage rotting inside.

Our last wall is the golden wall of money. This is a fatal wall. It cuts us off from life, from vitality, from the alive sun and the alive earth, as *nothing* can. Nothing, not even the most fanatical dogmas of an iron-bound religion, can insulate us from the inrush of life and inspiration, as money can.

We are losing vitality: losing it rapidly. Unless we seize the torch of inspiration, and drop our money-bags, the moneyless will be kindled by the flame of flames, and they will consume us like old rags.

We are losing vitality, owing to money and money-standards. The torch in the hands of the moneyless will set our house on fire, and burn us to death, like sheep in a flaming corral.

LOREN EISELEY

the judgment of the birds

It is a commonplace of all religious thought, even the most primitive, that the man seeking visions and insight must go apart from his fellows and live for a time in the wilderness. If he is of the proper sort, he will return with a message. It may not be a message from the god he set out to seek, but even if he has failed in that particular, he will have had a vision or seen a marvel, and these are always worth listening to and thinking about.

The world, I have come to believe, is a very queer place, but we have been part of this queerness for so long that we tend to take it for granted. We rush to and fro like Mad Hatters upon our peculiar errands, all the time imagining our surroundings to be dull and ourselves quite ordinary creatures. Actually, there is nothing in the world to encourage this idea, but such is the mind of man, and this is why he finds it necessary from time to time to send emissaries into the wilderness in the hope of learning of great events, or plans in store for him, that will resuscitate his waning taste for life. His great news services, his world-wide radio network, he knows with a last remnant of healthy distrust will be of no use to him in this matter. No miracle can withstand a radio broadcast, and it is certain that it would be no miracle if it could. One must seek, then, what only the solitary approach can give—a natural revelation.

Let it be understood that I am not the sort of man to whom is entrusted direct knowledge of great events or prophecies. A naturalist, however, spends much of his life alone, and my life is no exception. Even in New York City there are patches of wilderness, and a man by himself is bound to undergo certain experiences falling into the class of which I speak. I set mine down, therefore: a matter of pigeons, a flight of chemicals, and a judgment of birds, in the hope that they will come to the eye of those who have retained a true taste for the marvelous, and who are capable of discerning in the flow of ordinary events the point at which the mundane world gives way to quite another dimension.

New York is not, on the whole, the best place to enjoy the downright miraculous nature of the planet. There are, I do not doubt, many remarkable stories to be heard there and many strange sights to be seen, but to grasp a marvel fully it must be savored from all aspects. This cannot be done while one is being jostled and hustled along a crowded street. Nevertheless, in any city there are true wildernesses where a man can be alone. It can happen in a hotel room, or on the high roofs at dawn.

One night on the twentieth floor of a midtown hotel I awoke in the dark and grew restless. On an impulse I climbed upon the broad old-fashioned window sill, opened the curtains and peered out. It was the hour just before dawn, the hour when men sigh in their sleep, or, if awake, strive to focus their wavering eyesight upon a world emerging from the shadows. I leaned out sleepily through the open window. I had expected depths, but not the sight I saw.

I found I was looking down from that great height into a series of curious cupolas or lofts that I could just barely make out in the darkness. As I looked, the outlines of these lofts became more distinct because the light was being reflected from the wings of pigeons who, in utter silence, were beginning to float outward upon the city. In and out through the open slits in the cupolas passed the white-winged birds on their mysterious errands. At this hour the city was theirs, and quietly, without the brush of a single wing tip against stone in that high, eerie place, they were taking over the spires of Manhattan. They were pouring upward in a light that was not yet perceptible to human eyes, while far down in the black darkness of the alleys it was still midnight.

As I crouched half asleep across the sill, I had a moment's illusion that the world had changed in the night, as in some immense snowfall, and that if I were to leave, it would have to be as these other inhabitants were doing, by the window. I should have to launch out into that great bottomless void with the simple confidence of young birds reared high up there among the familiar chimney pots and interposed horrors of the abyss.

I leaned farther out. To and fro went the white wings, to and fro. There were no sounds from any of them. They knew man was asleep and this light for a little while was theirs. Or perhaps I had only dreamed about man in this city of wings—which he could surely never have built. Perhaps I, myself, was one of these birds dreaming unpleasantly a moment of old dangers far below as I teetered on a window ledge.

Around and around went the wings. It needed only a little courage, only a little shove from the window ledge to enter that city of light. The muscles of my hands were already making little premonitory lunges. I wanted to enter that city and go away over the roofs in the first dawn. I wanted to enter it so badly that I drew back carefully into the room and opened the hall door. I found my coat on the chair, and it slowly became clear to me that there was a way down through the floors, that I was, after all, only a man.

I dressed then and went back to my own kind, and I have been rather more than usually careful ever since not to look into the city of light. I had seen, just once, man's greatest creation from a strange inverted angle, and it was not really his at all. I will never forget how those wings went round and round, and how, by the merest pressure of the fingers and a feeling for air, one might go away over the roofs. It is a knowledge, however, that is better kept to oneself. I think of it sometimes in such a way that the wings, beginning far down in the black depths of the mind, begin to rise and whirl till all the mind is lit by their spinning, and there is a sense of things passing away, but lightly, as a wing might veer over an obstacle.

To see from an inverted angle, however, is not a gift allotted merely to the human imagination. I have come to suspect that within their degree it is sensed by animals, though perhaps as rarely as among men. The time has to be right; one has to be, by chance or intention, upon the border of two worlds. And sometimes these two borders may shift or interpenetrate and one sees the miraculous.

I once saw this happen to a crow.

This crow lives near my house, and though I have never injured him, he takes good care to stay up in the very highest trees and, in general, to avoid humanity. His world begins at about the limit of my eyesight.

On the particular morning when this episode occurred, the whole countryside was buried in one of the thickest fogs in years. The ceiling was absolutely zero. All planes were grounded, and even a pedestrian could hardly see his outstretched hand before him.

I was groping across a field in the general direction of the railroad station, following a dimly outlined path. Suddenly out of the fog, at about the level of my eyes, and so closely that I flinched, there flashed a pair of immense black wings and a huge beak. The whole bird rushed over my head with a frantic cawing outcry of such hideous terror as I have never heard in a crow's voice before, and never expect to hear again.

He was lost and startled, I thought, as I recovered my poise. He ought not to have flown out in this fog. He'd knock his silly brains out.

All afternoon that great awkward cry rang in my head. Merely being lost in a fog seemed scarcely to account for it—especially in a tough, intelligent old bandit such as I knew that particular crow to be. I even looked once in the mirror to see what it might be about me that had so revolted him that he had cried out in protest to the very stones.

Finally, as I worked my way homeward along the path, the solution came to me. It should have been clear before. The borders of our worlds had shifted. It was the fog that had done it. That crow, and I knew him well, never under normal circumstances flew low near men. He had been lost all right, but it was more than that. He had thought he was high up, and when he encountered me looming gigantically through the fog, he had perceived a ghastly and, to the crow mind, unnatural sight. He had seen a man walking on air, desecrating the very heart of the crow kingdom, a harbinger of the most profound evil a crow mind could conceive of—air-walking men. The encounter, he must have thought, had taken place a hundred feet over the roofs.

He caws now when he sees me leaving for the station in the morning, and I fancy that in that note I catch the uncertainty of a mind that has come to know things are not always what they seem. He has seen a marvel in his heights of air and is no longer as other crows. He has experienced the human world from an unlikely perspective. He and I share a viewpoint in common: our worlds have interpenetrated, and we both have faith in the miraculous.

It is a faith that in my own case has been augmented by two remarkable sights. As I have hinted previously, I once saw some very odd chemicals fly across a waste so dead it might have been upon the moon, and once, by an even more fantastic piece of luck, I was present when a group of birds passed a judgment upon life.

On the maps of the old voyageurs it is called *Mauvaises Terres,* the evil lands, and, slurred a little with the passage through many minds, it has come down to us anglicized as the Badlands. The soft shuffle of moccasins has passed through its canyons on the grim business of war and flight, but the last of those slight disturbances of immemorial silences died out almost a century ago. The land, if one can call it a land, is a waste as lifeless as that valley in which lie the kings of Egypt. Like the Valley of the Kings, it is a mausoleum, a place of dry bones in what once was a place of life. Now it has silences as deep as those in the moon's airless chasms.

Nothing grows among its pinnacles; there is no shade except under great toadstools of sandstone whose bases have been eaten to the shape of wine glasses by the wind. Everything is flaking, cracking, disintegrating, wearing away in the long, imperceptible weather of time. The ash of ancient volcanic outbursts still sterilizes its soil, and its colors in that waste are the colors that flame in the lonely sunsets on dead planets. Men come there but rarely, and for one purpose only, the collection of bones.

It was a late hour on a cold, wind-bitten autumn day when I climbed a great hill spined like a dinosaur's back and tried to take my bearings. The tumbled waste fell away in waves in all directions. Blue air was darkening into purple along the bases of the hills. I shifted my knapsack, heavy with the petrified bones of long-vanished creatures, and studied my compass. I wanted to be out of there by nightfall, and already the sun was going sullenly down in the west.

It was then that I saw the flight coming on. It was moving like a little close-knit body of black specks that danced and darted and closed again. It was pouring from the north and heading toward me with the undeviating relentlessness of a compass needle. It streamed through the shadows rising out of monstrous gorges. It rushed over towering pinnacles in the red light of the sun, or momentarily sank from sight within their shade. Across that desert of eroding clay and wind-worn stone they came with a faint wild twittering that filled all the air about me as those tiny living bullets hurtled past into the night.

It may not strike you as a marvel. It would not, perhaps, unless you stood in the middle of a dead world at sunset, but that was where I stood. Fifty million years lay under my feet, fifty million years of bellowing monsters moving in a green world now gone so utterly that its very light was traveling on the farther edge of space. The chemicals of all that vanished age lay about one in the ground. Around me still lay the shearing molars of dead titanotheres, the delicate sabers of soft-stepping cats, the hollow sockets that had held the eyes of many a strange, outmoded beast. Those eyes had looked out upon a world as real as ours; dark, savage brains had roamed and roared their challenges into the steaming night.

Now they were still here, or, put it as you will, the chemicals that made them were here about me in the ground. The carbon that had driven them ran blackly in the eroding stone. The stain of iron was in the clays. The iron did not remember the blood it had once moved within, the phosphorus had forgot the savage brain. The little individual moment had ebbed from all those strange combinations of chemicals as it would ebb from our living bodies into the sinks and runnels of oncoming time.

I had lifted up a fistful of that ground. I held it while that wild flight of south-bound warblers hurtled over me into the oncoming dark. There went phosphorus, there went iron, there went carbon, there beat the calcium in those hurrying wings. Alone on a dead planet I watched that incredible miracle speeding past. It ran by some true compass over field and waste land. It cried its individual ecstasies into the air until the gullies rang. It swerved like a single body, it knew itself and, lonely, it bunched close in the racing darkness, its individual entities feeling about them the rising night. And so, crying to each other their identity, they passed away out of my view.

I dropped my fistful of earth. I heard it roll inanimate back into the gully at the base of the hill: iron, carbon, the chemicals of life. Like men from those wild tribes who had haunted these hills before me seeking visions, I made my sign to the great darkness. It was not a mocking sign, and I was not mocked. As I walked into my camp late that night, one man, rousing from his blankets beside the fire, asked sleepily, "What did you see?"

"I think, a miracle," I said softly, but I said it to myself. Behind me that vast waste began to glow under the rising moon.

I have said that I saw a judgment upon life, and that it was not passed by men. Those who stare at birds in cages or who test minds by their closeness to our own may not care for it. It comes from far away out of my past, in a place of pouring waters and green leaves. I shall never see an episode like it again if I live to be a hundred, nor do I think that one man in a million has ever seen it, because man is an intruder into such silences. The light must be right, and the observer must remain unseen. No man sets up such an experiment. What he sees, he sees by chance.

You may put it that I had come over a mountain, that I had slogged through fern and pine needles for half a long day, and that on the edge of a little glade with one long, crooked branch extending across it, I had sat down to rest with my back against a stump. Through accident I was concealed from the glade, although I could see into it perfectly.

The sun was warm there, and the murmurs of forest life blurred softly away into my sleep. When I awoke, dimly aware of some commotion and outcry in the clearing, the light was slanting down through the pines in such a way that the glade was lit like some vast cathedral. I could see the dust motes of wood pollen in the long shaft of light, and there on the extended branch sat an enormous raven with a red and squirming nestling in his beak.

The sound that awoke me was the outraged cries of the nestling's parents, who flew helplessly in circles about the clearing. The sleek black monster was indifferent to them. He gulped, whetted his beak on the dead branch a moment and sat still. Up to that point the little tragedy had followed the usual pattern. But suddenly, out of all that area of woodland, a soft sound of complaint began to rise. Into the glade fluttered small birds of half a dozen varieties drawn by the anguished outcries of the tiny parents.

No one dared to attack the raven. But they cried there in some instinctive common misery, the bereaved and the unbereaved. The glade filled with their soft rustling and their cries. They fluttered as though to point their wings at the murderer. There was a dim intangible ethic he had violated, that they knew. He was a bird of death.

And he, the murderer, the black bird at the heart of life, sat on there, glistening in the common light, formidable, unmoving, unperturbed, untouchable.

The sighing died. It was then I saw the judgment. It was the judgment of life against death. I will never see it again so forcefully presented. I will never hear it again in notes so tragically prolonged. For in the midst of protest, they forgot the violence. There, in that clearing, the crystal note of a song sparrow lifted hesitantly in the hush. And finally, after painful fluttering, another took the song, and then another, the song passing from one bird to another, doubtfully at first, as though some evil thing were being slowly forgotten. Till suddenly they took heart and sang from many throats joyously together as birds are known to sing. They sang because life is sweet and sunlight beautiful. They sang under the brooding shadow of the raven. In simple truth they had forgotten the raven, for they were the singers of life, and not of death.

I was not of that airy company. My limbs were the heavy limbs of an earthbound creature who could climb mountains, even the mountains of the mind, only by a great effort of will. I knew I had seen a marvel and observed a judgment, but the mind which was my human endowment was sure to question it and to be at me day by day with its heresies until I grew to doubt the meaning of what I had seen. Eventually darkness and subtleties would ring me round once more.

And so it proved until, on the top of a stepladder, I made one more observation upon life. It was cold that autumn evening, and, standing under a suburban street light in a spate of leaves and beginning snow, I was suddenly conscious of some huge and hairy shadows dancing over the payment. They seemed attached to an odd, globular shape that was magnified above me. There was no mistaking it. I was standing under the shadow of an orb-weaving spider. Gigantically projected against the street, she was about her spinning when everything was going underground. Even her cables were magnified upon the sidewalk and already I was half-entangled in their shadows.

"Good Lord," I thought, "she has found herself a kind of minor sun and is going to upset the course of nature."

I procured a ladder from my yard and climbed up to inspect the situation. There she was, the universe running down around her, warmly arranged among her guy ropes attached to the lamp supports—a great black and yellow embodiment of the life force, not giving up to either frost or stepladders. She ignored me and went on tightening and improving her web.

I stood over her on the ladder, a faint snow touching my cheeks, and surveyed her universe. There were a couple of iridescent green beetle cases turning slowly on a loose strand of web, fragment of luminescent eye from a moth's wing and a large indeterminable object, perhaps a cicada, that had struggled and been wrapped in silk. There were also little bits and slivers, little red and blue flashes from the scales of anonymous wings that had crashed there.

Some days, I thought, they will be dull and gray and the shine will be out of them; then the dew will polish them again and drops hang on the silk until everything is gleaming and turning in the light. It is like a mind, really, where everything changes but remains, and in the end you have these eaten-out bits of experience like beetle wings.

I stood over her a moment longer, comprehending somewhat reluctantly that her adventure against the great blind forces of winter, her seizure of this warming globe of light, would come to nothing and was hopeless. Nevertheless it brought the birds back into my mind, and that faraway song which had traveled with growing strength around a forest clearing years ago—a kind of heroism, a world where even a spider refuses to lie down and die if a rope can still be spun on to a star. Maybe man himself will fight like this in the end, I thought, slowly realizing that the web and its threatening yellow occupant had been added to some luminous store of experience, shining for a moment in the fogbound reaches of my brain.

The mind, it came to me as I slowly descended the ladder, is a very remarkable thing; it has gotten itself a kind of courage by looking at a spider in a street lamp. Here was something that ought to be passed on to those who will fight our final freezing battle with the void. I thought of setting it down carefully as a message to the future: *In the days of the frost seek a minor sun.*

But as I hesitated, it became plain that something was wrong. The marvel was escaping—a sense of bigness beyond man's power to grasp, the essence of life in its great dealings with the universe. It was better, I decided, for the emissaries returning from the wilderness, even if they were merely descending from a stepladder, to record their marvel, not to define its meaning. In that way it would go echoing on through the minds of men, each grasping at that beyond out of which the miracles emerge, and which, once defined, ceases to satisfy the human need for symbols.

In the end I merely made a mental note: One specimen of Epeira observed building a web in a street light. Late autumn and cold for spiders. Cold for men, too. I shivered and left the lamp glowing there in my mind. The last I saw of Epeira she was hauling steadily on a cable. I stopped carefully over her shadow as I walked away.

EDMUND WILSON

on first reading genesis

I discovered a few years ago, in going through the attic of my mother's house, an old Hebrew Bible that had belonged to my grandfather, a Presbyterian minister, as well as a Hebrew dictionary and a Hebrew grammar. I had always had a certain curiosity about Hebrew, and I was perhaps piqued a little at the thought that my grandfather could read something that I couldn't, so, finding myself one autumn in Princeton, with the prospect of spending the winter, I enrolled in a Hebrew course at the Theological Seminary, from which my grandfather had graduated in 1846. I have thus acquired a smattering that has enabled me to work through Genesis, with constant reference to the English translation and the notes of the Westminster Commentaries, and this first acquaintance with the Hebrew text has, in several ways, been to me a revelation. In the first place, the study of a Semitic language gives one insights into a whole point of view, a system of mental habits, that differs radically from those of the West. But, besides this, I had never read Genesis before. In college I had taken the second half year of a course in Old Testament literature, so I did have some familiarity with the prophets and the later phases of Biblical history, but the Pentateuch and the earlier historical books were known to me only in patches or through simplified versions of Bible stories that had been read to me when I was a child. I came to them in the original for the first time rather late in life, when I had already read many other books, and since such an experience is probably rare—Hebrew being studied mainly by Christian seminarists and orthodox Jews, both of whom come to it early and with definite religious predispositions—I am going to give a report on it. I am myself neither a Jew nor a Christian, and I propose to disregard, in doing so, the little I know of the tons of theological commentary that have been written by the various churches. I do not propose to take for granted—as, from recent conversations on this subject with even well-educated people, I conclude I am warranted in not doing—that the reader is any better acquainted with even the most famous Bible stories than I was when I recently began to explore them.

First of all, the surprises of the language. The Bible in Hebrew is far more a different thing from the Bible in any translation than the original Homer, say, is from the best of the translations of Homer, because the language in which it is written is more different from English than Greek is. To speak merely from the point of view of style, the writing of the earliest books is a good deal tighter and tougher—Renan calls it a twisted cable—than is easy to imitate with the relatively loose weave of English. It is also much more poetic, or, rather, perhaps—since the King James Version does partly take care of this with its seventeenth-century rhythms—poetic in a more primitive way. Certain passages are composed in a kind of verse, and even the prose has a metrical basis. The first verse of Genesis, for instance, almost corresponds to a classical hexameter, and we soon feel we are reading an epic or a saga or something of the sort. The progress of the chronicle is interspersed with old prophecies and fragments of ballads that have evidently been handed down by word of mouth and that stand out from the background of the narrative by reason of their oracular obscurity and their "parallelistic" form. There are many plays on words and jingles that disappear in our solemn translations, and the language itself is extremely expressive, full of onomatopoetic effects. The word for "to laugh" is *tsakháq* ("kh" as in "Chekhov"), and thus Isaac is called Isaac (*Yitskháq*) because Sarah, in her delightful scene with God, cannot refrain from laughing when He tells her she shall yet bear a child; a light rain is called *matár*, a heavier downpour *géshem* (it was a *géshem* that caused the Deluge). The words for the emotions are likely to come from the physical states that accompany them. The verbs for "to love" and "to hate" are both based on heavy breathing: *aháv* and *ayáv*. Patience and impatience are rendered as the taking of long or short breaths.

The Hebrew language is also emphatic to a degree with which our language can hardly compete. The device for affirming something strongly is to repeat the important word, and God's warning to Adam that he will "dying, die," if he disobeys His orders, seems weakened in our version—"thou shalt surely die"—as does Joseph's assertion that "stolen, I was stolen out of the land of the Hebrews" by "indeed I was stolen." Nor can we match the vehement expression of the violent Hebrew emotions. When Jehovah, about to invoke the Flood, has become disgusted with man, it is not adequate to say that the thoughts of man's heart were "only evil continually"; in the "*raq ra kol hayyóm*" of the text, we seem to hear the Creator actually spitting on his unworthy creation. "And Isaac trembled very exceedingly" is the rendering of the King James Version of the passage in which Isaac discovers that Jacob has deceived him, which falls short of "Isaac trembled mightily a great trembling," and in the next verse we read that Esau "cried mightily a great and bitter cry." This violence and vehemence of the Hebrews is implicit in the structure of the language itself. They did not conjugate their verbs for tenses, as the modern Western languages do, since our modern conception of time was something at which they had not yet arrived—a significant feature of the language that I want, in a later section of this essay, to discuss by itself at length. What the Hebrews had instead of tenses were two fundamental conjugations for perfect and imperfect—that is, for action completed and action uncompleted. And both of these two "aspects" theoretically exist in seven variations for every verb (though actually the complete set is rare) that have nothing to do with time. The primary form of the verb is known as the "light" or simple form, and the second is the passive of this. So much seems plain enough sailing, but what follow are three intensive forms—active, passive and reflexive—and two causatives—active and passive.

These verbs, which take little account of time, are the instruments, then, of a people who, at the period when this language was formed, must have been both passionate and energetic. It is not a question of *when* something happens, but whether the thing is completed or certain to be completed. There are special forms, the causatives, for getting things done: "I will multiply your descendants," "They made Joseph take off his coat." The intensives are unexpected to the non-Semitic reader, who has difficulty in getting the hang of them, but feels a dynamic element in the bone of the language, and soon begins to find them fascinating. The translator of these strange verb forms, which double the middle consonant and vary the pattern of vowels, is obliged to resort to an adverb or a stronger verb. The intensive form of one of the words for "to kill," the paradigm verb that the student learns, is given in the grammars as "kill brutally." So you have "break" and "break to pieces," "grow" and "grow luxuriantly." A curious example, which occurs in Genesis 24:21, illustrates the problems of translators. When the emissary of Abraham meets Rebecca at the well and watches her attentively in silence, to see whether she will behave in the way by which he has proposed to God that the wife appointed for Isaac may be made to reveal herself, a verb that means "to look at" is put in the intensive form. The old Revised Version made it "And the man looked steadfastly on her"; the new Revised Version has it "gazed at her"—the first of these, that is, adds an adverb, the second tries to find an appropriate verb, and the nuances conveyed are different.

These intensives are sometimes baffling. It is not always easy to see what is implied in a given context. The forms may, in certain cases, turn intransitive into transitive verbs; the intensive of "to learn" may mean "to teach," or indicate multiplicity or frequency. The student soon finds himself groping amid modes of being and acting that cannot be accommodated to our Western categories, and of which the simplified descriptions supplied by his beginner's grammar do not really give him much grasp. The intensive reflexive, for example, has uses that are puzzling to render or even to understand. It seems to imply behavior that ranges from what Henry James, borrowing from the French, meant by "abounding in one's own sense" to what we mean by "throwing one's weight around." When Enoch or Noah "walks with God," he does so in this form of the verb "to walk," and nobody has ever known how to render it. Yet one gets from the Hebrew original the impression that the walking of these patriarchs was of a very special kind, that it had the effect of making them both more important and more highly charged. This expression, in the Old Testament, says Dr. John Skinner, the author of the volume on Genesis in the International Critical Commentary series, in general "signifies intimate companionship, and here denotes a fellowship with God morally and religiously perfect. . . . We shall see, however, that originally it included the idea of initiation into divine mysteries." I have looked Enoch up in a number of translations, and the only attempts I have found to give the verb form its special force are in the independent modern translations by James Moffatt and Monsignor Knox, the former of whom says that Enoch "lived close to God," the latter that he was "the close friend of God." The flaming sword set by God at the gate of the Garden of Eden is made to "turn" in the intensive reflexive, and the English translations, from the King James Version to the Revised Standard Version, render this as "turned every way." I imagine something a little more spectacular. Gesenius's standard lexicon seems to bear me out in suggesting "brandished, glittering." Yet as soon as you are beginning to pride yourself on seizing the force of the intensive reflexive, you are pulled up by finding that this variation of the verb that means "to shave" implies, in the hygienic prescriptions of Leviticus, nothing more interesting than "to shave oneself" or "to get oneself shaved."

When Abraham, foreseeing that the beauty of Sarah will cause Pharaoh to want her for his harem, has passed her off as his sister, in order that Pharaoh may not be impelled to put him out of the way, and when Pharaoh, afflicted by God for a sin he has committed unknowingly, learns at last what is causing the trouble and sends Abraham about his business, he says, "Here is your wife. Take her and go!" We are amused, when we first read this incident, to find "send" in the intensive form and to hear the brusque snap of "*qakh valékh!*" Yet we later on find that these words are more or less a conventional formula that does not necessarily imply irritation and that "send" in the intensive occurs when the sending is not necessarily ejective. There is something, we become aware, peremptory in the language itself. You have drawn-out "cohortative" forms that express, for the first person, exhortation, strong intention or earnest entreaty, along with clipped jussive forms for other people or things, as when God says, "Let this or that happen." The whole language is intensely purposeful, full of the determination to survive by force or by wit, to accomplish certain objectives, to lay down laws that will stabilize life and ensure its perpetuation, to fix the future by positive prophecies.

As this will of the ancient Hebrew finds expression in the dynamic verb forms, so the perdurability of the people is manifested in what may be called the physical aspects of the language. The prime unit of Hebrew is a group of three consonants. Nearly every verb consists of such a trinity. The values may be modified—the consonant may be doubled or be altered to a kindred sound, as "f" to "p," "v" to "b"—by a dot written inside the letter, and the intervening vowels may be indicated by a system of dots and dashes written above and below, but they were not so originally written and are not—except in poetry and in a single daily paper—so written today in Israel. The Hebrew alphabet thus differs from our alphabet in not including characters for the vowels, or even, in every case, different characters for kindred consonantal sounds. It is a system of twenty-two integers, a set of unsupplantable blocks, and each Hebrew word makes a shell into which a varying content of vowel sounds may be poured. The verbs are modified by prefixes and endings, and some of the conjugations take prefixes, but, to a Westerner, the most striking feature of the Hebrew conjugations is the way in which a shift of meaning (from active to passive, for example) is effected by a vowel change inside this consonantal shell—the kind of thing that we do on a lesser scale in inflecting our so-called strong verbs: e.g., "sing, sang, sung." We may put in an "o" for the noun and get "song," and the Jews, too, can use the same shell, with a different vowel content, for a noun. What impresses is the hardness of this shell.

Our first look at the text of the Bible, when we have mastered the alphabet, is likely to give us the feeling that this system is extremely impractical. It requires what must seem to the beginner an annoying and easily avoidable effort to coördinate with the heavy consonants the elusive little dashes and dots that hover about them like midges, especially since two of the former are not consonants in our sense at all but gutturals, no longer pronounced, which have to be regarded as blanks and read with the sounds of the vowels that are indicated above or below them. Even the printing of these signs is difficult, impossible for a linotype machine, since they appear in innumerable combinations. The result is that, even in learned books, the consonants are, if possible, written without "pointings," and what you get is a kind of shorthand. You must already know the words extremely well in order to be able to recognize them. Yet some further acquaintance induces respect, and a perception that this method is appropriate, an inalienable element of the Jewish tradition. The characters themselves are impressive—not so fluent as the Roman and Greek, and retaining even more than these the look of having been once cut in stone.* To write out Hebrew vocabulary, with black ink and a stub pen, affords a satisfaction that may give one a faint idea of the pleasures of Chinese calligraphy, as well as a feeling of vicarious authority as one traces the portentous syllables. One remembers the hand of Jehovah writing on Belshazzar's wall (though He had to write Aramaic in order to be understood by that alien and uninstructed king). These twenty-two signs that Moses was believed to have brought back from Egypt graven on the Tables of the Law, and from which, in their early Phoenician form, all our European alphabets have been derived, have, austere in their vowelless terseness, been steadily proceeding from right to left, over a period of two thousand years, among people that read from left to right; and in the Bible they take on an aspect exalted and somewhat mysterious: the square letters holding their course, with no capitals for proper names and no punctuation save the firm double diamond that marks the end of a verse, compact in form as in meaning, stamped on the page like a woodcut, solid verse linked to solid verse with the ever recurrent "and," the sound of which is modulated by changes of vowel, while above and below them a dance of accents shows the pattern of the metrical structure and the rise and fall of the chanting, and, above and below, inside and out, the vowel pointings hang like motes, as if they were the molecules the consonants breathed. Difficult for the foreigner to penetrate and completely indifferent to this, they have withstood

* The movement from right to left is supposed to have been determined by the engraver's having held the chisel in his left hand and the hammer in his right, and thus naturally having worked from the right.

even the drive toward assimilation—to their Spanish and Germanic neighbors—of the Jews of the Middle Ages; and in the dialect of German that is Yiddish, in newspapers spread in the subway, they still march in the direction opposite to that of all the other subway newspapers, English or Spanish or Italian, Hungarian or Russian or Greek, with only a light sprinkling of points to indicate Germanic vowels. And we have seen them reassemble in Israel, reconstituting their proper language—not embarrassed in the least by the fear that the newspaper reader of our century, even knowing Hebrew perfectly, may have difficulty in distinguishing, in the British reports, a vowelless Bevan from a vowelless Bevin. They march on through our modern events as if they were invulnerable, eternal.

But in the meantime, the Bible confronts us, in the dignity and beauty of its close-packed page.

The opening of Genesis is wonderful: the spirit of God in the darkness that hovers or broods on the waters, the sudden decree of light, the teeming of earth, sea and sky. The story of the Garden of Eden and the episode of Cain and Abel are imperfectly disengaged from some very ancient matrix of folklore, and parts of them are blotted in obscurity. What is the explanation of the phrase that so strangely recurs? "Your desire shall be for your husband," says God to Eve, "and he shall dominate you." "If you do not do well," He tells Cain, "sin is lurking at the door. His desire is for you, but you will dominate him." Is the second the mistake of a copyist, whose eye has slipped back to the earlier passage, or an obsessive idea of the author's? The serpent here is not the Devil, as the Jews later thought him to have been, but simply "the wiliest of all the beasts of the field." The Fall here has not the importance that it was later to take on for the Christians. Except for one reference to Adam in Job, the Old Testament does not mention it again. It was Paul who set up Original Sin, with the dreadful results we know for Catholic and Calvinist doctrine. The Creator here is all too human—we should nowadays say He was manic-depressive or something of the sort. He immediately becomes jealous of the man He has molded, angry at Adam for eating the fruit that has made him "like one of us" by imparting to him the knowledge of good and evil, and fearful lest he eat of the tree of life and so become immortal, too—as He is later, out of jealousy of human success, to frustrate the building of the city in which everyone speaks the same language and to impose the confusion of the Tower of Babel. What we do find in the story of Adam and his family are those living and salient traits—the relations of Adam and Eve, the sullen personality of Cain—that give these fragmentary legends a human truth and have caused them to haunt our imaginations; and you have, also, the earliest examples of that specialty of the Jewish genius—the development of the moral consciousness, of man's relations with God. This dawning of the moral sense brings with it, for Adam and Eve, an immediate awareness of their animal nature and the impulse to clothe themselves.

After Adam, the chronicle is almost lost in a cloudy domain of myth. Methuselah lives nine hundred and sixty-nine years; Enoch walks with God, then vanishes, "for God took him." The formidable race that the Septuagint calls "giants" and the Masoretic Bible "Nephilim" (fallen ones?) are dwelling on the earth. The sons of God interbreed with the daughters of men. Something in all this has gone wrong, though it is not clear precisely what. The Creator, at an earlier stage so nervously suspicious of man, so anxious lest man try to compete with Him, now decides he has gone to the bad and regrets He has ever made him. He decides to wipe mankind out, but relents in favor of the family of Noah. There follows the account of a flood which, according to Sir Leonard Woolley, must actually have occurred locally some three thousand years before Christ, in the region between the Tigris and the Euphrates—an account that seems less poetic as well as less realistic than the similar record preserved in the Babylonian epic *Gilgamesh*. It is curious to compare the two stories. The Babylonian one mentions reed huts, the remnants of which Woolley found below a thick layer of river silt, and the adventures of the Ark are "lived," described here in much more detail than in the Biblical tale of the Flood. One is struck by the behavior of these earlier gods. "The gods were frightened by the deluge, and, shrinking back, they ascended to the heaven of Anu. The gods cowered like dogs crouched against the outer wall." Later, when the waters are going down and a sacrifice is offered. "The gods smelled the savor, the gods smelled the sweet savor, the gods crowded like flies about the sacrificer."* This was not the way of Jehovah,

* I quote from the translation by E. A. Speiser, so excellent in its literary quality, included in *Ancient Near Eastern Texts*, Princeton University Press, 1950.

who has absolute authority and absolute power, and could not behave so abjectly.

It should be said at this point that the text of Genesis is regarded as a patching together of texts by two different hands, combined, perhaps, with passages from still older sources. One sees clearly in the Hebrew the reasons that certain points seem confused in translation—though actually they have partially been ironed out—for the original is still more confused. In the two recensions that have been here brought together, it is evident that one of the scribes had referred to God as "Elohím," the other by the name that we call "Jehovah." The first of these words is a plural—most commonly used with a singular, but occasionally with a plural verb—which seems to designate spirits or powers that preside over the phenomena of the universe. It will be noticed that the Creator in the Eden story expresses his displeasure that Adam has "become like one of *us*," and this plurality of Elohím, the indeterminateness of his or their identity, lends mystery to certain incidents—the wrestling of Jacob with the "angel," the destruction of Sodom and Gomorrah—in which a "man" or several "messengers" turn out to be what we translate as "God," though the names of Elohím and Jehovah, sometimes alternating, sometimes appearing together, make the ancient conception of deity rather difficult, at this early stage, to grasp. Jehovah is a definitely singular God, the pillar of monotheism. He figures in the Bible at first as the national divinity of the Hebrews, competing with neighboring divinities, but He is later, without ever losing His special relation to the Hebrews, to become a universal God; and one of the things that make Genesis interesting is to see how this universal Deity develops out of primitive conceptions, incompletely fused, of a personal Hebrew patron and a host of primeval spirits. The Jehovah who is to figure for the Christian as an omniscient Heavenly Father, brought closer to humanity by sending them a Son, for the Jew as a transcendent principle that cannot be given a name—"Jehovah" is itself a substitute for the unpronounceable name of God, and the Jew, in his religious services, substitutes for this "Adonái" (my Lord)—this soaring and awful conception is only trying here its first brief flights. Nor are there here any Christian angels, with flowing white robes and great wings, only divine "messengers," easily mistaken for human beings. The Hebrew word for "messenger" was translated by the Greek word "ἄγγελος" and this later gave rise to "angel," which has come to connote a being that does not exist in the Hebrew text. Nor is there as yet a Devil; even the Satan who appears in Job but is otherwise scarcely mentioned is merely "the Adversary," an antagonist opposing Jehovah. There are only the men of a nomad tribe groping after some understanding with a superhuman power or powers. The scribe himself is groping for their history, and his narrative is blurred not only by an undetermined conception of God but also by other discrepancies that result from his pious unwillingness to deal boldly with his differing sources. In comparison with this unknown editor, the unknown writer or writers who turned out the Homeric poems did a smooth and harmonious job on the ancient materials that he or they worked with. But that was not the Oriental way. The Semitic peoples, it seems, liked to preserve all the versions, with the result, in the text of Genesis, that the factual elements are rarely consistent: the chronologies do not come out right, the enumerations do not add up correctly. In the case of the episode mentioned above, of the imposture practiced by Abraham on Pharoah in passing off Sarah as his sister, you are given the same story three times—told the second time of Abraham and Abimelech, the third time of Isaac and Abimelech. The men of the passing caravan to whom Joseph is sold by his brothers are designated first as Midianites, and then, in succession, as Ishmaelites, Midianites and Ishmaelities. The wonder is, with all this untidiness, these absurdities and incongruities, that the dialogue should be so telling, the situations presented with so sure a stroke, that the personalities of the principal characters should remain so convincing and so interesting. Abraham, Jacob and Joseph are created as living figures in a way that makes relatively trifling the imprecisions of the different versions; it is even perhaps true that their outlines are thrown into a kind of relief by the factual uncertainty of the legend. Renan tells us of one of his teachers at the seminary of St. Sulpice that, in expounding this episode of Abraham in Egypt, he had difficulty in explaining how Sarah, who is apparently supposed to be nearly seventy, was capable of exciting the desire of Pharaoh. He "would call our attention," says Renan, "to the fact that, after all, such things had been known, and that 'Mlle. de Lenclos,' at seventy, had inspired passions and precipitated duels." The extraordinary thing is that, in the course of all the centuries during which these stories have been read and pondered, such outrageous anomalies as this have not bothered people more.

With the emergence of the patriarch Abraham, there begins that remarkable narrative which also includes the careers of his descendants, Isaac, Jacob and Joseph. We may wonder that these personages should run so true to familiar Jewish types till we realize that Jewish children, for more than three thousand years, have been brought up with these Biblical figures before them.

The relations of Abraham with Jehovah strike a note that today sounds feudal. He is respectful toward Him, even obsequious, yet their intercourse exhibits at the same time an element of what may almost be called homely intimacy. Abraham may argue with Jehovah, and Jehovah, who has made with him a covenant and chosen him as "father of many nations," never thunders against him as the Jehovahs of the prophets do. It is natural for this Jehovah to visit His earthly agent, in the guise of a human traveler and in the company of two other travelers (throughout this visit called "men," but later described as "messengers"), at noon, by the oaks of Mamre, as Abraham is sitting in front of his tent. The travelers ask him where his wife is, and he tells them that she is inside the tent. The visitor who is Jehovah explains to Abraham that He will come that way again in the spring, and that Sarah shall then have a son. She has been barren, and she and Abraham have already been through the episode, so painful for everyone concerned, of Hagar, the Egyptian maid, to whom Abraham has given a child and whom Sarah has driven away. Sarah has been listening inside the tent door, and when she hears this prediction, she laughs to herself. "Now that I am worn out," she says, "how should I have pleasure, and my husband an old man?" "Why did Sarah laugh?" asks the visitor. "Does she think that God cannot do it?" "I didn't laugh," says Sarah, frightened. "No, but you did laugh," says God.

In the meantime, Jehovah reflects that He had better take Abraham into His confidence and explain to him that recent reports as to what is going on in Sodom and Gomorrah make the situation sound so serious that He has decided to have it looked into: He may be obliged to destroy these cities. When He broaches this subject to Abraham, the latter thinks at once of his nephew Lot, who at the moment is living in Sodom. There ensues a significant dialogue, in which Abraham, playing on Jehovah's sense of justice, gradually beats Him down in such a way as to insure Lot's survival. Is it right that the good men in Sodom, Abraham puts it up to Him, should be punished along with the vicious? "The Judge of the whole earth will surely not commit an injustice! Suppose there are fifty good men: would it not be unjust that these should perish?" Jehovah feels the force of this; very well, He will spare the city if He finds in it fifty good men. "Behold, I have dared to speak to my Lord," Abraham is quick to add, relapsing into abysmal humility now that he has won his point—"I who am dust and ashes!" But he persists: "Suppose five of the fifty are lacking?" Jehovah is obliged to admit that this would not be fair either, and gradually, step by step, begging God not to be annoyed and protesting his own unworthiness, he persuades Him to agree that for ten good men He will refrain from exterminating the Sodomites. (Nothing is said of Gomorrah, where Abraham has no relations.)

The messengers of Jehovah arrive at the city, where they find Lot sitting at the gate. He cordially invites them to his house, where he gives them an excellent dinner, but before they have gone to bed, the whole male population of Sodom—to a man, the narrator says—gather outside the house and demand that the visitors be surrendered to them. They have seen the divine messengers and found them all too attractive. In this scene, there is a real terror (echoed with less effect in the similar episode of Judges 19, though the latter is more brutal and more gruesome). Lot goes out and shuts the door behind him. He offers the Sodomites his daughters, if they want them (knowing, perhaps, that he is perfectly safe), but he cannot betray the guests whom he has taken under his roof. "You are not one of us!" shout the Sodomites, with the jeer that was so often to be made to the Jew. "You're all by yourself here—you're only a sojourner! You can't tell us what to do! We'll see that you get it worse than they do!" They yell at him to stand aside, mob him, are about to break down the door, but the messengers pull Lot inside, strike the invaders with blindness, and shut the door in their faces. "Now gather all your family together," the messengers order Lot, "and get them away from here. This place has become such a scandal that Jehovah has sent us to wipe it out." But the Sodomite husbands of Lot's two daughters imagine that the visitors are joking, and Lot himself is reluctant to go. When they have not left at dawn the next morning, the messengers drag Lot and his family out—the sons-in-law are left behind—and tell them to flee for their lives before the brimstone begins.

The insistence all through these episodes of the earlier part of Genesis is on family—i.e., race survival, the importance, by measures however extreme, of perpetuating the consecrated seed. One feels in the story of Sodom, coming after the promise that Sarah shall still bear a child in old age, that the horror for the Jews of the Sodomites is the menace of "genocide." When Lot's daughters, deprived of their husbands, are living miserably with their father in a cave, they have no way of saving this seed except by getting him drunk and inducing him to make them pregnant. We are made to feel not that the daughters of Lot have here committed a sin, but rather that their action is justified by the desperateness of the situation. With this fierceness of the will to persist goes a sense, which redeems the sternness of the patriarchal relations, of the pathos of parental feelings. When Hagar is about to bear Abraham's child, she cannot help being insolent to Sarah, and Sarah retaliates by treating her so harshly that she runs away. She is met by a messenger of God, who reassures her and makes her return; but later, after Isaac has been born, when Sarah has fears lest Ishmael, Hagar's child, may come to share with him Abraham's heritage, she drives her away again. Abraham gets up early and gives Hagar some bread and a skin of water. With the child, she goes into the wilderness, and when all her water is gone, she puts Ishmael under a bush and sits down some distance away, saying, "Let me not look on the death of the child!" Then the little boy begins to cry, and God hears him and shows Hagar a well of water. So later, God, testing Abraham, orders him to sacrifice Isaac. When they are going up together to the mountaintop, the boy speaks up: "My father!" "Here am I, my son." "We've got the wood and the fire, but where is the lamb for the offering?" The father is obliged to reply, "God, my son, will provide the lamb." These strokes of human feeling, of insight, are so trenchant and so authentic, and they so surely awake a response in all kinds and conditions of people, that there are moments when the gods and heroes of the so much more expertly handled, the so much more sophisticated Homeric poems seem less real than the nomads of Genesis when the finger of the unknown scribe, tracing the ancient story, flashes across the page the verses that make them live. This finger also makes the contact, momentous in its day and place, between God and the humblest life, and the God of the patriarchal chronicle is a much more attractive deity than the God of the Garden of Eden, the Flood and the Tower of Babel. The mind that created Hagar, dying of thirst with her baby, had also to create the God who would pity them and allow them their role in the world.

The composer of the conversation between Abraham and Isaac on their way to the sacrifice could not admit of a God who would compel His chosen agent to go through with this cruel ordeal. In these fumbling and awkward old stories, we can see man becoming aware of the conscience that begins to dignify him, that seems to tower above him.

The adventures of Abraham's grandson Jacob are distinguished by no such tenor of submissive and patient piety. His life has a strange discontinuity, for his ultimately successful career is characterized, on the one hand, by exploits of outrageous cunning and, on the other, as it were, broken into by visitations of Jehovah that strike a note quite different from Abraham's intercourse with a deity who treats him as a trusted servant. Jacob, described as a quiet boy, is his mother's favorite son, but his father prefers his twin brother, the more virile and active Esau. The young Jacob first induces his brother, who has come back hungry from hunting, to trade his birthright for a supper of lentils, the smell of which is driving him crazy; then later, when their father is dying, incited by his partial mother, he tricks the old half-blind Isaac into mistaking him for his brother, in order to make sure of receiving his father's special blessing that will establish him as the head of the family. Esau, learning of this, swears to kill Jacob, and their mother sends Jacob away to live with his uncle Laban. On his journey, Jacob sleeps out-of-doors, and in a dream sees the messengers of God ascending and descending by a ladder between Heaven and earth. At the top of the ladder is Jehovah, who tells Jacob that He is the God of his grandfather and his father, and that Jacob can count on his backing; that his family shall multiply and that through them the peoples of the earth shall be blessed. When Jacob wakes up, he is frightened: "What a fearful place this is!" he says. "It must be God's house and the gate of Heaven!"

We now have a long account of Jacob's sojourn with his uncle Laban. He falls in love with Laban's daughter Rachel, but Laban will not let him marry her till he has worked for Laban seven years —a period that, so great is Jacob's love for her, seems to pass, the narrator tells us, like only a few days. But at the end of this time, when Jacob has earned her, Laban fails to keep his promise; in the darkness of the marriage night, he succeeds in passing off on Jacob his older daughter Leah, whom he wishes to get married off first, but then offers Jacob Rachel, too—the marriage to take place at once—if the young man will agree to work for him seven years longer. While Jacob is serving this second term, the relations between him and his wives are subjected to a good deal of strain, because Rachel, whom he loves, has no children while Leah is producing four. Because she is not beloved—because she is "hated," the narrative says—God has taken pity on Leah and is trying in this way to console her. But Rachel makes her maid sleep with Jacob and then claims the resulting two sons as her own. Leah, who has now stopped bearing, makes Jacob give *her* maid, too, two sons. During the wheat harvest, an incident occurs. One of Leah's sons finds some mandrakes and brings them to his mother. The Hebrew word for mandrake has the same connotation as our "love apple"; it was supposed to be an aphrodisiac and also to promote conception. Rachel asks Leah for some of these, but the bitter Leah replies that Rachel has taken her husband's love; will she rob her of even her mandrakes? If Leah will give her the mandrakes, says Rachel, she will let her sleep with Jacob. The result is that Leah again conceives, while poor Rachel has no luck with the mandrakes. But at last God remembers Rachel and allows her to give birth to Joseph. Jacob decides, at this point, that he has had enough of working for Laban, but Laban has come to realize that Jacob is under divine protection, that he has prospered because of his nephew's presence. He offers to pay Jacob whatever he asks, and a duel of cunning commences.

This conflict has its comic aspect. Jacob offers to stay on awhile if Laban will allow him to take for his own all the spotted goats and sheep and all the black lambs. Laban agrees, but then removes these from the flocks and has his sons keep them apart from the rest. Jacob, encouraged by God, as he afterwards tells his wives, secures a mixed-colored breed simply by setting up striped sticks at the water troughs where the animals mate. He also sees to it that the spotted breed is produced from the most vigorous specimens. This makes Jacob extremely rich, and he finally decides to leave Laban. Without forewarning his uncle, he goes off with his wives and his children, his camels, his sheep, goats and asses, his male and his female servants. Rachel, without Jacob's knowing it, carries away her father's household gods, the Hebrew equivalents of lares and penates. Laban comes after them and makes a scene. Why has Jacob left his uncle in this furtive way instead of allowing him to kiss his daughters good-by and to send them away with music? He searches the tents for the household gods, which Rachel hides in her camel's saddle.

Jacob, not knowing she has them, becomes angry and denounces Laban. "If I hadn't had God with me," he says, "I should never have got away from you with anything to show for my work!" Laban is obliged to back down. They make a covenant, and Laban goes home. Jacob proceeds on his way and encounters divine messengers. "This is God's army," he says.

But the thought of reunion with Esau now begins to worry Jacob. He devises a strategy for propitiating his brother or keeping out of his reach, in case Esau still wants to kill him. First of all, he sends out men to announce his return, and they report that Esau is coming to meet him, accompanied by four hundred followers. Jacob is apprehensive. He divides his company in two in order that, if one part should get massacred, the other should have a chance to escape. He then prays, reminding God that He has promised to stand behind him and to see to it that his children survive. After this, he instructs his servants to go ahead of him with a present for Esau consisting of over five hundred animals. They are to drive them in procession, drove by drove, with intervals between the droves, so as to make the strongest possible impression. They must wait until Esau has seen the first drove and demands to know whose they are, then they will tell him it is a present for him, sent by his servant Jacob, who is following close behind. Each new drove will come as a fresh surprise. Soon Jacob himself will appear, and perhaps this will do the trick. Yet Jacob is evidently anxious and tense. He sends his wives and his children to the farther side of the Jabbok River. Now he is all alone, and he passes through a strange experience, a crisis and test of the spirit that accompanies this critical moment of his meeting his brother again and perhaps predetermines its upshot. This is the episode that has come to be known as the struggle of Jacob with the angel—perhaps out of euphemism, since the editors of the sacred text had a tendency to play down passages that appeared disrespectful to God. Actually, no angel is ever mentioned. Jacob wrestles all night with a "man." That they all but literally went to the mat is shown by the Hebrew verb, found only here, which is made from one of the nouns for "dust" (which is similar in sound to the name of the Jabbok). They are "dusting" one another. The mysterious opponent realizes that he cannot get Jacob down, so he strikes him on the socket of the thigh and puts his thigh out of joint. "Let me go," he bids Jacob, "for the day is breaking." But Jacob is still able to hold his own: "I shall not let you go till you bless me."

The being asks Jacob's name, and when Jacob tells him, he says, "Your name shall no longer be Jacob, but Israel"—meaning "striver with God"—"for you have striven with both God and men, and prevailed." Jacob asks his opponent's name; the other refuses to answer, but blesses him before he departs. Jacob knows that he has wrestled with God, that he has seen Him face to face, yet still lives. The sun rises, and he goes away limping. Thereafter, he is sometimes called Israel. It is the first time the name occurs. Is there some implication here of a rivalry of God with His creation? What is striking for us today in this passage is that even the chosen leader, who identifies himself with the spirits that preside over man's destiny and the forces of nature, must pit himself against them, like Prometheus, in order to win something from them; that this name the Jews gave themselves contained, or was afterwards made to contain, the idea that they had conquered, at a maiming cost, some share in the power of God.

The meeting with Esau goes off very well, though Jacob is plainly nervous. There follows a hideous episode of the kind that even devout readers of the Bible have not often cared to remember. Such stories are in themselves far from elevating; they do not provide texts for sermons or suggest subjects for paintings, yet, in the narrative of the Bible, their savagery has the effect of setting off the strong purposes, the flashes of revelation, that represent the emergence of the moral sense, of the nobler human ambitions—those principles and aspirations that seemed to the ancient Jew so much on a different level from the ferocity and the duplicity which were also a part of his history that he regarded them as promises and precepts handed down to him by a higher being. Jacob now buys some land in Canaan, and Shechem, the son of the local prince, seduces Jacob's only daughter, Dinah—"and humbled her," the narrative adds, which seems to imply rape. But Shechem's "soul was attached to Dinah; he loved her, and he spoke to the heart of the girl." Shechem goes to his father and asks him to arrange for him to marry Dinah. The father takes it up with Jacob and proposes that his people and Jacob's should live on good terms together, intermarry and trade with one another, that Jacob should settle among them. Shechem, whose soul longs for Dinah, offers Jacob and her brothers any gift they ask, if they will let him make her his wife. But Jacob's sons have just come in from the cattle, and, still furious at the wrong done Dinah but not betraying their feelings, they make the objection to Jacob that they cannot allow their sister to be married to a man who has not beeen circumcised, and insist that if there is to be intermarriage between Shechem's people and theirs, all the former must undergo this operation. Young Shechem at once consents, and his father, who has always humored him, goes to the gate of the city and announces that this drastic measure is forthwith to be carried out. Every man who goes out of the gate must be stopped and subjected to circumcision. When this has been going on three days and the male inhabitants of the city are all suffering from the effects of the operation and unprepared to defend themselves, two of Jacob's sons, Simeon and Levi, descend on them and slaughter them all, including, of course, Shechem and his father, and they carry away Dinah, who has been kept in Shechem's house. They also plunder the city and devastate the countryside, driving off all the animals and enslaving the women and children. When Jacob finds out what has happened, he rebukes his revengeful sons; he shows then what a mess they have made, that his name is now a stink to the people there. He has only a handful of followers, and his neighbors will combine against him and kill them all. The stupid young men reply, "Could we let him treat our sister like a harlot?"

God tells Jacob to go to Bethel, and Jacob makes his household purify themselves and hand over to him all their images of the false local gods. He reaches Bethel without interference, because God has restrained his enemies, and he builds an altar there. God now repeats his promises, and Jacob moves on to another place. But Rachel has conceived again, and on the way she falls into labor. "Don't be afraid," says the midwife, when her pains become agonizing. "You will bear another son." But Rachel dies in giving birth to this son, and, dying, names his Ben-oni, Son of My Suffering. Jacob, however, changes this to Ben-yamin, Son of the Right Hand. He marks Rachel's grave and journeys on. The last thing we hear of him in this section is that one of his sons, Reuben, has gone to bed with Rachel's former maid, his father's concubine, by whom Jacob has had two sons. "And Israel," the narrator says, "heard about this"—Israel, the striver with God.

There follows the story of Joseph, which I shall not attempt to retell. It is, of course, a success story, the prototype of all success stories. Joseph is the able Jew who makes good in a foreign land. In his function as Pharaoh's governor, he reminds us of Disraeli Prime Minister and of the powerful Jewish viziers of the tenth and eleventh centuries in Spain. He scores off his envious brothers, who have sold him into Egypt, first by putting them to a great deal of inconvenience, then by forgiving them and setting them up in Egypt; and he gratifies his father Jacob and arranges for him a serene old age. There are moments when we feel about Joseph that he is a little what is meant by the Yiddish word *allrightnik*, when we are tempted to sympathize with the brothers in their resentment at his reading of dreams that is always to his own advantage. Except for this gift of interpreting dreams, he has little communication with the Deity, and we may easily find Jacob more interesting, with his trickery, his love for Rachel, his victimization by Laban and his finally sending his father-in-law about his business, his difficult domestic relations and his uncontrollable children, his sporadic contacts with God that jolt him into consciousness of his destiny. But Joseph, with his solid character, his career of worldly advancement, makes a necessary intermittence—or, rather, an intermittence that convinces us we are dealing with a human world—in this chronicle of intercourse with the Deity, so that the next advance in this intercourse will come with a peculiar impressiveness: the Moses of Exodus, who will talk to God, face to face, on a loftier level than Abraham, who will derive from Him authority and leadership of a more compelling kind than Jacob's.

All these incidents take place in a world in which the time values are always vague, because Hebrew verbs have no real tenses. This whole question of time is so interesting, the time-sense of a people is so fundamental, so important for understanding its mentality, that I want to discuss it in a more general way, and not merely in connection with the Bible.

"What was perhaps most astonishing to the modern European," a former governor, of Kenya, Sir Philip Mitchell (quoted in the issue of August 1953 of the German magazine *Der Monat*). has reported of the natives of that region, "was their not having any calendar or way of telling time, the fact that they oriented themselves solely by the moon and the seasons, the rising and the setting of the sun. Before the modern Europeans took over, there did not, except for the Swahili spoken on the coast, exist in any language from Abyssinia to the Transvaal any way of saying 'on January 1, 1890,' or 'at two-thirty in the afternoon,' or of expressing an other such idea."

Now, the Jews of the Old Testament were not, of course, quite in this primitive state, but their time-sense was so little developed that they did not even have a word for "hour," and, as we have seen, they took no interest in accurate chronology. The Babylonians evidently had sundials three hundred years before Christ, but the only possible reference in the Bible to any such time-telling device is a dubious one in Isaiah 38:8, where the "grades" that have been interpreted as the degrees of a dial might mean also a flight of steps. We so much take for granted, in our part of the world, our schedules of clock and calendar time that it is difficult to adjust ourselves to the mental habits of peoples who do not share our conventions.

This is certainly one difference that throws us off in our attempts to deal with the Russians. The visitor to Moscow may at first be misled by the fact that he and the Muscovites make use of similar clocks, and that the Russians, since the Revolution, have adjusted their calendar to ours; he may assume that appointments will be kept, that meetings will begin on time, and he is likely to become impatient when he discovers that *seichás* (this hour) is often equivalent to "never." Yet if he studies the language, he should realize that the Russians are living in an older, a much less closely scheduled world.* The tenses of the verbs in any language are the key to a people's idea of time, and the tenses of the Russians are different from ours and different from those, I believe, of any of the Romance or Teutonic languages. The basic thing to grasp here is that the Slavs lack the Western conception of a definite moment in the present, of the present as a definite moment. You cannot say in Russian, "I tell you 'No!,'" or, like John Burroughs in his well-known poem, "Serene, I fold my hands and wait." The Russians, like the ancient Jews, make their fundamental distinction between action completed and action going on. You can only say in Russian, "I am telling you 'No!'"—that is, put the verb in the "imperfective." In the "perfective," there is no present tense; you can have an action completed only in the future or in the past. The line from John Burroughs would have to be rendered in Russian either "I am folding my hands and shall wait" or "I have folded my hands and am waiting." The language does not allow for an action completed in

* Old Slavonic, a literary language, had a fuller equipment of tenses, but—except for a few survivals among the southern tongues—these were lost by the Slavic languages when they developed in a colloquial way.

the present, and the past is also lacking in precisions that our Western languages make. The Russian past is an old past participle that is inflected (quite uselessly, from our point of view) for gender as well as number, but the use of which is otherwise exactly like the illiterate use of the past participle that is current in the American South: "I taken her out for a walk." In Russian there is no pluperfect; you cannot, by a change of the tense, make it clear that some action or event has taken place before some other. Nor is there any distinction such as we make between a perfect and a simple past: though I have written, "I have folded my hands" above, for the sake of natural English, the Russians would be simply "I folded." When something is past, it is past, and the antiquated Russian language does not worry about the chronology of past events in relation to one another. Nor does it have any grammatical machinery for adjusting events in the past to the point of view of the present—that is, to the point of view of the moment when the speaker is speaking.* Thus, it could not be said in Russian of Chekhov's three sisters that they thought they would go to Moscow. A neighbor of theirs would have said, "They thought they *will* go to Moscow." The difference between us and the Russians is that, here again, we are equipped with the conception of the present as a definite point. This point, for us, stands as a limit to the past, and the past, as seen from this moment, falls into an ordered perspective. With us, the conditional "would" relegates the intention of the sisters to a moment when it was not yet possible to know whether or not their intention would be carried out; they might or might not have gone. Chekhov knows, of course, that they will never get off, but if he told you about it in Russian, the language would not provide him with any way of even hinting that there was anything problematic about it. It sets no limit and adjusts no perspective. In telling of the sisters' hopes, the language must transport the speaker to the period when these hopes were being entertained, and at that period, as I have earlier pointed out, there was no way in Russian for the sisters to say, "Today we shake the dust of this place from our feet and definitely clear out for

* There is a Russian conditional mode, but it is only used for the past in connection with definitely negative ideas, or when, speaking from the point of view of the present, one is quite sure that something has not occurred. It may be mentioned that the same form of the conditional is used for the past and the future. *I should have done something* and *I should do something* are said in the same way.

Moscow!" It is easier in Russian than it is for us indefinitely to put things off, as Chekhov knows his three sisters will do; so far as their grammar goes, the time of departure may never come, and from the moment when this ceases to be future, it is bound to be conceived as continuous: action still uncompleted. It will take them a long time to prepare, it will take them a long time to travel.

What cannot be grasped by your Russian friend who keeps you waiting an hour and a half is that for you a moment of the present will come when you stand with your watch in your hand and the hands of the watch at, say, two-forty-five (the times for which appointments are made in Russia often seem to us incomprehensible and soon cease to carry conviction, as when soneone says, "Two, or perhaps half past two, or perhaps better a quarter to three").* If you make sure to arrive at a meeting a little in advance of the hour set and find that you must wait some time before the doors will be opened, it is because the time for beginning is understood differently by the Russians and the hour officially mentioned has nothing whatever to do with it. Eventually they will drift in, and the moment to start will come; they will feel it, not check it on their watches. Nor will their watches tell them when to stop. Once a meeting, a performance at the theater, a banquet, an interview, a lecture, a lesson has got itself under way, it will go on till the subject has been covered, till the drama has run its course, till everyone has had enough. And, as a result of this willingness to squander time, the theatrical entertainment or the novel or the serious discussion, with Russians, is likely to flourish more richly and to develop in a way more organic than enterprises of this kind usually do with us. As the performance will not be cramped, so the preparation will not have been hurried. Rehearsal, rewriting, preliminary study will not have been menaced by a deadline, by the last train to Montclair or Stamford, by an engagement to meet somebody at six o'clock and talk about something else till you dine with somebody else at seven. And this lack of our sense of clock-time is also one reason the Russians—excelling at research and pure science—have proved themselves, since the Revolution, so ill suited for industrial operations, which depend on close timing and deadlines, the kind of thing

* Turgenev—in other ways, a scrupulous man—used to tax Henry James's patience and sometimes offend Flaubert by never turning up at the appointed time.

perfected by our Taylor system. The programs of the Five-Year Plans were attempts to impose on the Russians the conception of clock and calendar time, to stampede them into the Western frame. In our mechanized part of the world, such a device is neither needed nor conceivable. Our industrial time runs on—the seconds clicking by like cogs—as steadily as the conveyor belt that carries the parts of the car that must always be the model of a particular calendar year. If some step in the process jams, it is soon got going again; our factories do not stop for lunch, as the Russian ones do, or as they did when I visited them in 1935. The accurate continuous functioning of the American industrial machine involves, more or less, our whole lives. But the Five-Year Plans of the Russians were like unaccustomed blocks of Western time set down in the Eastern eternity, as their plants were set down on the steppes; and though their front ends were squarely presented, a triumph of theatrical décor, they would tend to melt away on the other side, to succumb to the Russian continuous present. The planners themselves, in the meantime, instead of starting work with the workers and keeping in touch with the plant, would have been coming to their offices late in the morning and escaping from the discipline of the clock by getting together for interminable conferences that would go on for most of the night. The recent order that Soviet officials must be at their desks from nine to six is one of the ever recurring, the almost Sisyphean attempts on the part of the governing group to synchronize Russia with the schedule of the West.

Now, the Jews of the Old Testament were living in a world of time that, from our modern Western point of view, was even less advanced than the Russian. In their language, as in Russian, the primary distinction was made between completed and incomplete action, but there were no definite tenses at all. The beginner is usually told, as the best rule of thumb to start out with, to translate the perfects as pasts and the imperfects as futures. But he soon finds out that this will not do. It is true that the ancient Jew usually thought of future action as uncompleted and completed action as past, but our categories of future and past can hardly be said to have existed for him. In my old grammar of 1838, the author, a Professor Isaac Nordheimer of the University of the City of New York, begins his discussion of the Hebrew tenses by explaining that the efforts of Europeans to work out a system of tenses has been "hitherto attended with very incomplete success," because of the fact that

"Occidental scholars" cannot help proceeding on assumptions "derived . . . from the manner in which the various points of time are indicated in the Indo-European languages, rather than from the nature of the subject itself." He goes on to try to grapple with the nature of the Hebrew idea of time, and he presents us with a diagram. Let the straight line AB, he says, represent the sequence of time. Let us assume that for the Jews this sequence extended beyond A into an infinite past and beyond B into an infinite future. Let us take, upon this line, a point C somewhere between A and B, which will represent the present, *our* conception of the present. But here the trouble begins. The Jews even more than the Russians lacked our Western conception of the present moment—a feature that, it seems, marks a very advanced state in the history of language development. For them, no point C could exist. When the narrator of a Biblical story tells of something that has happened in the past, he does not keep it in a definite relation to a fixed point of reference in the present, the point at which the story is supposed to be told. He puts himself back into the time of the story, and by a logic not unlike that which is exemplified by the Russian sisters who thought they *will* go to Moscow, he may put in the imperfect ("future")—since the action has not yet been completed at the time of which he is telling—some event which, from our point of view, is already completed and belongs to the past. If we should try to proceed by our rule of thumb in translating Genesis 41:50, we should find ourselves putting it that Joseph "begat two sons before the years of famine will come." Dr. Nordheimer's diagram elucidates this by showing that the moment the storyteller puts himself back to a point D, between A and C, the happenings between D and C will be shifted from the past to the future; but he tries also to make it account for a feature of Hebrew grammar that must be one of the strangest in the history of language—the principle that when a verb-form follows the conjunction "and," the imperfect is written for the perfect and the perfect for the imperfect. That is, if you relied on the rule of thumb, you would find yourself translating, "And God *will say*, 'Let there be light,'" instead of, "And God *said*." It seems to me that this phenomenon eludes Dr. Nordheimer's argument, and that the Hebrew line of eternity ends by slipping away from all his alphabetical points and retaining only the property of extending indefinitely in either direction; nor have I seen any other explanation that appeared to me satisfactory. I shall not discuss this problem except to point out that it illustrates how difficult it is for us today to grasp the old Hebrew idea of time.

The points on Dr. Nordheimer's line cannot even be used to demonstrate other features of the Hebrew verbs more accessible than the "*and* conversive." A striking example of this, and a very significant one, is the so-called "prophetic" use of the perfect. If Jehovah or a prophet declares with the utmost conviction of certaintly that something is going to happen, the action or event is put—since its eventual completion is not to be doubted—in the form of the verb that denotes completion. The implication is "It's as good as done." If you translate, as everybody has had to do, these prophetic perfects as futures, you miss an important nuance. When Jehovah says to Moses, "I am what I am," we are faced with the converse problem. Both verbs are in the imperfect, so, if we followed our rule of thumb, it would give us "I shall be what I shall be"—which again would be incorrect, since what the author of Exodus means to say is that God's existence has never ceased, that it is still going on and will never end. (This passage seems to be echoed in John 8:58: "Before Abraham was, I am.") Both these instances of usage are much to the point, for they both imply the conception of a single and eternal God, which was fundamental to Hebrew thought. For this Deity, the point C, the present moment, is a matter of little importance. Hence the carelessness of chronology in the Bible, the long shadows cast by the patriarchs, the habit of feeling that the prophets are still, like Jehovah, in being (the verb that means "to prophesy" has no "light" active but is always in the light passive, which indicates that God is speaking *through* the prophet, or in the intensive reflexive, which indicates raving or exaltation), so that it shocked no one's sense of reality to attribute to them writings that dealt with events occurring years after their deaths or to read back into them predictions of happenings—the coming of the Messiah, for example—that in their lifetimes had not even been imagined. "Instead of narrating, Israel predicts, that is to say, systematizes," says Renan in this connection. "That is why it has prophets, not historians. The invasion of the Scythians, for example, is not narrated anywhere. The episode of Gog, in Ezekiel, is a description of it, transformed into a symbol for the future. In this curious state of mind, everything becomes a type and a general formula. The thing that has actually happened counts for almost nothing." The book of Daniel, which is written in terms of Belshazzar and Nebuchadnezzar and the Babylonian captivity, was intended to apply to a situation four hundred years later, when the Jews, then returned to Jerusalem, were being persecuted by Antiochus Epiphanes.

Renan believed also that this vagueness of the time sense, this lack of an equipment of tenses, which is common, it seems, to the Semitic languages, had been one of the factors that contributed to preventing the Semitic peoples from acquiring techniques and "progressing" along the same lines as the European world. They had never been geared into our time-system. Though modern clocks were not used in Europe till some time in the thirteenth century, it seems to have been the Romans who established our clock and our calendar. The Greeks, of course, had water clocks and sundials and an elaborate system of tenses that indicated with precision, as the Semitic languages could not do, the relation of happenings to one another. But the Romans, with their conquests, imposed their system wherever their armies came; they left the construction of their language along with their other constructions. The Romance languages inherited them, and the Teutonic ones took their stamp. We live today in a Roman structure of present, past, pluperfect, future and future perfect. (The current tendency to drop this last tense, to slur the relations of events in the future, is probably due to our desperate rush to pull future events into the present.) And we live not merely, as the Romans did, in a world of years, months, weeks and days, but in a world of minutes, seconds, and infinitesimally split seconds.

Does the Westernized modernized Jew not live in this structure, too? He has mastered it; in a practical way, he lives by it. Yet his Bible and the language in which it was written seem never to be quite absent from the background of his mind. The Talmud has kept them alive as immediate inalienable realities that have annihilated time and space through fifteen centuries of exile and dispersion. Most Jews have a dimension of eternity, and this is one thing that sets them off from, and to some extent makes them seem strange to, the people whose view of the world is conditioned by self-limiting historical units: the development of civilizations, the births and the deaths of nations. Our myths are the temporal myths of Caesar and Pericles, of Charlemagne, Washington, Hitler; but the myths of the Jews are timeless—the patriarchs and prophets who never die, the Messiah who never comes. The legend of the Wandering Jew is an attempt by the Gentiles to synchronize the Jewish eternalness with the vicissitudes of their own intensely temporal history. The sense of persistent values that survive and transcend our historical epochs, as it has always been inherent in Jewish religion, is also implied in their language; and some acquaintance with the Hebrew Bible may be useful in making us realize how much our conception of time is an artificial contrivance; that tonight at eight-thirty, when we hope for a new revelation afforded by some popular drama, the night of August 9th, when we did or did not commit the crime, the point C that fixes the moment of the present, have an importance that is purely conventional. I do not mean that we ought to go back to the world of the Hebrew prophets or that the Jews as a people still live in this world, though one sometimes gets the impression that there are rabbis and scholars who do; but today one begins to be dubious of our passion for historicity, which seems at moments to become maniacal. I have lately been typing old notebooks of mine that go back to 1914, and I find that, for every year, I have recorded the current slang and the favorite popular songs. Is this valuable? I thought it was, and I expect to make some use of this data. Like everyone else in our part of the world, I am incurably history-minded. But what about all the issues of all the innumerable newspapers recorded on microfilm, all the minutes of all the meetings carefully filed away? We are shocked and indignant when the Russians, with their less highly developed historical sense, do not hesitate to sponge out the record of a decade or of half a century and to substitute something simpler, which will be more advantageous to the party in power (remember that the Russian verb does not indicate the relations of events in the past; when an action is past, it is simply past). We are amused by the rabbinical mind, which occupies itself with the moral situation of Jonah inside the whale as if it were a permanently important problem. But how long can our civilization go on storing up and stuffing our heads with so much minute historical information?

M. André Malraux, in his novel *The Walnut Trees of Altenburg,* written in the midst of the last World War, presents an international group of thinkers in various departments of knowledge discussing those basic conceptions that underlie the mentality of every civilization without ever being subjected to criticism, because they are so taken for granted that people are not aware of them. And one of these, a great anthropologist, arrives at the conclusion that, for us, the uncriticized conception is not "the nation," as somebody else has suggested, but the historical point of view itself.

We live, he insists, in history "as the religious civilizations lived in God," and behind our conception of history is our special conception of time.

Shall we someday come to reckon differently—to abridge historical processes, to range over longer periods, to see events in different relations, to have a different conception of events themselves? Our present conception of time, which has till recently dominated our imaginative writing and is still extremely strong, seems essential to our mechanics, to our science, which has merged with our study of morals. Now, the critical study of the Bible that has been one of the features of our scientific period has shown that the Jewish ideas about morals, the principles ascribed to Jehovah, were modified from prophet to prophet—and hence, from era to era, under pressure of varying situations, economic, political, social. And yet there is something there that is less affected than one might expect by these changes in time and locale: the principles of rectitude and justice, represented by the permanent Jewish God (as later, with Christianity, the claims of human fellow-feeling). When the resolute Western grammarian makes an effort to introduce our time sequence into the timeless Hebrew verbs, they continue to remain something else. "Many have concluded," says Dr. Kyle M. Yates, the author of an excellent beginner's grammar, *The Essentials of Biblical Hebrew,* "that uniformity in the determination and translation of these points [the nuances of mood and tense] is impossible," but he insists that they must exist, and he draws up a table of them. The weakness of such systems is that they are bound to wear the aspect of gratuitous creations, since the meanings assigned by their formulators cannot, except in a very few instances, be shown to have any connection with the actual mechanism of the verb-forms. And so, when the garbled events of the Bible are subjected to an exact rearrangement that satisfies our Western chronology, we see that they still remain something else—something that is scarcely impaired by the extreme improbability that Methuselah lived almost a thousand years, that Sarah was nearly seventy when she proved irresistible to Pharoah, that Jacob's great love for Rachel kept him working for Laban seven years. It is something that has done a good deal to sustain the morale of the Gentile as well as that of the Jew through the strictly historical happenings—the wars, the persecutions, the conquests, the migrations and the natural disasters of the last three thousand years.

Yet the Biblical "aspect of eternity" has its disadvantages, too.

It is the Jews who have given to the Western world all four of its great religions—Judaism, Christianity, Mohammedanism and the half-religion Marxism—and they all of them have in common a compelling and delusive utopianism. The Jew expected the Messiah, who was to lead him out of capitivity; the Mohammedan looked forward to his paradise; the medieval Christian expected the Judgment Day and the reign of Christ for infinity. Karl Marx, who liked to bait the utopian socialists and believed himself free from their errors, actually derived his appeal in great part from his vision of a socialist Armageddon and a socialist Judgment Day, when the sheep would be separated from the goats and the reign of Justice begin, as his "History" was also an omnipotent God that guided a chosen group. All these visions were solemn promises that gave people the courage to live, and in which they believed so vividly that it was almost as if the visions were already fulfilled. They belong to the "prophetic perfect," that phase of the Hebrew verb which indicates that something is as good as accomplished. And the escape from historical time—from the compromise, the modification, the incomplete satisfaction, the accepted misunderstanding, the complicated adjustments of every day—may bring with it something obsessive, as all four of these religions have shown, that easily produces intolerance on the other side. To believe in a word of God unchangeable and eternal (as promulgated by any of these prophets) is to stop human self-improvement, human self-creation dead—in the literal, as it always turns out, as well as in the "spiritual" way. This sense of transcendent principle has always had to be corrected by the realistic observation, the practical worldliness, of the Graeco-Roman tradition. It is the reciprocal relation of the two that has made what there is of our civilization.

MARY McCARTHY

artists in uniform

The Colonel went out sailing,
He spoke with Turk and Jew. . . .

"Pour it on, Colonel," cried the young man in the Dacron suit excitedly, making his first sortie into the club-car conversation. His face was white as Roquefort and of a glistening, cheeselike texture; he had a shock of tow-colored hair, badly cut and greasy, and a snub nose with large gray pores. Under his darting eyes were two black craters. He appeared to be under some intense nervous strain and had sat the night before in the club car drinking bourbon with beer chasers and leafing through magazines which he frowningly tossed aside, like cards into a discard heap. This morning he had come in late, with a hangdog, hangover look, and had been sitting tensely forward on a settee, smoking cigarettes and following the conversation with little twitches of the nose and quivers of the body, as a dog follows a human conversation, veering its mistrustful eyeballs from one speaker to another and raising its head eagerly at its master's voice. The colonel's voice, rich and light and plausible, had in fact abruptly risen and swollen, as he pronounced his last sentence. "I can tell you one thing," he had said harshly. "They weren't named Ryan or Murphy!"

A sort of sigh, as of consummation, ran through the club car. "Pour it on, Colonel, give it to them, Colonel, that's right, Colonel," urged the young man in a transport of admiration. The colonel fingered his collar and modestly smiled. He was a thin, hawklike, black-haired handsome man with a bright blue bloodshot eye and a well-pressed, well-tailored uniform that did not show the effects of the heat—the train, westbound for St. Louis, was passing through Indiana, and, as usual in a heat wave, the air-conditioning had not met the test. He wore the Air Force insignia, and there was something in his light-boned, spruce figure and keen, knifelike profile that suggested a classic image of the aviator, ready to cut, piercing, into space. In base fact, however, the colonel was in procurement, as we heard him tell the mining engineer who had just bought him a drink. From several silken hints that parachuted into the talk, it was patent to us that the colonel was a man who knew how to enjoy this earth and its pleasures: he led, he gave us to think, a bachelor's life of abstemious dissipation and well-rounded sensuality. He had accepted the engineer's drink with a mere nod of the glass in acknowledgment, like a genial Mars quaffing a libation; there was clearly no prospect of his buying a second in return, not if the train were to travel from here to the Mojave Desert. In the same way, an understanding had arisen that I, the only woman in the club car, had become the colonel's perquisite; it was taken for granted, without an invitation's being issued, that I was to lunch with him in St. Louis, where we each had a wait between trains—my plans for seeing the city in a taxicab were dished.

From the beginning, as we eyed each other over my volume of Dickens ("*The Christmas Carol?*" suggested the colonel, opening relations), I had guessed that the colonel was of Irish stock, and this, I felt, gave me an advantage, for he did not suspect the same of me; strangely so, for I am supposed to have the map of Ireland written on my features. In fact, he had just wagered, with a jaunty, sidelong grin at the mining engineer, that my people "came from Boston from way back," and that I—narrowed glance, running, like steel measuring-tape, up and down my form—was a professional sculptress. I might have laughed this off, as a crudely bad guess like his *Christmas Carol,* if I had not seen the engineer nodding gravely, like an idol, and the peculiar young man bobbing his head up and down in mute applause and agreement. I was wearing a bright apple-green raw silk blouse and a dark-green rather full raw silk skirt, plus a pair of pink glass earrings; my hair was done up in a bun. It came to me, for the first time, with a sort of dawning horror, that I had begun, in the course of years, without ever guessing it, to look irrevocably Bohemian. Refracted from the three men's eyes was a strange vision of myself as an artist, through and through, stained with my occupation like the dyer's hand. All I lacked, apparently, was a pair of sandals. My sick heart sank to my Ferragamo shoes; I had always particularly preened myself on being an artist in disguise. And it was not only a question of personal vanity—it seemed to me that the writer or intellectual had a certain missionary usefulness in just such accidental gatherings as this, if he spoke not as an intellectual but as a normal member of the public. Now, thanks to the colonel, I slowly became aware that my contributions to the club-car conversation were being watched and assessed as coming from *a certain quarter.* My costume, it seemed, carefully assembled as it had been at an expensive shop, was to these observers simply a uniform that blazoned a caste and allegiance just as plainly as the colonel's khaki and eagles. "*Gardez,*" I said to myself. But, as the conversation grew tenser and I endeavored to keep cool, I began to writhe within myself, and every time I looked down, my contrasting greens seemed to be growing more and more lurid and taking on an almost menacing light, like leaves just before a storm that lift their bright undersides as the air becomes darker. We had been speaking, of course, of Russia, and I had mentioned a study that had been made at Harvard of political attitudes among Iron Curtain refugees. Suddenly, the colonel had smiled. "They're pretty Red at Harvard, I'm given to understand," he observed in a comfortable tone, while the young man twitched and quivered urgently. The eyes of all the men settled on me and waited. I flushed as I saw myself reflected. The woodland greens of my dress were turning to their complementary red, like a color-experiment in psychology or a traffic light changing. Down at the other end of the club car, a man looked up from his paper. I pulled myself together. "Set your mind at rest, Colonel," I remarked dryly. "I know Harvard very well and they're conservative to the point of dullness. The only thing crimson is the football team." This disparagement had its effect. "So . . .?" queried the colonel. "I thought there was some professor. . . ." I shook my head. "Absolutely not. There used to be a few fellow-travelers, but they're very quiet these days, when they haven't absolutely recanted. The general atmosphere is more anti-Communist than the Vatican." The colonel and the mining engineer exchanged a thoughtful stare and seemed to agree that the Delphic oracle that had just pronounced knew whereof it spoke. "Glad to hear it," said the colonel. The engineer frowned and shook his fat wattles; he was a stately, gray-haired, plump man with small hands and feet and the pampered, finical tidiness of a small-town widow. "There's so much hearsay these days," he exclaimed vexedly. "You don't know *what* to believe."

I reopened my book with an air of having closed the subject and read a paragraph three times over. I exulted to think that I had made a modest contribution to sanity in our times, and I imagined my words pyramiding like a chain letter—the colonel telling a fellow-officer on the veranda of a club in Texas, the engineer halting a works-superintendent in a Colorado mine shaft: "I met a woman on the train who claims. . . . Yes, absolutely. . . ." Of course, I did not know Harvard as thoroughly as I pretended, but I forgave myself by thinking it was the convention of such club-car symposia in our positivistic country to speak from the horse's mouth.

Meanwhile, across the aisle, the engineer and the colonel continued their talk in slightly lowered voices. From time to time, the colonel's polished index-fingernail scratched his burnished black head and his knowing blue eye forayed occasionally toward me. I saw that still I was a doubtful quantity to them, a movement in the bushes, a noise, a flicker, that was figuring in their crenelated thought as "she." The subject of Reds in our colleges had not, alas, been finished; they were speaking now of another university and a woman faculty-member who had been issuing Communist statements. This story somehow, I thought angrily, had managed to appear in the newspapers without my knowledge, while these men were conversant with it; I recognized a big chink in the armor of my authority. Looking up from my book, I began to question them sharply, as though they were reporting some unheard-of natural phenomenon. "When?" I demanded. "Where did you see it? What was her name?" This request for the professor's name was a headlong attempt on my part to buttress my position, the implication being that the identities of all university professors were known to me and that if I were but given the name I could promptly clarify the matter. To admit that there was a single Communist in our academic system whose activities were hidden from me imperiled, I instinctively felt, all the small good I had done here. Moreover, in the back of my mind, I had a supreme confidence that these men were wrong: the story, I supposed, was some tattered piece of misinformation they had picked up from a gossip column. Pride, as usual, preceded my fall. To the colonel, the demand for the name was not specific but generic: what *kind* of name was the question he presumed me to be asking. "Oh," he said slowly with a luxurious yawn, "Finkelstein or Fishbein or Feinstein." He lolled back in his seat with a side glance at the engineer, who deeply nodded. There was a voluptuary pause, as the implication sank in. I bit my lip, regarding this as a mere diversionary tactic. "Please!" I said impatiently. "Can't you remember exactly?" The colonel shook his head and then his spare cheekbones suddenly reddened and he looked directly at me. "I can tell you one thing," he exclaimed irefully. "They weren't named Ryan or Murphy."

The colonel went no further; it was quite unnecessary. In an instant, the young man was at his side, yapping excitedly and actually picking at the military sleeve. The poor thing was transfromed, like some creature in a fairy tale whom a magic word releases from silence. "That's right, Colonel," he happily repeated. "I know them. *I* was at Harvard in the business school, studying accountancy. I left. I couldn't take it." He threw a poisonous glance at me, and the colonel, who had been regarding him somewhat doubtfully, now put on an alert expression and inclined an ear for his confidences. The man at the other end of the car folded his newspaper solemnly and took a seat by the young man's side. "They're all Reds, Colonel," said the young man. "They teach it in the classroom. I came back here to Missouri. It made me sick to listen to the stuff they handed out. If you didn't hand it back, they flunked you. Don't let anybody tell you different." "You are wrong," I said coldly and closed my book and rose. The young man was still talking eagerly, and the three men were leaning forward to catch his every gasping word, like three astute detectives over a dying informer, when I reached the door and cast a last look over my shoulder at them. For an instant, the colonel's eye met mine and I felt his scrutiny processing my green back as I tugged open the door and met a blast of hot air, blowing my full skirt wide. Behind me, in my fancy, I saw four sets of shrugging brows.

In my own car, I sat down, opposite two fat nuns, and tried to assemble my thoughts. I ought to have spoken, I felt, and yet what could I have said? It occurred to me that the four men had perhaps not realized why I had left the club car with such abruptness: was it possible that they thought I was a Communist, who feared to be unmasked? I spurned this possibility, and yet it made me uneasy. For some reason, it troubled my *amour-propre* to think of my anti-Communist self living on, so to speak, green in their collective memory as a Communist or fellow-traveler. In fact, though I did not give a fig for the men, I hated the idea, while a few years ago I should have counted it a great joke. This, it seemed to me, was a measure of the change in the social climate. I had always scoffed at the notion of liberals "living in fear" of political demagoguery in America, but now I had to admit that if I was not fearful, I was at least uncomfortable in the supposition that anybody, anybody whatever, could think of me, precious me, as a Communist. A remoter possibility was, of course, that back there my departure was being ascribed to Jewishness, and this too annoyed me. I am in fact a quarter Jewish, and though I did not "hate" the idea of being taken for a Jew, I did not precisely like it, particularly under these circumstances. I wished it to be clear that I had left the club car for intellectual and principled reasons; I wanted those men to know that it was not I, but my principles, that had been offended. To let them conjecture that I had left because I was Jewish would imply that only a Jew could be affronted by an anti-Semitic outburst; a terrible idea. Aside from anything else, it voided the whole concept of transcendence, which was very close to my heart, the concept that man is more than his circumstances, more even than himself.

However you looked at the episode, I said to myself nervously, I had not acquitted myself well. I ought to have done or said something concrete and unmistakable. From this, I slid glassily to the thought that those men ought to be punished, the colonel, in particular, who occupied a responsible position. In a minute, I was framing a businesslike letter to the Chief of Staff, deploring the colonel's conduct as unbecoming to an officer and identifying him by rank and post, since unfortunately I did not know his name. Earlier in the conversation, he had passed some comments on "Harry" that bordered positively on treason, I said to myself triumphantly. A vivid image of the proceedings against him presented itself to my imagination: the long military tribunal with a row of stern soldierly faces glaring down at the colonel. I myself occupied only an inconspicuous corner of this tableau, for, to tell the truth, I did not relish the role of the witness. Perhaps it would be wiser to let the matter drop . . .? We were nearing St. Louis now; the colonel had come back into my car, and the young accountant had followed him, still talking feverishly. I pretended not to see them and turned to the two nuns, as if for sanctuary from this world and its hatred and revenges. Out of the corner of my eye, I watched the colonel, who now looked wry and restless; he shrank against the window as the young man made a place for himself amid the colonel's smart luggage and continued to express his views in a pale breathless voice. I smiled to think that the colonel was paying the piper. For the colonel, anti-Semitism was simply an aspect of urbanity, like a knowledge of hotels or women. This frantic psychopath of an accountant was serving him as a nemesis, just as the German people had been served by their psychopath, Hitler. Colonel, I adjured him, you have chosen, between him and me;

measure the depth of your error and make the best of it! No intervention on my part was now necessary; justice had been meted out. Nevertheless, my heart was still throbbing violently, as if I were on the verge of some dangerous action. What was I to do, I kept asking myself, as I chatted with the nuns, if the colonel were to hold me to that lunch? And I slowly and apprehensively revolved this question, just as though it were a matter of the most serious import. It seemed to me that if I did not lunch with him—and I had no intention of doing so—I had the dreadful obligation of telling him why.

He was waiting for me as I descended the car steps. "Aren't you coming to lunch with me?" he called out and moved up to take my elbow. I began to tremble with audacity. "No," I said firmly, picking up my suitcase and draping an olive-green linen duster over my arm. "I can't lunch with you." He quirked a wiry black eyebrow. "Why not?" he said. "I understood it was all arranged." He reached for my suitcase. "No," I said, holding on to the suitcase. "I can't." I took a deep breath. "I have to tell you. I think you should be *ashamed* of yourself, Colonel, for what you said in the club car." The colonel stared: I mechanically waved for a redcap, who took my bag and coat and went off. The colonel and I stood facing each other on the emptying platform. "What do you mean?" he inquired in a low, almost clandestine tone. "Those anti-Semitic remarks," I muttered, resolutely. "You ought to be *ashamed*." The colonel gave a quick, relieved laugh. "Oh, come now," he protested. "I'm sorry," I said. "I can't have lunch with anybody who feels that way about the Jews." The colonel put down his attaché case and scratched the back of his lean neck. "Oh, come now," he repeated, with a look of amusement. "You're not Jewish, are you?" "No," I said quickly. "Well, then . . ." said the colonel, spreading his hands in a gesture of bafflement. I saw that he was truly surprised and slightly hurt by my criticism, and this made me feel wretchedly embarrassed and even apologetic, on my side, as though I had called attention to some physical defect in him, of which he himself was unconscious. "But I might have been," I stammered. "You had no way of knowing. You oughtn't to talk like that." I recognized, too late, that I was strangely reducing the whole matter to a question of etiquette: "Don't start anti-Semitic talk before making sure that are no Jews present." "Oh, hell," said the colonel, easily. "I can tell a Jew." "No, you can't," I retorted, thinking of my Jewish grandmother, for by Nazi criteria I was Jewish. "Of course I can," he insisted. "So can you." We had begun to walk down the platform side by side disputing with a restrained passion that isolated us like a pair of lovers. All at once, the colonel halted, as though struck with a thought. "What *are* you, anyway?" he said meditatively, regarding my dark hair, green blouse, and pink earrings. Inside myself, I began to laugh. "Oh," I said gaily, playing out the trump I had been saving. "I'm Irish, like you, Colonel." "How did you know?" he said amazedly. I laughed aloud. "I can tell an Irishman," I taunted. The colonel frowned. "What's your family name?" he said brusquely. "McCarthy." He lifted an eyebrow, in defeat, and then quickly took note of my wedding ring. "That your maiden name?" I nodded. Under this peremptory questioning, I had the peculiar sensation that I get when I am lying; I began to feel that "McCarthy" was a nom de plume, a coinage of my artistic personality. But the colonel appeared to be satisfied. "Hell," he said, "come on to lunch, then. With a fine name like that, you and I should be friends." I still shook my head, though by this time we were pacing outside the station restaurant; my baggage had been checked in a locker; sweat was running down my face and I felt exhausted and hungry. I knew that I was weakening and I wanted only an excuse to yield and go inside with him. The colonel seemed to sense this. "Hell," he conceded. "You've got me wrong. I've nothing against the Jews. Back there in the club car, I was just stating a simple fact: you won't find an Irishman sounding off for the Commies. You can't deny that, can you?"

His voice rose persuasively; he took my arm. In the heat, I wilted and we went into the air-conditioned cocktail lounge. The colonel ordered two old-fashioneds. The room was dark as a cave and produced, in the midst of the hot midday, a hallucinated feeling, as though time had ceased, with the weather, and we were in eternity together. As the colonel prepared to relax, I made a tremendous effort to guide the conversation along rational, purposive lines; my only justification for being here would be to convert the colonel. "There *have* been Irishmen associated with the Communist party." I said suddenly, when the drinks came. "I can think of two." "Oh, hell," said the colonel, "every race and nation has its traitors. What I mean is, you won't find them in numbers. You've got to admit the Communists in this country are ninety per cent Jewish." "But the Jews in this country aren't ninety per cent Communist," I retorted.

As he stirred his drink, restively, I began to try to show him the reasons why the Communist movement in America had attracted such a large number, relatively, of Jews: how the Communists had been anti-Nazi when nobody else seemed to care what happened to the Jews in Germany; how the Communists still capitalized on a Jewish fear of fascism; how many Jews had become, after Buchenwald, traumatized by this fear. . . .

But the colonel was scarcely listening. An impatient frown rested on his jaunty features. "I don't get it," he said slowly. "Why should you be for them, with a name like yours?" "I'm *not* for the Communists," I cried. "I'm just trying to explain to you—" "For the Jews," the colonel interrupted, irritable now himself. "I've heard of such people but I never met one before." "I'm not 'for' them," I protested. "You don't understand. I'm not for *any* race or nation. I'm against those who are against them." This word, *them*, with a sort of slurring circle drawn round it, was beginning to sound ugly to me. Automatically, in arguing with him, I seemed to have slipped into the colonel's style of thought. It occurred to me that defense of the Jews could be a subtle and safe form of anti-Semitism, an exercise of patronage: as a rational Gentile, one could feel superior both to the Jews and the anti-Semites. There could be no doubt that the Jewish question evoked a curious stealthy lust or concupiscence. I could feel it now vibrating between us over the dark table. If I had been a good person, I should unquestionably have got up and left.

"I don't get it," repeated the colonel. "How were you brought up? Were your people this way too?" It was manifest that an odd reversal had taken place; each of us regarded the other as "abnormal" and was attempting to understand the etiology of a disease. "Many of my people think just as you do," I said, smiling coldly. "It seems to be a sickness to which the Irish are prone. Perhaps it's due to the potato diet," I said sweetly, having divined that the colonel came from a social stratum somewhat lower than my own.

But the colonel's hide was tough. "You've got me wrong," he reiterated, with an almost plaintive laugh. "I don't dislike the Jews. I've got a lot of Jewish friends. Among themselves, they think just as I do, mark my words. I tell you what it is," he added ruminatively, with a thoughtful prod of his muddler, "I draw a distinction between a kike and a Jew," I groaned. "Colonel, I've never heard an anti-Semite who didn't draw that distinction. You know what Otto Kahn said? 'A kike is a Jewish gentleman who has just left the room.'" The colonel did not laugh. "I don't hold it against some of them," he persisted, in a tone of pensive justice. "It's not their fault if they were born that way. That's what I tell them, and they respect me for my honesty. I've had a lot of discussions; in procurement, you have to do business with them, and the Jews are the first to admit that you'll find more chiselers among their race than among the rest of mankind." "It's not a race," I interjected wearily, but the colonel pressed on. "If I deal with a Jewish manufacturer, I can't bank on his word. I've seen it again and again, every damned time. When I deal with a Gentile, I can trust him to make delivery as promised. That's the difference between the two races. They're just a different breed. They don't have standards of honesty, even among each other." I sighed, feeling unequal to arguing the colonel's personal experience.

"Look," I said, "you may be dealing with an industry where the Jewish manufacturers are the most recent comers and feel they have to cut corners to compete with the established firms. I've heard that said about Jewish cattle-dealers, who are supposed to be extra sharp. But what I think, really, is that you notice it when a Jewish firm fails to meet an agreement and don't notice it when it's a Yankee." "Hah," said the colonel. "They'll tell you what I'm telling you themselves, if you get to know them and go into their homes. You won't believe it, but some of my best friends are Jews," he said, simply and thoughtfully, with an air of originality. "They may be *your* best friends, Colonel," I retorted, "but you are not theirs. I defy you to tell me that you talk to them as you're talking now." "Sure," said the Colonel, easily. "More or less." "They must be very queer Jews you know," I observed tartly, and I began to wonder whether there indeed existed a peculiar class of Jews whose function in life was to be "friends" with such people as the colonel. It was difficult to think that all the anti-Semites who made the colonel's assertion were the victims of a cruel self-deception.

A dispirited silence followed. I was not one of those liberals who believed that the Jews, alone among peoples, possessed no characteristics whatever of a distinguishing nature—this would mean they had no history and no culture, a charge which should be leveled against them only by an anti-Semite. Certainly, types of Jews could be noted and patterns of Jewish thought and feeling: Jewish humor, Jewish rationality, and so on, not that every Jew reflected every attribute of Jewish life or history. But somehow, with the colonel, I dared not concede that there was such a thing as a Jew: I saw the sad meaning of the assertion that a Jew was a person whom other people thought was Jewish.

Hopeless, however, to convey this to the colonel. The desolate truth was that the colonel was extremely stupid, and it came to me, as we sat there, glumly ordering lunch, that for extremely stupid people anti-Semitism was a form of intellectuality, the sole form of intellectuality of which they were capable. It represented, in a rudimentary way, the ability to make categories, to generalize. Hence a thing I had noted before but never understood: the fact that anti-Semitic statements were generally delivered in an atmosphere of profundity. Furrowed brows attended these speculative distinctions between a kike and a Jew, these little empirical laws that you can't know one without knowing them all. To arrive, indeed, at the idea of a Jew was, for these grouping minds, an exercise in Platonic thought, a discovery of essence, and to be able to add the great corollary, "Some of my best friends are Jews," was to find the philosopher's cleft between essence and existence. From this, it would seem, followed the querulous obstinacy with which the anti-Semite clung to his concept; to be deprived of this intellectual tool by missionaries of tolerance would be, for persons like the colonel, the equivalent of Western man's losing the syllogism: a lapse into animal darkness. In the club car, we had just witnessed an example: the colonel with his anti-Semitic observation had come to the mute young man like the paraclete, bearing the gift of tongues.

Here in a bar, it grew plainer and plainer that the colonel did not regard himself as an anti-Semite but merely as a heavy thinker. The idea that I considered him anti-Semitic sincerely outraged his feelings. "Prejudice" was the last trait he could have imputed to himself. He looked on me, almost respectfully, as a "Jew-lover," a kind of being he had heard of but never actually encountered, like a centaur or a Siamese twin, and the interest of relating this prodigy to the natural state of mankind overrode any personal distaste. There I sat, the exception which was "proving" or testing the rule, and he kept pressing me for details of my history that might explain my deviation in terms of the norm. On my side, of course, I had become fiercely resolved that he would learn nothing from me that would make it possible for him to dismiss my anti-anti-Semitism as the product of special circumstances: I was stubbornly sitting on the fact of my Jewish grandmother like a hen on a golden egg. I was bent on making *him* see himself as a monster, a deviation, a heretic from Church and State. Unfortunately, the colonel, owing perhaps to his military training, had not the glimmering of an idea of what democracy meant; to him, it was simply a slogan that was sometimes useful in war. The notion of an ordained inequality was to him "scientific."

"Honestly," he was saying in lowered tones, as our drinks were taken away and the waitress set down my sandwich and his corned-beef hash, "don't you, brought up the way you were, feel about them the way I do? Just between ourselves, isn't there a sort of inborn feeling of horror that the very word, Jew, suggests?" I shook my head, roundly. The idea of an *innate* anti-Semitism was in keeping with the rest of the colonel's thought, yet it shocked me more than anything he had yet said. "No," I sharply replied. "It doesn't evoke any feeling one way or the other." "Honest Injun?" said the colonel. "Think back; when you were a kid, didn't the word, Jew, make you feel sick?" "There was a dreadful sincerity about this that made me answer in an almost kindly tone. "No, truthfully, I assure you. When we were children, we learned to call the old-clothes man a sheeny, but that was just a dirty word to us, like 'Hun' that we used to call after workmen we thought were Germans."

"I don't get it," pondered the colonel, eating a pickle. "There must be something wrong with you. Everybody is born with that feeling. It's natural; it's part of nature." "On the contrary," I said. "It's something very unnatural that you must have been taught as a child." "It's not something you're *taught*," he protested. "You must have been," I said. "You simply don't remember it. In any case, you're a man now; you must rid yourself of that feeling. It's psychopathic, like that horrible young man on the train." "You thought he was crazy?" mused the colonel, in an idle, dreamy tone. I shrugged my shoulders. "Of course. Think of his color. He was probably just out of a mental institution. People don't get that tattletale gray except in prison or mental hospitals." The colonel suddenly grinned. "You might be right," he said. "He was quite a case." He chuckled.

I leaned forward. "You know, Colonel," I said quickly, "anti-Semitism is contrary to the Church's teaching. God will make you do penance for hating the Jews. Ask your priest; he'll tell you I'm right. You'll have a long spell in Purgatory, if you don't rid yourself of this sin. It's a deliberate violation of Christ's commandment, 'Love thy neighbor.' The Church holds that the Jews have a sacred place in God's design. Mary was a Jew and Christ was a Jew. The Jews are under God's special protection. The Church teaches that the millennium can't come until the conversion of the Jews; therefore, the Jews must be preserved that the Divine Will may be accomplished. Woe to them that harm them, for they controvert God's Will!" In the course of speaking, I had swept myself away with the solemnity of the doctrine. The Great Reconciliation between God and His chosen people, as envisioned by the Evangelist, had for me at that moment a piercing, majestic beauty, like some awesome Tintoretto. I saw a noble spectacle of blue sky, thronged with gray clouds, and a vast white desert, across which God and Israel advanced to meet each other, while below in hell the demons of disunion shrieked and gnashed their teeth.

"Hell," said the colonel, jovially, "I don't believe in all that. I lost my faith when I was a kid. I saw that all this God stuff was a lot of bushwa." I gazed at him in stupefaction. His confidence had completely returned. The blue eyes glittered debonairly, the eagles glittered; the narrow polished head cocked and listened to itself like a trilling bird. I was up against an airman with a bird's-eye view, a man who believed in nothing but the law of kind: the epitome of godless materialism. "You still don't hold with that bunk?" the colonel inquired in an undertone, with an expression of stealthy curiosity. "No," I confessed, sad to admit to a meeting of minds. "You know what got me?" exclaimed the colonel. "That birth-control stuff. Didn't it kill you?" I made a neutral sound. "I was beginning to play around," said the colonel, with a significant beam of the eye, "and I just couldn't take that guff. When I saw through the birth-control talk, I saw through the whole thing. They claimed it was against nature, but I claim, if that's so, an operation's against nature. I told my old man that when he was having his kidney stones out. You ought to have heard him yell!" A rich, reminiscent satisfaction dwelt in the colonel's face.

This period of his life, in which he had thrown off the claims of the spiritual and adopted a practical approach, was evidently one of those "turning points" to which a man looks back with pride. He lingered over the story of his break with church and parents with a curious sort of heat, as though the flames of old sexual conquests stirred within his body at the memory of those old quarrels. The looks he rested on me, as a sharer of that experience, grew more and more lickerish and assaying. "What got *you* down?" he finally inquired, settling back in his chair and pushing his coffee cup aside. "Oh," I said wearily, "it's a long story. You can read it when it's published." "You're an author?" cried the colonel, who was really very slow-witted. I nodded, and the colonel regarded me afresh. "What do you write? Love stories?" He gave a half-wink. "No," I said. "Various things. Articles. Books. Highbrowish stories." A suspicion darkened in the colonel's sharp face. "That McCarthy," he said. "Is that your pen name?" "Yes," I said, "but it's my real name too. It's the name I write under *and* my maiden name." The colonel digested this thought. "Oh," he concluded.

A new idea seemed to visit him. Quite cruelly, I watched it take possession. He was thinking of the power of the press and the indiscretions of other military figures, who had been rewarded with demotion. The consciousness of the uniform he wore appeared to seep uneasily into his body. He straightened his shoulders and called thoughtfully for the check. We paid in silence, the colonel making no effort to forestall my dive into my pocketbook. I should not have let him pay in any case, but it startled me that he did not try to do so, if only for reasons of vanity. The whole business of paying, apparently, was painful to him; I watched his facial muscles contract as he pocketed the change and slipped two dimes for the waitress onto the table, not daring quite to hide them under the coffee cup—he had short-changed me on the bill and the tip, and we both knew it. We walked out into the steaming station and I took my baggage out of the checking locker. The colonel carried my suitcase and we strolled along without speaking. Again, I felt horribly embarrassed for him. He was meditative, and I supposed that he too was mortified by his meanness about the tip.

"Don't get me wrong," he said suddenly, setting the suitcase down and turning squarely to face me, as though he had taken a big decision. "I may have said a few things back there about the Jews getting what they deserved in Germany." I looked at him in surprise; actually, he had not said that to me. Perhaps he had let it drop in the club car after I had left. "But that doesn't mean I approve of Hitler." "I should hope not," I said. "What I mean is," said the colonel, "that they probably gave the Germans a lot of provocation, but that doesn't excuse what Hitler did." "No," I said, somewhat ironically, but the colonel was unaware of anything satiric in the air. His face was grave and determined; he was sorting out his philosophy for the record. "I mean, I don't approve of his methods," he finally stated. "No," I agreed. "You mean, you don't approve of the gas chamber." The colonel shook his head very severely. "Absolutely not! That was terrible." He shuddered and drew out a handkerchief and slowly wiped his brow. "For God's sake," he said, "don't get me wrong. I think they're human beings." "Yes," I assented, and we walked along to my track. The colonel's spirits lifted, as though, having stated his credo, he had both got himself in line with public policy and achieved an autonomous thought. "I mean," he resumed, "you may not care for them, but that's not the same as killing them, in cold blood, like that." "No, Colonel," I said.

He swung my bag onto the car's platform and I climbed up behind it. He stood below, smiling, with upturned face. "I'll look for your article," he cried, as the train whistle blew. I nodded, and the colonel waved, and I could not stop myself from waving back at him and even giving him the corner of a smile. After all, I said to myself, looking down at him, the colonel was "a human being." There followed one of those inane intervals in which one prays for the train to leave. We both glanced at our watches. "See you some time," he called. "What's your married name?" "Broadwater," I called back. The whistle blew again. "Brodwater?" shouted the colonel, with a dazed look of unbelief and growing enlightenment; he was not the first person to hear it as a Jewish name, on the model of Goldwater. B-r-o-a-d," I began, automatically, but then I stopped. I disdained to spell it out for him; the victory was his. "One of the chosen, eh?" his brief grimace seemed to commiserate. For the last time, and in the final fullness of understanding, the hawk eye patrolled the green dress, the duster, and the earrings; the narrow flue of his nostril contracted as he curtly turned away. The train commenced to move.

MARY McCARTHY

settling the colonel's hash

Seven years ago, when I taught in a progressive college, I had a pretty girl student in one of my classes who wanted to be a short-story writer. She was not studying writing with me, but she knew that I sometimes wrote short stories, and one day, breathless and glowing, she came up to me in the hall, to tell me that she had just written a story that her writing teacher, a Mr. Converse, was terribly excited about. "He thinks it's wonderful," she said, "and he's going to help me fix it up for publication."

I asked what the story was about; the girl was a rather simple being who loved clothes and dates. Her answer had a deprecating tone. It was just about a girl (herself) and some sailors she had met on the train. But then her face, which had looked perturbed for a moment, gladdened.

"Mr. Converse is going over it with me and we're going to put in the symbols."

Another girl in the same college, when asked by us in her sophomore orals why she read novels (one of the pseudo-profound questions that ought never to be put) answered in a defensive flurry: "Well, *of course* I don't read them to find out what happens to the hero."

At the time, I thought these notions were peculiar to progressive education: it was old-fashioned or regressive to read a novel to find out what happens to the hero or to have a mere experience empty of symbolic pointers. But I now discover that this attitude is quite general, and that readers and students all over the country are in a state of apprehension, lest they read a book or story literally and miss the presence of a symbol. And like everything in America, this search for meanings has become a socially competitive enterprise; the best reader is the one who detects the most symbols in a given stretch of prose. And the benighted reader who fails to find any symbols humbly assents when they are pointed out to him; he accepts his mortification.

I had no idea how far this process had gone until last spring, when I began to get responses to a story I had published in *Harper's*. I say "story" because that was what it was called by *Harper's*. I myself would not know quite what to call it; it was a piece of reporting or a fragment of autobiography—an account of my meeting with an anti-Semitic army colonel. It began in the club car of a train going to St. Louis; I was wearing an apple-green shirtwaist and a dark-green skirt and pink earrings; we got into an argument about the Jews. The colonel was a rather dapper, flashy kind of Irish-American with a worldly blue eye; he took me, he said, for a sculptress, which made me feel, to my horror, that I looked Bohemian and therefore rather suspect. He was full of the usual profound clichés that anti-Semites air, like original epigrams, about the Jews: that he could tell a Jew, that they were different from other people, that you couldn't trust them in business, that some of his best friends were Jews, that he distinguished between a Jew and a kike, and finally that, of course, he didn't agree with Hitler: Hitler went too far; the Jews were human beings.

All the time we talked, and I defended the Jews, he was trying to get my angle, as he called it; he thought it was abnormal for anybody who wasn't Jewish not to feel as he did. As a matter of fact, I have a Jewish grandmother, but I decided to keep this news to myself: I did not want the colonel to think that I had any interested reason for speaking on behalf of the Jews, that is, that I was prejudiced. In the end, though, I got my comeuppance. Just as we were parting, the colonel asked me my married name, which is Broadwater, and the whole mystery was cleared up for him, instantly; he supposed I was married to a Jew and that the name was spelled B-r-o-d-w-a-t-e-r. I did not try to enlighten him; I let him think what he wanted; in a certain sense, he was right; he had unearthed my Jewish grandmother or her equivalent. There were a few details that I must mention to make the next part clear: in my car, there were two nuns, whom I talked to as a distraction from the colonel and the moral problems he raised. He and I finally had lunch together in the St. Louis railroad station, where we continued the discussion. It was a very hot day. I had a sandwich; he had roast-beef hash. We both had an old-fashioned.

The whole point of this "story" was that it really happened; it is written in the first person; I speak of myself in my own name, McCarthy; at the end, I mention my husband's name, Broadwater. When I was thinking about writing the story, I decided not to treat it fictionally; the chief interest, I felt, lay in the fact that it happened, in real life, last summer, to the writer herself, who was a good deal at fault in the incident. I wanted to embarrass myself and, if possible, the reader too.

Yet, strangely enough, many of my readers preferred to think of this account as fiction. I still meet people who ask me, confidentially, "That story of yours about the colonel—was it really true?" It seemed to them perfectly natural that I would write a fabrication, in which I figured under my own name, and sign it, though in my eyes this would be like perjuring yourself in court or forging checks. Shortly after the "story" was published, I got a kindly letter from a man in Mexico, in which he criticized the menu from an artistic point of view: he thought salads would be better for hot weather and it would be more in character for the narrator-heroine to have a Martini. I did not answer the letter, though I was moved to, because I had the sense that he would not understand the distinction between what *ought* to have happened and what *did* happen.

Then in April I got another letter, from an English teacher in a small college in the Middle West, that reduced me to despair. I am going to cite it at length.

"My students in freshman English chose to analyze your story, 'Artists in Uniform,' from the March issue of *Harper's*. For a week I heard oral discussions on it and then the students wrote critical analyses. In so far as it is possible, I stayed out of their discussions, encouraging them to read the story closely with your intentions as a guide to their understanding. Although some of them insisted that the story has no other level than the realistic one, most of them decided it has symbolic overtones.

"The question is: how closely do you want the symbols labeled? They wrestled with the nuns, the author's two shades of green with pink accents, with the 'materialistic godlessness' of the colonel. . . . A surprising number wanted exact symbols; for example, they searched for the significance of the colonel's eating hash and the author eating a sandwich. . . . From my standpoint, the story was an entirely satisfactory springboard for understanding the various shades of prejudice, for seeing how much of the artist goes into his painting. If it is any satisfaction to you, our campus was alive with discussions about 'Artists in Uniform.' We liked the story and we thought it amazing that an author could succeed in making readers dislike the author—for a purpose, of course!"

I probably should have answered this letter, but I did not. The gulf seemed to me too wide. I could not applaud the backward students who insisted that the story has no other level than the realistic one without giving offense to their teacher, who was evidently a well-meaning person. But I shall try now to address a reply, not to this teacher and her unfortunate class, but to a whole school of misunderstanding. There were no symbols in this story; there was no deeper level. The nuns were in the story because they were on the train; the contrasting greens were the dress I happened to be wearing; the colonel had hash because he had hash; materialistic godlessness meant just what it means when a priest thunders it from the pulpit—the phrase, for the first time, had meaning for me as I watched and listened to the colonel.

But to clarify the misunderstanding, one must go a little further and try to see what a literary symbol is. Now in one sense, the colonel's hash and my sandwich can be regarded as symbols; that is, they typify the colonel's food tastes and mine. (The man in Mexico had different food tastes which he wished to interpose into our reality.) The hash and the sandwich might even be said to show something very obvious about our characters and bringing-up, or about our sexes; I was a woman, he was a man. And though on another day I might have ordered hash myself, that day I did not, because the colonel and I, in our disagreement, were polarizing each other.

The hash and the sandwich, then, could be regarded as symbols of our disagreement, almost conscious symbols. And underneath our discussion of the Jews, there was a thin sexual current running, as there always is in such random encounters or pickups (for they have a strong suggestion of the illicit). The fact that I ordered something conventionally feminine and he ordered something conventionally masculine represented, no doubt, our awareness of a sexual possibility; even though I was not attracted to the colonel, nor he to me, the circumstances of our meeting made us define ourselves as a woman and a man.

The sandwich and the hash were our provisional, *ad hoc* symbols of ourselves. But in this sense all human actions are symbolic because they represent the person who does them. If the colonel had ordered a fruit salad with whipped cream, this too would have represented him in some way; given his other traits, it would have pointed to a complexity in his character that the hash did not suggest.

In the same way, the contrasting greens of my dress were a symbol of my taste in clothes and hence representative of me—all too representative, I suddenly saw, in the club car, when I got an "artistic" image of myself flashed back at me from the men's eyes. I had no wish to stylize myself as an artist, that is, to parade about as a symbol of flamboyant unconventionality, but apparently I had done so unwittingly when I picked those colors off a rack, under the impression that they suited me or "expressed my personality" as salesladies say.

My dress, then, was a symbol of the perplexity I found myself in with the colonel; I did not want to be categorized as a member of a peculiar minority—an artist or a Jew; but brute fate and the colonel kept resolutely cramming me into both those uncomfortable pigeonholes. I wished to be regarded as ordinary or rather as universal, to be anybody and therefore everybody (that is, in one sense, I wanted to be on the colonel's side, majestically above minorities); but every time the colonel looked at my dress and me in it with my pink earrings I shrank to minority status, and felt the dress in the heat shriveling me, like the shirt of Nessus, the centaur, that consumed Hercules.

But this is not what the students meant when they wanted the symbols "labeled." They were searching for a more recondite significance than that afforded by the trite symbolism of ordinary life, in which a dress is a social badge. They supposed that I was engaging in literary or artificial symbolism, which would lead the reader out of the confines of reality into the vast fairy tale of myth, in which the color green would have an emblematic meaning (or did the two greens signify for them what the teacher calls "shades" of prejudice), and the colonel's hash, I imagine, would be some sort of Eucharistic mincemeat.

Apparently, the presence of the nuns assured them there were overtones of theology; it did not occur to them (a) that the nuns were there because pairs of nuns are a standardized feature of summer Pullman travel, like crying babies, and perspiring businessmen in the club car, and (b) that if I thought the nuns worth mentioning, it was also because of something very simple and directly relevant: the nuns and the colonel and I all had something in common—we had all at one time been Catholics—and I was seeking common ground with the colonel, from which to turn and attack his position.

In any account of reality, even a televised one, which comes closest to being a literal transcript or replay, some details are left out as irrelevant (though nothing is really irrelevant). The details that are not eliminated have to stand as symbols of the whole, like stenographic signs, and of course there is an art of selection, even in a newspaper account: the writer, if he has any ability, is looking for the revealing detail that will sum up the picture for the reader in a flash of recognition.

But the art of abridgment and condensation, which is familiar to anybody who tries to relate an anecdote, or give a direction—the art of natural symbolism, which is at the basis of speech and all representation—has at bottom a centripetal intention. It hovers over an object, an event, or series of events and tries to declare what it is. Analogy (that is, comparison to other subjects) is inevitably one of its methods. "The weather was soupy," i.e., like soup. "He wedged his way in," i.e., he had to enter, thin edge first, as a wedge enters, and so on. All this is obvious. But these metaphorical aids to communication are a far cry from literary symbolism, as taught in the schools and practiced by certain fashionable writers. Literary symbolism is centrifugal and flees from the object, the event, into the incorporeal distance, where concepts are taken for substance and floating ideas and archetypes assume a hieratic authority.

In this dream-forest, symbols become arbitrary; all counters are interchangeable; anything can stand for anything else. The colonel's hash can be a Eucharist or a cannibal feast or the banquet of Atreus, or all three, so long as the actual dish set before the actual man is disparaged. What is depressing about this insistent symbolization is the fact that while it claims to lead to the infinite, it quickly reaches very finite limits—there are only so many myths on record, and once you have got through Bulfinch, the Scandinavian, and the Indian, there is not much left. And if all stories reduce themselves to myth and symbol, qualitative differences vanish, and there is only a single, monotonous story.

American fiction of the symbolist school demonstrates this mournful truth, without precisely intending to. A few years ago, when the mode was at its height, chic novels and stories fell into three classes: those which had a Greek myth for their framework, which the reader was supposed to detect, like finding the faces in the clouds in old newspaper puzzle contests; those which had symbolic modern figures, dwarfs, hermaphrodites, and cripples, illustrating maiming and loneliness; and those which contained symbolic animals, cougars, wild cats, and monkeys. One young novelist, a product of the Princeton school of symbolism, had all three elements going at once, like the ringmaster of a three-ring circus, with the freaks, the animals, and the statues.

The quest for symbolic referents had as its object, of course, the deepening of the writer's subject and the reader's awareness. But the result was paradoxical. At the very moment when American writing was penetrated by the symbolic urge, it ceased to be able to create symbols of its own. Babbitt, I suppose, was the last important symbol to be created by an American writer; he gave his name to a type that henceforth would be recognizable to everybody. He passed into the language. The same thing could be said, perhaps, though to a lesser degree, of Caldwell's Tobacco Road, Eliot's Prufrock, and possibly of Faulkner's Snopeses. The discovery of new symbols is not the only function of a writer, but the writer who cares about this must be fascinated by reality itself, as a butterfly collector is fascinated by the glimpse of a new specimen. Such a specimen was Mme. Bovary or M. Homais or M. de Charlus or Jupien; these specimens were precious to their discoverers, not because they repeated an age-old pattern but because their markings were new. Once the specimen has been described, the public instantly spots other examples of the kind, and the world seems suddenly full of Babbitts and Charlus, where none had been noted before.

A different matter was Joyce's Mr. Bloom. Mr. Bloom can be called a symbol of eternal recurrence—the wandering Jew, Ulysses the voyager—but he is a symbol thickly incarnate, fleshed out in a Dublin advertising canvasser. He is not *like* Ulysses or vaguely suggestive of Ulysses; he is Ulysses, circa 1905. Joyce evidently believed in a cyclical theory of history, in which everything repeated itself; he also subscribed in youth to the doctrine that declares that the Host, a piece of bread, is also God's body and blood. How it can be both things at the same time, transubstantially, is a mystery, and Mr. Bloom is just such a mystery: Ulysses in the visible appearance of a Dublin advertising canvasser.

Mr. Bloom is not a symbol of Ulysses, but Ulysses-Bloom together, one and indivisible, symbolize or rather demonstrate eternal recurrence. I hope I make myself clear. The point is transubstantiation: Bloom and Ulysses are transfused into each other and neither reality is diminished. Both realities are locked together, like the protons and neutrons of an atom. *Finnegans Wake* is a still more ambitious attempt to create a fusion, this time a myriad fusion, and to exemplify the mystery of how a thing can be itself and at the same time be something else. The world is many and it is also one.

But the clarity and tension of Joyce's thought brought him closer in a way to the strictness of allegory than to the diffuse practices of latter-day symbolists. In Joyce, the equivalences and analogies are very sharp and distinct, as in a pun, and the real world is almost querulously audible, like the voices of the washerwomen on the Liffey that come into Earwicker's dream. But this is not true of Joyce's imitators or of the imitators of his imitators, for whom reality is only a shadowy pretext for the introduction of a whole *corps de ballet* of dancing symbols in mythic draperies and animal skins.

Let me make a distinction. There are some great writers, like Joyce or Melville, who have consciously introduced symbolic elements into their work; and there are great writers who have written fables or allegories. In both cases, the writer makes it quite clear to the reader how he is to be read; only an idiot would take *Pilgrim's Progress* for a realistic story, and even a young boy, reading *Moby Dick,* realizes that there is something more than whale-fishing here, though he may not be able to name what it is. But the great body of fiction contains only what I have called natural symbolism, in which selected events represent or typify a problem, a kind of society or psychology, a philosophical theory, in the same way that they do in real life. What happens to the hero becomes of the highest importance. This symbolism needs no abstruse interpretation, and abstruse interpretation will only lead the reader away from the reality that the writer is trying to press on his attention.

I shall give an example or two of what I mean by natural symbolism and I shall begin with a rather florid one: Henry James' *The Golden Bowl.* This is the story of a rich American girl who collects European objects. One of these objects is a husband, Prince Amerigo, who proves to be unfaithful. Early in the story, there is a visit to an antique shop in which the Prince picks out a gold bowl for his fiancée and finds, to his annoyance, that it is cracked. It is not hard to see that the cracked bowl is a symbol, both of the Prince himself, who is a valuable antique but a little flawed, morally, and also of the marriage, which represents an act of acquisition or purchase on the part of the heroine and her father. If the reader should fail to notice the analogy, James calls his attention to it in the title.

I myself would not regard this symbol as necessary to this particular history; it seems to me, rather, an ornament of the kind that was fashionable in the architecture and interior decoration of the period, like stylized sheaves of corn or palms on the façade of a house. Nevertheless, it is handsome and has an obvious appropriateness to the theme. It introduces the reader into the Gilded Age attitudes of the novel. I think there is also a scriptural echo in the title that conveys the idea of punishment. But having seen and felt the weight of meaning that James put into this symbol, one must not be tempted to press further and look at the bowl as a female sex symbol, a chalice, a Holy Grail, and so on; a book is not a pious excuse for reciting a litany of associations.

My second example is from Tolstoy's *Anna Karenina.* Toward the beginning of the novel, Anna meets the man who will be her lover, Vronsky, on the Moscow-St. Petersburg express; as they meet, there has been an accident; a workman has been killed by the train. This is the beginning of Anna's doom, which is completed when she throws herself under a train and is killed; and the last we see of Vronsky is in a train, with a toothache; he is off to the wars. The train is necessary to the plot of the novel, and I believe it is also symbolic, both of the iron forces of material progress that

Tolstoy hated so and that played a part in Anna's moral destruction, and also of those iron laws of necessity and consequence that govern human action when it remains on the sensual level.

One can read the whole novel, however, without being conscious that the train is a symbol; we do not have to "interpret" to feel the import of doom and loneliness in the train's whistle—the same import we ourselves can feel when we hear a train whistle blow in the country, even today. Tolstoy was a deeper artist than James, and we cannot be sure that the train was a conscious device with him. The appropriateness to Anna's history may have been only a *felt* appropriateness; everything in Tolstoy has such a supreme naturalness that one shrinks from attributing contrivance to him, as if it were a sort of fraud. Yet he worked very hard on his novels—I forget how many times Countess Tolstoy copied out *War and Peace* by hand.

The impression one gets from his diaries is that he wrote by ear; he speaks repeatedly, even as an old man, of having to start a story over again because he has the wrong tone, and I suspect that he did not think of the train as a symbol but that it sounded "right" to him, because it was, in that day, an almost fearsome emblem of ruthless and impersonal force, not only to a writer of genius but to the poorest peasant in the fields. And in Tolstoy's case I think it would be impossible, even for the most fanciful critic, to extricate the train from the novel and try to make it say something that the novel itself does not say directly. Every detail in Tolstoy has an almost cruel and viselike meaningfulness and truth to itself that make it tautological to talk of symbolism; he was a moralist and to him the tiniest action, even the curiosities of physical appearance, Vronsky's bald spot, the small white hands of Prince Andrei, told a moral tale.

It is now considered very old-fashioned and tasteless to speak of an author's "philosophy of life" as something that can be harvested from his work. Actually, most of the great authors did have a "philosophy of life" which they were eager to communicate to the public; this was one of their motives for writing. And to disentangle a moral philosophy from a work that evidently contains one is far less damaging to the author's purpose and the integrity of his art than to violate his imagery by symbol-hunting, as though reading a novel were a sort of paperchase.

The images of a novel or a story belong, as it were, to a family, very closely knit and inseparable from each other; the parent "idea" of a story or a novel generates events and images all bearing a strong family resemblance. And to understand a story or a novel, you must look for the parent "idea," which is usually in plain view, if you read quite carefully and literally what the author says.

I will go back, for a moment, to my own story, to show how this can be done. Clearly, it is about the Jewish question, for that is what the people are talking about. It also seems to be about artists, since the title is "Artists in Uniform." Then there must be some relation between artists and Jews. What is it? They are both minorities that other people claim to be able to recognize by their appearance. But artists and Jews do not care for this categorization; they want to be universal, that is, like everybody else. They do not want to wear their destiny as a badge, as the soldier wears his uniform. But this aim is really hopeless, for life has formed them as Jews or artists, in a way that immediately betrays them to the majority they are trying to melt into. In my conversation with the colonel, I was endeavoring to play a double game. I was trying to force him into a minority by treating anti-Semitism as an aberration, which, in fact, I believe it is. On his side, the colonel resisted this attempt and tried to show that anti-Semitism was normal, and he was normal, while I was the queer one. He declined to be categorized as anti-Semite; he regarded himself as an independent thinker, who by a happy chance thought the same as everybody else.

I imagined I had a card up my sleeve; I had guessed that the colonel was Irish (i.e., that he belonged to a minority) and presumed that he was a Catholic. I did not see how he could possibly guess that I, with my Irish name and Irish appearance, had a Jewish grandmother in the background. Therefore when I found I had not convinced him by reasoning, I played my last card; I told him that the Church, his Church, forbade anti-Semitism. I went even further; I implied that God forbade it, though I had no right to do this, since I did not believe in God, but was only using Him as a whip to crack over the colonel, to make him feel humble and inferior, a raw Irish Catholic lad under discipline. But the colonel, it turned out, did not believe in God, either, and I lost. And since, in a sense, I had been cheating all along in this game we were playing, I had to concede the colonel a sort of moral victory in the end; I let him think that my husband was Jewish and that that "explained" everything satisfactorily.

Now there are a number of morals or meanings in this little tale, starting with the simple one: don't talk to strangers on a train. The chief moral or meaning (what I learned, in other words, from this experience) was this: you cannot be a universal unless you accept the fact that you are a singular, that is, a Jew or an artist or what-have-you. What the colonel and I were discussing, and at the same time illustrating and enacting, was the definition of a human being. I was trying to be something better than a human being; I was trying to be the voice of pure reason; and pride went before a fall. The colonel, without trying, was being something worse than a human being, and somehow we found ourselves on the same plane—facing each other, like mutually repellent twins. Or, put in another way: it is dangerous to be drawn into discussions of the Jews with anti-Semites: you delude yourself that you are spreading light, but you are really sinking into muck; if you endeavor to be dispassionate, you are really claiming for yourself a privileged position, a little mountain top, from which you look down, impartially, on both the Jews and the colonel.

Anti-Semitism is a horrible disease from which nobody is immune, and it has a kind of evil fascination that makes an enlightened person draw near the source of infection, supposedly in a scientific spirit, but really to sniff the vapors and dally with the possibility. The enlightened person who lunches with the colonel in order, as she tells herself, to improve him, is cheating herself, having her cake and eating it. This attempted cheat, on my part, was related to the question of the artist and the green dress; I wanted to be an artist but not to pay the price of looking like one, just as I was willing to have Jewish blood but not willing to show it, where it would cost me something—the loss of superiority in an argument.

These meanings are all there, quite patent, to anyone who consents to look *into* the story. They were *in* the experience itself, waiting to be found and considered. I did not perceive them all at the time the experience was happening; otherwise, it would not have taken place, in all probability—I should have given the colonel a wide berth. But when I went back over the experience, in order to write it, I came upon these meanings, protruding at me, as it were, from the details of the occasion. I put in the green dress and my mortification over it because they were part of the truth, just as it had occurred, but I did not see how they were related to the general question of anti-Semitism and my grandmother until they *showed* me their relation in the course of writing.

Every short story, at least for me, is a little act of discovery. A cluster of details presents itself to my scrutiny, like a mystery that I will understand in the course of writing or sometimes not fully until afterward, when, if I have been honest and listened to these details carefully, I will find that they are connected and that there is a coherent pattern. This pattern is *in* experience itself; you do not impose it from the outside and if you try to, you will find that the story is taking the wrong tack, dribbling away from you into artificiality or inconsequence. A story that you do not learn something from while you are writing it, that does not illuminate something for you, is dead, finished before you started it. The "idea" of a story is implicit in it, on the one hand; on the other hand, it is always ahead of the writer, like a form dimly discerned in the distance; he is working *toward* the "idea."

It can sometimes happen that you begin a story thinking that you know the "idea" of it and find, when you are finished, that you have said something quite different and utterly unexpected to you. Most writers have been haunted all their lives by the "idea" of a story or a novel that they think they want to write and see very clearly: Tolstoy always wanted to write a novel about the Decembrists and instead, almost against his will, wrote *War and Peace*; Henry James thought he wanted to write a novel about Napoleon. Probably these ideas for novels were too set in their creators' minds to inspire creative discovery.

In any work that is truly creative, I believe, the writer cannot be omniscient in advance about the effects that he proposes to produce. The suspense in a novel is not only in the reader, but in the novelist himself, who is intensely curious too about what will happen to the hero. Jane Austen may know in a general way that Emma will marry Mr. Knightley in the end (the reader knows this too, as a matter of fact); the suspense for the author lies in the how, in the twists and turns of circumstance, waiting but as yet unknown, that will bring the consummation about. Hence, I would say to the student of writing that outlines, patterns, arrangements of symbols may have a certain usefulness at the outset for some kinds of minds, but in the end they will have to be scrapped. If the story does not contradict the outline, overrun the pattern, break the symbols, like an insurrection against authority, it is surely a still birth. The natural symbolism of reality has more messages to communicate than the dry Morse code of the disengaged mind.

The tree of life, said Hegel, is greener than the tree of thought; I have quoted this before but I cannot forbear from citing it again in this context. This is not an incitement to mindlessness or an endorsement of realism in the short story (there are several kinds of reality, including interior reality); it means only that the writer must be, first of all, a listener and observer, who can pay attention to reality, like an obedient pupil, and who is willing, always, to be surprised by the messages reality is sending through to him. And if he gets the messages correctly he will not have to go back and put in the symbols; he will find that the symbols are there, staring at him significantly from the commonplace.

AFTERWORD

going home to the duke

Customarily, we think of art and its makers as comprising a world wholly apart from our own. And we are right, in part. The graceful line, the right word in the right place, we do not achieve often, and the work of art, with its illusion of perfection, its grace, its rightness, offends us. Most of my readers, odeless and odorless, will live many more years than Keats's twenty-five, and I shall not, like Rimbaud, run guns in Africa.

But we are right only in part. Art is made by men out of the materials—color, line, sound—of our world, and the process by which these materials become art is an activity of the mind we have all experienced, for we are all engaged in the creation of narratives with ourselves as protagonists. Memory functions in terms of selection, character, and event. Under the pressure of our emotions, we choose to remember out of all the events that have occurred those we can bear to remember. We assert that a cause and effect relationship exists among the events chosen, and we call the pattern that results our lives. If the process is carried out with some regard for truth, with some knowledge of the materials involved, we are able to function. If we lie to ourselves, if we are ignorant of the nature of our materials, we end up, if we are lucky, on the psychiatrist's couch, revising our creation.

Art is a simplification, intensification, and refinement of human experience, and if we find little taste for art in our society, it may be because our society has little taste for what is human. Those of us, middle class but poor, who grew up during the thirties and forties were confronted by a prevalent fear of and distaste for the human. Our parents lied to us. And it was easy to believe at least one of their lies. The stork must have brought us, for our parents were seemingly devoid of the passions we already felt stirring within us. Maybe storks had bad thoughts, or maybe they had brought us from some dark duchy and would reappear disguised as chauffeurs, driving the limousines that would take us home to our true father, the Duke.

The art of living begins, like all the arts, in imitation. Our parents failed us as models. What we felt, they pretended not to feel. What they believed in, the principles of the middle class, soon failed us, too. I remember a young friend who had a very successful career as a cat burglar, and his anger at the merchants who claimed greater losses than he had inflicted upon them. I think it may have been the realization that the merchants in their insurance claims were thieves, too, that led him to retire from crime. They were the enemy, and one did not want to be like them.

Like most Americans my age, I found the image I wanted to approximate in the neighborhood movie house. Humphrey Bogart was my hero. I had neither his looks nor his lisp, but that did not matter: I had his image, twenty feet high, on the screen before me, and it was a meaningful image. It was that of a man in whom thought and action were united, a man of integrity. I don't suppose *integrity* was then a part of my vocabulary, but I understood emotionally that when Bogie sent Ingrid off with Paul, who needed her, and who was needed by the Underground, or when he sent the lovely and greedy Mary Astor to prison, he did so out of some inner strength. There were drawbacks, of course. Neither *Casablanca* nor *The Maltese Falcon*, both rich in loss, were any guide to winning *and* keeping a woman. Still, there was that dream of integrity; the image flickering on the screen was a beacon toward which one might journey.

What I yearned after was some realization of myself. Not all of my friends were so fortunate in their choice of an ideal. Jack wasn't. There was in him—and here I'm playing at the psychiatrist he should have had—a kind of self-loathing. I suppose he had accepted in his early years the enemy's appraisal of his worth. In any event, he did not respect the materials out of which his life had to be formed, and turned elsewhere, to John, still another friend.

John was, to borrow a phrase from a fashion magazine, one of the beautiful people. Oh, not in looks, and not, certainly, in the sense the magazine intends the phrase—money and the style money buys—but in the happy sense of being who you are and extending your identity into the world. John looked somewhat like an Italian organ grinder, and liked the way he looked. He affected what was in part dictated by economic necessity, a rough elegance wholly unlike the rigid conformity the rest of us showed. I mention the matter of clothing because that was the first area into which Jack moved.

If John carried a J. C. Penney bandana for a handkerchief, Jack soon carried one, too. If John wore cords when the rest of us wore levis, you could be certain Jack would next appear in cords. I'm sure that John was flattered in the beginning, but gradually during the two or three years that followed, though more slowly than the rest of us who delighted in each new feat of imitation, John came to feel differently, for finally Jack was imitating John even in the choice of girls. If John dated Sue Bigelow on the weekend, you could count on Jack's asking her out the following week.

There was, of course, something absurd and sad about Jack—and something frightening: Jack wearing cords, carrying a bandana, dating John's girls, and Jack always the first with a bad word for John. Of course, Jack hated John, for even if he had become John—and one sometimes felt he had—he could never be unique until he had destroyed John. That World War II did put John in a grave in Holland is almost beside the point, for Jack found another model and began imitating him.

You may ask, what do John and Jack, Bogie and the Duke, have to do with art? Only what I have already suggested, that the process by which we shape our lives and commit them to memory, and having done so, determine the choices of the future, is a process more than analogous to the artistic process. The artist differs from us in that he has a talent for sound, or line, or color, and if he is a great artist, in having a better mind, but the way his mind works—the selection of given materials and the shaping of them into a unique and meaningful pattern—is the way our minds work.

To experience art is to experience our humanity. If a society is not interested in the human experience, is afraid of it, and endeavors to curtail it, it will exhibit that lack of interest, that fear, that endeavor in its attitude toward art.

One of the most ancient sources of wonder for man must be that he survives growing up, and perhaps he never does, but to the extent that he does grow and survive, he does so by means of the creative processes of his mind. If his parents fail him, if society fails him, he can, if he is lucky, still turn to the great works of art, and learn from them something of what it is to be human. If the noble Oedipus, that Everyman of the ancient world, cannot know everything, and hence unwittingly kills has father, marries his mother, and fathers his own brothers and sisters, he can still come to knowledge—not foresight, the province of the gods, but that knowledge of man's capacities which can only be gained by having lived. He can come to this knowledge, accept it, and find redemption.

Art is a mirror in which we can see our parents forgiven, our society changed, ourselves blessed—all by our own hand, the hand of the only duke worth going home to.

HENRI COULETTE

4

about america

WILLIAM CARLOS WILLIAMS

the destruction of tenochtitlan

Upon the orchidean beauty of the new world the old rushed inevitably to revenge itself after the Italian's return. Such things occur in secret. Though men may be possessed by beauty while they work that is all they know of it or of their own terrible hands; they do not fathom the forces which carry them. Spain cannot be blamed for the crassness of the discoverers. They moved out across the seas stirred by instincts, ancient beyond thought as the depths they were crossing, which they obeyed under the names of King or Christ or whatever it might be, while they watched the recreative New unfolding itself miraculously before them, before *them,* deafened and blinded. Steering beyond familiar horizons they were driven to seek perhaps self-justification for victorious wars against Arab and Moor; but these things are the surface only. At the back, as it remains, it was the evil of the whole world; it was the perennial disappointment which follows, like smoke, the bursting of ideas. It was the spirit of malice which underlies men's lives and against which nothing offers resistance. And bitter as the thought may be that Tenochtitlan, the barbaric city, its people, its genius wherever found should have been crushed out because of the awkward names men give their emptiness, yet it was no man's fault. It was the force of the pack whom the dead drive. Cortez was neither malicious, stupid nor blind, but a conqueror like other conquerors. Courageous almost beyond precedent, tactful, resourceful in misfortune, he was a man of genius superbly suited to his task. What his hand touched went down in spite of him. He was one among the rest. Velasquez, the Cuban Governor who sent him out, traitorously attacked him from the rear a week afterward. His own captains would have deserted him, so hard was he to follow. But the entire enterprise lived for many years on the verge of being allowed to languish, ruin to succeed destruction, because of the fortuitous anger which blossomed so naïvely, so mysteriously in Fonseca, Bishop of Burgos, President of the Council of the Indies. This the man, Cortez' most powerful enemy, already so notorious for the spiteful malevolence with which he thwarted the views of Columbus—a logic clearer had there been two Fonsecas instead of the one. After a rough voyage from Cuba, across the gulf, Cortez landed his small force safely before what is now Vera Cruz, near the native city of Cempoal. There, lest his men should desert him in view of the hardships which lay ahead, he had his vessels beached, under pretext of their being no longer seaworthy, and destroyed them.

Montezuma immediately sent gifts, at the same time begging the Spaniard not to risk coming up into the back country: a gold necklace of seven pieces, set with many gems like small rubies, a hundred and eighty-three emeralds and ten fine pearls, and hung with twenty-seven little bells of gold.—Two wheels, one of gold like the sun and the other of silver with the image of the moon upon it, made of plates of those metals, twenty-eight hands in circumference, with figures of animals and other things in bas relief, finished with great skill and ingenuity.—A headpiece of wood and gold, adorned with gems, from which hung twenty-five little bells of gold, and, on it, instead of plume, a green bird with eyes, beak and feet of gold.—Several shoes of the skin of deer, sewed with gold thread, the soles of which were made of blue and white stones of a brilliant appearance.—A shield of wood and leather, with little bells hanging to it and covered with plates of gold, in the middle of which was cut the image of the god of war between four heads of a lion, a tiger, an eagle and an owl represented alive with their hair and feathers.—Twenty-four curious and beautiful shields of gold, of feathers and very small pearls, and four of feathers and silver only.—Four fishes, two ducks and some other birds of molten gold.—A large mirror adorned with gold, and many small.—Miters and crowns of feathers and gold ornamented with pearls and gems.—Several large plumes of beautiful feathers, fretted with gold and small pearls.—Several fans of gold and silver mixed together; others of feathers only, of different forms and sizes.—A variety of cotton mantles, some all white, others chequered with white and black, or red, green, yellow and blue; on the outside rough like shaggy cloth and within destitute of color and nap.—A number of under-waistcoats, handkerchiefs, counterpanes, tapestries and carpets of cotton, the workmanship superior to the materials of which they were composed.—And books made of tablets with a smooth surface for writing, which being joined might be folded together or stretched out to a considerable length, "the characters inscribed thereon resembling nothing so much as Egyptian hieroglyphics."—But Cortez was unwilling to turn back; rather these things whetted his appetite for the adventure. Without more ado he sent letters to his king advising him that having come to these lands to conquer them, in the royal name and that of the true church, he would forthwith proceed to take Montezuma, dead or alive, unless he should accept the faith and acknowledge himself a subject to the Spanish throne.

The advance was like any similar military enterprise: it accomplished its purpose. Surmounting every difficulty Cortez went his way into the country past the quiet Cempoalan maizefields, past the smoking summit of Popocatepetl, until, after weeks of labor, he arrived upon the great lakes and the small cities in them adjoining Tenochtitlan itself. Montezuma seeing that there was nothing else for it, sent envoys accompanied by three hundred warriors, who met the Spaniard advancing on the lake road and there welcomed him to the district with great ceremony and show of friendliness. Noticeable among them was one young man of magnificent appearance who descended from his litter and walked to meet the Conqueror while his followers ran before him, picking up stones and other small obstructions which lay in his path. Cortez now passed over his first causeway into one of the lesser lake cities, built of well-hewn stone sheer from the water. He was overcome with wonder. The houses were so excellently put together, so well decorated with cloths and carven wood, so embellished with metalwork and other marks of a beautiful civilization; the people were so gracious; there were such gardens, such trees, such conservatories of flowers that nothing like it had ever been seen or imagined. At the house where the Conqueror was entertained that day and night he especially noted a pool built of stone into the clear waters of which stone steps descended, while round it were paven paths lined with sweet-smelling shrubs and plants and trees of all sorts. Also he noted the well-stocked kitchen garden. The following day at noon he arrived at the end of his journey.

There it lay! a city as large as Cordova or Seville, entirely within the lake two miles from the mainland: Tenochtitlan. Four avenues or entrances led to it, all formed of artificial causeways. Along the most easterly of these, constructed of great beams perfectly hewn and fitted together, and measuring two spears-lengths in width, the Christian advanced. Running in at one side of the city and out at the other this avenue constituted at the same time its principal street. As Cortez drew nearer he saw, right and left, magnificent houses and temples, close to the walls of which, each side, moved parallel rows of priests in black robes, and, between them, supported by two attendants, Montezuma, on foot, down the center of the roadway. Cortez stepped forward but the attendants interceded. The Emperor then advanced alone and with great simpleness of manner placed a golden chain about the Christian's neck. Then taking him by the hand, and the whole procession following, he conducted him to the quarters which had been chosen for the visitors, a great building close to the royal palaces in the center of the city. Everything had been prepared in advance: all the material needs together with rich gifts, as before: precious metals, gems, male and female apparel of remarkable elegance, ornamental hangings for bed-chambers, tapestries for halls and temples, counterpanes composed of feathers interwoven with cotton, and many beautiful and curious artifices "of so costly and unusual workmanship that considering their novelty and wonderful beauty no price could be set on them." Here in this large building whose great hall was to serve the Spaniards for barracks from that time until the end, Montezuma and Cortez found themselves seated at last face to face. Montezuma spoke: "They have told you that I possess houses with walls of gold and many other such things and that I am a god or make myself one. The houses you see are of stone and lime and earth."—Then opening his robe: "You see that I am composed of flesh and bone like yourselves and that I am mortal and palpable to the touch."—To this smiling sally, so full of gentleness and amused irony, Cortez could reply nothing save to demand that the man declare himself a subject of the Spanish King forthwith and that, furthermore, he should then and there announce publicly his allegiance to the new power.—Whatever the Aztec may have felt during the weeks of Cortez' slow advance upon his capital from the seashore, nothing at the present moment seemed to disturb his aristocratic reserve. He had thought and he had made up his mind. Without semblance of anger, fear or impatience; without humility or protest but with the force bred of a determination to face at any cost a situation fast going beyond his control, he spoke again. He explained that his people were not the aborigines of the land but that they had emigrated there in times past and ended by accepting the Spanish Monarch as his rightful and hereditary master. After due announcements and explanations had been made to the people Cortez became the acknowledged regent, in the name of Castile and the true church, for all that country.

Streets, public squares, markets, temples, palaces, the city spread its dark life upon the earth of a new world, rooted there, sensitive to its richest beauty, but so completely removed from those foreign contacts which harden and protect, that at the very breath of conquest it vanished. The whole world of its unique associations sank back into the ground to be reënkindled, never. Never, at least, save in spirit; a spirit mysterious, constructive, independent, puissant with natural wealth; light, if it may be, as feathers; a spirit lost in that soil. Scarcely an element in the city's incredible organization but evidenced an intellectual vigor full of resource and delicacy which had given it distinction. Half land and half water the streets were navigated by canoes and bridged at the intersections by structures of great timbers over which ten horses could go abreast. For water supply a masonry pipe, two paces broad and five feet high, ran from the mainland over one of the great causeways, carrying excellent drinking water. There were two such aqueducts, side by side, each to be used alternately while the other was cleaning. There were public squares, and one of great size surrounded by porticoes where daily sixty thousand souls engaged in buying and selling under the supervision of twelve central magistrates and numbers of inspectors. Here "everything which the world affords" was offered for purchase, from the personal services of laborers and porters to the last refinements of bijouterie; gold, silver, lead, brass, copper, tin; wrought and unwrought stone, bricks burnt and unburnt, timber hewn and unhewn, of different sorts; game of every variety, fowls, quails, partridges, wild ducks, parrots, pigeons, reed-birds, sparrows, eagles, hawks, owls, likewise the skins of some birds of prey with their feathers, head, beak and claws; rabbits, hares, deer and little dogs, which they raised for eating; wood and coals in abundance and brasiers of earthenware for burning coals; mats of various kinds; all kinds of green vegetables, especially onions, leeks, watercresses, nasturtium, sorrel, artichokes and golden thistle; fruits, fish, honey, grain—either whole, in the form of flour or baked into loaves; different kinds of cotton thread of all colors; jars, jugs, pots and an endless variety of vessels, all made of fine clay, most of them glazed and painted; eggs, cakes, pâtés of birds and fish; wine from the maguey; finally everything that could be found throughout the whole country was sold there, each kind of merchandise in a separate street or quarter of the market assigned to it exclusively, and thus the best order was preserved. There was an herb street, there were shops where they shaved and washed the head, and restaurateurs who furnished food and drink at a price.

Large numbers of temples existed throughout the great city, but for grandeur and excellence of architectural detail one far surpassed the rest. Forty towers, lofty and well built, rose from within its sacred precinct, the largest of which, constructed of hewn stone remarkably hard in texture, had fifty steps leading to its main body. A mass higher than the cathedral of Seville. Three halls of wonderful extent and height, adorned with figures sculptured in wood and stone, contained the principal idols. And from these, through very small doors, opened the chapels, to which no light was admitted, nor any person except the priests, and not all of them. Decorated with curious imagery in stone, the woodwork carved in relief and painted with figures of monsters and other things, unpaved, darkened and bloodstained, it was in these chapels that the religious practices which so shocked the Christian were performed. Here it was that the tribe's deep feeling for a reality that stems back into the permanence of remote origins had its firm hold. It was the earthward thrust of their logic; blood and earth; the realization of their primal and continuous identity with the ground itself, where everything is fixed in darkness. The priests in black robes, tribal men, never cutting or combing the hair; the instinctive exclusion of women from all places of worship; the debarring of priests from female society: it was a ceremonial acknowledgment of the deep sexless urge of life itself, the hungry animal, underlying all other power; the mysterious secret of existence whose cruel beauty they, the living, inherited from the dead. The same for their sculpture. It is the mystery of the past which monsters, grotesques, beasts combined with the human, truly signify—gentle animal associations distorted by the invasions of night—and not a debased instinct whose reliance is necessarily upon oppression and fear. The earth is black and it is there: only art advances. The figures of the idols themselves were of extra-human size and composed, significantly, of a paste of seeds and leguminous plants, commonly used for food, ground and mixed together and kneaded with human blood, the whole when completed being consecrated with a bath of blood from the heart of a living victim. The chief of these idols Cortez precipitated from their pedestals and cast down the temple steps; an act of extraordinary daring; at the same time purifying the chapels and setting up in them images of Our Lady and the saints.

Such a stroke could not fail to have proved of the most serious consequence to all had not Montezuma again displayed his tact, self-control and remarkable grasp of the changing situation. The new state of affairs was accepted, human sacrifice was abolished and the orderly significance of the events taking place was publicly made evident. In person, together with many of the principal citizens, he, Montezuma, assisted at the final purification of the chapels. Whether or not this be evidence on the Aztec's part of weakness or the deepest forbearance, surely nothing like it for quiet flexibility of temper and retained dignity has ever been recorded. Perhaps by a sudden, daring stroke this man might have rid himself of the intestine enemy who was each day, each week, striking deeper at the nation's life. Perhaps fear had unmanned him. Perhaps what we call forbearance was no more than the timidity which is an overwhelming agony of heart inspired by the sight of a resistless force aimed at our destruction. Still, if this be so, Montezuma has left no trace of cowardice upon the records. But weakling or genius, about the suave personality of this barbaric chieftain the liveliest, most airily expansive moods of the race did flower, just as the black permanence of tribal understanding stood rooted in the priesthood. Perhaps it was a conscious knowledge of this that inspired and moved Montezuma in the present action.

Surely no other prince has lived, or will ever live, in such state at did this American cacique: The whole waking aspirations of his people, opposed to and completing their religious sense, seemed to come off in him and in him alone: the drive upward, toward the sun and the stars. He was the very person of their ornate dreams, so delicate, so prismatically colorful, so full of tinkling sounds and rhythms, so tireless of invention. Never was such a surface lifted above the isolate blackness of such profound savagery. It is delightful to know that Montezuma changed his clothes four times a day, donning four different suits, entirely new, which he never wore again; that at meals he was served in a great clean-swept chamber on mats upon the floor, his food being kept warm in chafing dishes containing live coals; that at meals he sat upon a small cushion "curiously wrought of leather." But nowhere in his state was the stark power of beauty, the refined and the barbaric, so exquisitely expressed as in his smaller palaces and places of amusement. "What can be more wonderful than that a barbarous monarch, as he is, should have every object in his domain imitated in gold, silver, precious stones and feathers; the gold and silver being wrought so naturally as not to be surpassed by any smith in the world; the stonework executed with such perfection that it is difficult to conceive what instruments could have been used, and the feather work superior to the finest production in wax and embroidery." "There is one palace inferior to the rest, attached to which is a beautiful garden with balconies extending over it supported by marble columns and having a floor formed of jasper elegantly inlaid. Belonging to it are ten pools, in which are kept the different species of water birds found in the country, all domesticated: for the sea birds there are pools of salt water and for the river birds, fresh water. Each species being supplied with the food natural to it when wild. Over the pools are corridors and galleries, to which Montezuma resorts, and from which he can look out and amuse himself with the sight of the birds there." "In an apartment of the same palace there are men, women, and children whose faces, bodies, hair, eyebrows and eyelashes were white from birth." "The Emperor has another very beautiful palace, with a large courtyard, paved with handsome flags in the style of a chessboard. There are cages about nine feet in height and six paces square, each of which is half covered with a roof of tiles, and the other half has over it a wooden grate, skilfully made. Every cage contains a bird of prey, of all species." "In the same palace there are several large halls on the ground floor, filled with immense cages built of heavy pieces of timber, well put together, in which are kept lions, wolves, foxes and a great variety of other animals of the cat kind." "The care of these animals and birds is assigned to three hundred men." Daily the Emperor's wine cellar and larder were open to all who wished to eat and drink. His meals were served by three or four hundred youths who brought on an infinite variety of dishes; indeed, whenever he dined or supped, the table was loaded with every kind of fish, flesh, fruits and vegetables which the country afforded. Both at the beginning and end of every meal they furnished water for the hands, and the napkins used on these occasions were never employed a second time.

And then the end: Cortez had demanded gold from the first. To satisfy him, small groups of two Spaniards and two Indians, bearing the proper credentials, had been despatched about the Aztec's domain, to distances in some cases of several hundred miles, that the tribute be collected. On one of these forays the two Christians were killed. Cortez immediately seized the person of

Montezuma, together with his daughters and sons, imprisoning them in the garrison-fortress. From that time on, it was merely a matter of detail and of time as to what form the final catastrophe would take. Events shifted back and forth until in May, seven months after the Spaniards' first entrance to the city, the people laid siege to the intolerable intruders, determined to have done with them. In answer to shouts from outside, Montezuma, a prisoner within, had appeared on the ramparts of the beseiged fortress whence he implored his people to give over their attacks. In reply he was struck on the head by a stone which killed him. Only the horse and the ordnance saved the Christians on that memorable retreat across the great causeway. Fighting madly to escape with some remnant of his forces through the masses of the enemy, and to retain at the same time his prisoners and treasure, Cortez lost everything. The children of Montezuma, the gold, everything perished over the sides of the breached and beleaguered avenue across the lake down which the Spaniards retreated, foot by foot, with swarms of Indians flinging themselves continually upon them. They escaped. Some months later they returned and continued the destruction, this time deliberately and with calculated malintention. Tenochtitlan surrounded, the water supply cut off, the augmented Spanish forces began to burrow forward and after weeks of desperate effort they succeeded in their plans. It was the horses the Indians feared most. At one time they had Cortez in their very hands only to have them cut off at the wrists by his followers. But nothing could bemuse them now. They knew now what it all meant and they opposed themselves to the intruder inflexibly and without murmur until the end. Neither the overwhelming means used against them, their desertion by friends of the nearby tribes, the lack of water, starvation, nor attempts to inspire them with fear, made the slightest impression. To every advance made inviting them to parley they had but the one answer: no! Cortez, dejected, seeing that it would be necessary to exterminate them before he could succeed in taking the city and dreading the horror of such a course, decided with reluctance, in order to impress them, to burn the noble edifices in the great square which had served Montezuma for aviaries. "It grieved me much but it grieved the enemy more." Each day he heard mass and returned to the city to renew the attack upon the now nearly starved inhabitants who had retreated to the market quarter and there still held out. At one time during a successful sally the Indians had killed two of the Spanish horses and in great spirits had sent the severed heads by messengers in canoes to the surrounding tribes for them to come to the rescue, but none dared. Most had already joined the Christian in his irresistible purpose. But Guatemotzin, the young nephew of Montezuma, would not give in. Women and children reduced to the last extremity by hunger and privation were wandering dazed about the streets when the Spaniards had made their final charge. But Guatemotzin, taken captive from a boat in an effort to get to the mainland, still maintained his pride and integrity of spirit. He had done all that he could and he was beaten. Placing his hand upon the hilt of Cortez' dagger, he asked the Spaniard to draw it and plunge it into his heart. Cortez refused. Later the Conqueror tried to rebuild the city. *Viva quien vence!*

DANIEL BELL

the racket-ridden longshoremen: the web of economics and politics

Rimmed off from the rest of the city by a steel-ribbed highway and a wall of bulkhead sheds is the New York waterfront, an atavistic world more redolent of the brawling money-grubbing of the nineteenth century than the smooth-mannered business transactions of the twentieth. Cross the shadow line and you are in a rough, racket-ridden frontier domain, ruled by the bull-like figure of the "shaping boss." Here brawn and muscle, sustained where necessary by baling hook and knife, enforce discipline among a motley group of Italian immigrant, Slavic, and Negro workers and a restless and grumbling group of Irish. Here one finds kickbacks, loansharking, petty extortion, theft, and pilferage—and murder—a commonplace of longshore life. Many of the docks are controlled directly or indirectly by mobsters who dominated the pier union local, parceled out the jobs, and ran the rackets. The rank and file, cynical of any settlement by the leadership of the union, sometimes took the only course it knew, i.e., of "voting with its feet," a wildcat strike—but then, only with the backing of dissident rack leaders who used the occasion to challenge the entrenched mobs. In the decade after the war every major collective bargaining agreement between the shipping companies and the longshore union was repudiated by the men.

Why this domination by rackets has persisted is the subject of this paper. The answer, broadly, involves an understanding of the economics of the industry, of the peculiar political relationships between the union and the urban Democratic party machine in the port cities, the ethnic patterns within the longshoremen groups, the psychology of the longshoremen as an "isolated mass" suspicious of the urban community around them, and the "Chinese warlord" structure of the union itself. But these elements only provide the setting. What is distinctive is the role of the industrial racketeer, initially performing a "quasi-legitimate" economic function and thus acting as the social cement which bound the structure together.

I make a necessary distinction between corruption and industrial racketeering. Corruption involves spoliation of union funds, payoffs, bribes, shakedowns, etc. It is a form of abuse of office or extortion from others for the personal gain of the malefactor. If the cost is not too high, or can be passed along easily to others as in the building trades, it becomes an accepted part of the way of doing business; if too exorbitant it may lead to a demand for government intervention. Industrial racketeering, however, performs the function—at a high price—which other agencies cannot do, of stabilizing a chaotic market and establishing an order and structure in the industry. Industrial racketeering can exist only in a specific type of economic market. It does not exist in steel, auto, chemical, rubber, etc., where a few giant firms, acting in oligopolistic fashion, establish an ordered price structure in the industry. It has existed in small-unit size, highly competitive, local-product markets, such as trucking, garment, baking, cleaning, and dyeing, where no single force other than the industrial racketeer was strong enough to stabilize the industry. This was especially true in the 1920's when industrial racketeering flourished. In the early 1930's, legalized price-fixing by the New Deal, through the NRA, undercut the role of the industrial racketeer. What hitherto had been a quasi-economic but necessary function now became outright and unnecessary extortion. And in the garment area (dominated by Lepke and Gurrah), in the restaurant field, and in similar industries infested with industrial racketeers, the employers and the union appealed to government for help. And that is how Tom Dewey, as district attorney of New York County in the mid-thirties, first came into prominence as a prosecutor. Following the demise of the NRA, the trade-unions in most of these fields were strong enough to take over the role of stabilizing and policing the industry. On the New York waterfront, the racket pattern continued. Why?

It is the thesis of this paper that the distinctive economic matrix of the port shaped a pattern of accommodation between the shippers and the racketeers and led to the continuation of the system. Without these economic requirements, the system would go under. In our fascination these days with power and manipulation, we often ignore the economic fulcrum underneath. The political intervention of the state and federal agencies and the AFL, in the New York waterfront situation in 1953 and after, was based on the belief that by changing the power relations in the longshore union the conditions which gave rise to racketeering might be eliminated. Certainly this was the justification for the extraordinary intervention by the Eisenhower and Dewey administrations in the waterfront strikes in 1955 and 1956, although the Republicans had previously proclaimed that government should keep its hands out of any labor dispute. The political effort failed. Yet if it had succeeded, it is doubtful whether the pattern of racketeering would have been upset, for without the reshaping and rationalization of the "technological" environment (using the word in its broadest sense to cover ecological, mechanized handling techniques, and economic aspect of operations), the conditions which gave rise to racketeering would persist. And that is what this paper seeks to show. If what follows, then, is in great measure history, it is history written through sociological perspectives: to explain how racketeering became an integral part of a union and to demonstrate the role of a particular type of market in shaping a set of complex social relations.

the economic fulcrum

It is a schoolboy's maxim that New York owes its commanding position as the largest city in the United States to its magnificent port. In the growing commerce of the country, no other city could match its assets: wide and deep channels and ice-free and rarely foggy waters allowed great freighters to sail a few miles inland into a set of vast natural harbors, into protected estuaries curving into the bays, and into long, navigable rivers, which offered numerous and accessible wharfs. It was thus inevitable that shipping would come to New York. The frequency of sailings, the availability of cargo space, the many converging railroad trunk lines, and the ready banking facilities soon made the port attractive both to factors who wanted to move goods from inland to Europe and to importers bringing goods from abroad for sale in the United States. Because of the heavy commerce, the nation's banks made it a practice to keep large reserve deposits on hand, and this accumulation of liquid capital made New York the security trading center of the country. By the turn of the century, New York had become the greatest concentration point of economic and social power in the United States. The spatial counterpoint of downtown financial skyscraper and squat West Side bulkhead became the topographical symbol of this reciprocal genuflection of finance and commerce.

Although the New York harbor curves in a sinuous perimeter of seven hundred miles, the hub of the port is the four to five miles of piers and landings along the west side of Manhattan. Here the ocean-going vessels dock. Here the tremendous amount of cargo and produce which is consumed in the city or shipped inland, and the cargo sent from the industrial East for export abroad, are loaded and unloaded. But Manhattan is an island, and its handicaps are unique. Although much of the general cargo tonnage is handled on narrow Manhattan, the island does not have a single steamship pier with direct track connection to a trunkline railroad. Rail freight has to be delivered to or taken from the ships either by lighters which float across the harbor or by truck. But the width of the slips between piers is insufficient both for the berthing of ocean-going freighters and for the squat lighters which hover alongside the ships to unload or deliver the bulk cargo. Hence, serious congestion and delay create costly shifting expenses. And the narrowness of the piers themselves works havoc on the dock for the trucks. Only a few of New York's piers can accommodate the forty-foot mammoth trucks which carry cargo, so that, for the most part, freight must be handled in the choked marginal streets outside the piers. Congestion is so fierce and waiting-time so high that the large motor carriers publish penalty rates for deliveries to steamship piers within the metropolitan area.

As a result of these antiquated facilities, shore-handling costs, which once were a minor factor in the operation of a boat, in most instances began to exceed the combined costs of vessel depreciation, crew's wages, insurance, supplies, overhead, maintenance, and fuel oil. The biggest single shore expense became longshoring, which accounted for 50 per cent of the ship's total expense in moving cargo. If a shipping company was to have a profitable run, it needed a quick "turn-around," i.e., speedy unloading and loading, and a quick get-away. And for this, it needed a ready and compliant labor force.

the shape of the labor supply

Shipping, by custom, is a "casual" operation. The industry itself is seasonal and cyclical, the volume of business subject to wars, to political blackouts of trade routes, etc. Individual schedules are subject to the vagaries of weather, port delays, the kind of bulk consignments, etc. The demand for labor fluctuates widely, depending upon the number of ships in port. To get a quick "turn-around" the steamship company wants an over-supply of labor which can be readily available, will work long and continuous hours a few feverish days in the week, and will wait patiently over the idle stretches until the next ship comes.

Because their needs are irregular, most of the shipping companies do not hire longshoremen directly, but contract with stevedoring concerns on a tonnage basis for the loading and unloading of their ships. Approximately sixty such stevedoring concerns hire all dock labor, and they, together with the shipping lines, constitute the New York Shipping Association, which negotiates with the union on wages and working conditions.

Historically, the way of maintaining the necessary over-supply was an "open shape," i.e., encouraging all kinds of transients to congregate at the dock and picking the men on a gypsy basis. For a cab driver, an idle teamster—and even a city fireman or policeman off duty!—the system was an easy way to pick up a few extra dollars, particularly on weekends or evenings, when overtime rates prevailed. Thousands of such workers put in small and irregular amounts of time on the docks. But for the thousands of workers who sought regular livelihood the conditions of an open shape, and the favoritism it encouraged, were intolerable.

Prior to World War II, all hiring was done by open shape. Twice a day, at 7:55 A.M. and at 1 P.M. (and, when necessary, a third time in the evening), the men "shaped up" in loose semicircle in front of the pier and were picked for a half-day's work by the hiring or "shaping boss." No formal system existed for informing the men where they might be needed from day to day. Some men got the information from bulletin boards on piers, some through gossip, some followed newspapers and trade papers. If a man was not hired at the 7:55 A.M. shape, he had little chance of working during the rest of the day. And not knowing where else in the Port there might be work, he squatted on his pier; even if he did go to some other pier, the chances were that he would be late or that some other transient had gotten the nod. In the absence of any information, men congregated at the piers where they had obtained work in the past. Each pier or group of piers, thus, tended to build up its own labor force. Some longshore locals, such as Local 968, an all-Negro one, had no particular pier, since it had been crowded off its Brooklyn docks by an Italian local, and its members roamed the city or sought to set up their own "labor exchange" in Harlem.

In April, 1942, Rear Admiral Land, then head of the War Shipping Administration, bitterly criticized the shape-up as inefficient and chaotic. Because of the manpower shortage, and for reasons of security, the open shape, i.e., picking a group at random, was modified by the creation of steady or regular gangs who remained intact and had first crack at jobs on the gang's regular pier. (After the war, the regular-gang system remained on most Hudson River docks. The others, along the East River and Brooklyn, reverted to open shapes or to the use of traveling gangs.)

The system of regular gangs did allow new solidarities to form. And it is significant that strikes erupted on the New York waterfront after the war—there were none in the twenties and thirties and during the war—only when some form of regularized employment had arisen.

The shape-up obviously gave the shipping companies the floating labor force they needed. In 1946, the peak postwar year, a total of 60,000 longshoremen were employed on the piers. In 1950, because of the decline of shipping, this had fallen to 40,000. This was the total labor supply—regular workers and transients. Actually, the "full-time" longshore force was between 16,000 to 20,000 men; the rest were floaters. Of the regular group, only between 5 to 8 per cent worked 2,000 hours a year (i.e., a regular forty-hour week for fifty weeks). Between 20 and 25 per cent worked between 1,200 to 2,000 hours a year. And the remaining 35 to 45 per cent worked from 700 to 1,200 hours a year. The simplest indicator of the low and unstable income status of a New York longshoreman is that banks and finance companies do not make personal loans to dockworkers, nor are longshoremen accepted, usually, as low-income tenants in public or private housing projects.

the padrone and the peons

The system of the shape tended to emphasize the uncertainties and insecurities of the job. Under a brawny leader, pier cliques grew up to assure the pick of the jobs for themselves. Rackets multiplied. By possessing two social security cards a man could work a minimum number of hours on one card and then collect insurance while working regularly on the other. Or the surplus work cards were used to pad the payroll by adding a fictitious work gang to the roster, and the extra money was divided by the hiring boss, the payroll clerk, and the clique. This type of payroll padding, as well as loansharking and any number of other parasitic practices, was possible because of the "brass check,"* a system which had died out almost everywhere else at that time in U.S. industry. The worker collected his pay by turning in the brass check, but so could anyone else who had the check. Longshoremen who went broke before pay day, or needed money in a hurry to pay bills, sold their checks for a percentage of their value. The stevedoring companies blinked at the padding because the sums were petty beside the vaster benefits obtained by a pliant hiring boss who would drive the men for greater productivity.

The key man on the dock was the hiring or "shaping" boss. Although the hiring boss was, in fact, a foreman, and thus a management representative, all the hiring bosses were members of the

* An old system of paying unskilled labor. A worker was given a brass check for each day worked, and these checks were turned in at the end of the week for cash. Thus bookkeeping was minimized and few records had to be kept. Since prostitutes were once also paid in this manner, the term, particularly among the Wobblies, became one of contempt and was used so by Upton Sinclair as the title of a book on the "kept" press.

International Longshoreman's Association, and their choice was dictated by the local union; in few cases could a steamship or stevedore company name a hiring boss. As a key patronage job, the choice fell to the union officer, who traded it to a friend.

It was quite common for the hiring bosses on many of the piers to possess criminal records. A cynical reason was supplied by an official of a large stevedoring concern: "If I have a choice of hiring a tough ex-convict or a man without a criminal record I am more inclined to take the ex-convict. Know why? Because if he is in a boss job he'll keep the men in line and get the maximum work out of them. They would be afraid of him."

the world of the ILA

Why did the union tolerate these conditions? Stated more simply, why didn't the International Longshoremen's Association act like a union? The classic pattern of American unionism, its *raison d'être,* is *job control.* Job control means limiting the number of jobs, or the number of men seeking jobs, and a defined system of seniority, in order to assure equity and security in the title to the job. Few unions in the United States encourage cutthroat competition among men for jobs or tolerate a condition of job insecurity. The ILA did.

The answer was obvious long ago. Msgr. Swanstrom, a Catholic priest who published a study in 1939 entitled "The Waterfront Labor Problem," wrote: "Merely as a statement of fact, [the union's] officers and delegates have a vested interest in keeping the membership at a high level." By encouraging a surplus of labor, the union accommodated the companies; by controlling the shape-up, the union leadership had an effective club over the men.

Actually, the International Longshoremen's Association has been less a trade union than a collection of Chinese warlords, each ruling a great or small province. In the New York region there are about seventy locals, some craft, others geographically based, whose memberships range from ten to fifteen hundred members each. Roughly thirty of these are longshore locals which normally have geographical jurisdiction over one or a small group of adjacent piers. In addition, the ILA also contains craft locals of carpenters, clerks, and checkers, and a large, miscellaneous collection of locals of lumberyard workers, warehousemen, oil handlers, lightermen, tugboat operators, grain-elevator workers, ship caulkers, captains of deck scows, and others with such fancy titles as "Steamship Horse and Cattle Fitters," "Grain Ceilers," "Marine Carpenters," "Sugar Samplers," "Grain Trimmers," "Boom Testing and Rigging Testing" workers, etc.

Within a local, the small membership and the "face-to-face" contact made it possible for small cliques to gain and "enforce" control. A tight machine of loyal followers was built up through the handing-out of regular jobs to a favored few. The rest of the membership was cowed by the discriminatory threats of loss of job. In the postwar years, when for the first time some records were kept, only seven locals, it was shown, held regular elections by secret ballot. The others voted openly, or not at all.

The violations of democracy were widespread not only in the locals but in the district regions as well. In the New York area, the longshore locals were grouped into a District Council which dealt with the problems of the longshoremen, checkers, cargo repairmen, maintenance men, etc. But the area itself was politically gerrymandered. By design, there were far too many longshore locals with a paper membership. Since all actions of any consequence had to be approved by the District Council, dissident locals were easily outvoted. On major strike issues, an archaic system of voting enabled the top officers to manipulate the results. When a poll was to be taken, the prevailing custom was to place ballot boxes in each of the union's locals from Maine to Virginia. The totals were telephoned to the offices of the International where they were tabulated, the results announced, and the letters confirming receipt of the totals forwarded to each local. In the 1951 strike vote, reported the New York State Inquiry board, "testimony discloses that not a single local in the Port of New York confirmed the report by telephone or telegram. The testimony also showed that no permanent record of the result of the balloting was made in the books of the locals examined. . . ."

the racket fulcrum

On the waterfront, control of a union local means much more than the ordinary prizes of political victory. Control of a union local means control of a pier, and control of a pier means control of the host of rackets that are spawned on the docks. A victorious clique has a number of concessions it can parcel out. These include bookmaking, loansharking, kickbacks for jobs, etc. Hence, the often bitter struggles for control, and the iron suppression of opposition once in power.

But the biggest prize of all was the "loading racket." Control of "loading" and its lucrative revenues was the major prize over which the bloody pier wars were fought on the New York docks for thirty years. The "loading racket" was the key to criminal infiltration and baronial domination of sections of the ILA, and its intricate political and economic accommodations among the power elements in New York waterfront history reveals all the facets.

Public loading arose out of a peculiar situation. When the steamship companies deposited a consignment from the ship onto the pier-shed floor, they took no further responsibility for it. A trucker who arrived to pick up the consignment had to lift the shipment onto the truck himself or get some help. Public loading was simply the act of employing a helper to take the stack of goods stored in the pier shed and to lift it manually or mechanically with a forktruck from the floor of the dock to the tailgate of the waiting truck. A lift of about a foot and a half. That was all.* Yet, for the privilege of controlling the loading "concessions" on different piers, more than a score of men were murdered, prominent shipping executives cowed, entire union locals taken over by mobsters, and city officials persuaded to look the other way. How come?

"Time," said Benjamin Franklin, "is money." Time is the answer. During World War I the number of vehicles trucking freight to and from the docks increased enormously. The cobbled streets along the waterfront right-of-way had not been built for such traffic. Nor were the city's narrow piers. The long lines piled up. The most expensive cost item in trucking became waiting time. Rather than pay a driver's helper for snoozing on the truck, the practice arose of sending a driver alone to the pier and having him hire a loader from among the "shenangos" or barflies at the nearby saloon.

Gradually, through a process of squatters' rights, various individuals began to assert a monopoly on loading at each pier. At first they offered a service; later they began to enforce compulsory service;

* The public loader, therefore, differed from the longshoremen who were hired by the stevedoring companies to load and unload ships. Public loaders were in origin roughly akin to public porters at rail stations who are not allowed through the train gate. They were, in effect, independent "middlemen" between the stevedoring operation and the trucker.

and, in classic monopoly fashion, they began to charge, literally, all that the traffic would bear. (Truckers in a special hurry could pay a "hurry-up" fee and go to the head of the line.) So the tollgate was established. Whether you needed a loader or not, you had to pay for the service, and on each ton of goods an extra tax was levied. So the industrial racketeer becomes established; he finds a strategic juncture and proceeds to occupy this point of vantage to his own profit.

When you have a good thing, said the devil, you organize it. And many men tried. "They hold their piers through a process of conquest and military occupation," wrote Alva Johnston in a New York *Tribune* series on loading in 1931. A gangster's crown, however, is like the Golden Bough of the priests of Nemi. One could succeed to the title of king only by slaying his predecessor. In the twenties a dozen members of the waterfront dynasty succeeded one another in rapid fashion.*

In the mid-twenties, however, peace was established. The various loading bosses in the West Side piers pooled their efforts and formed an organization known as Varick Enterprises, Inc., which served as a central collection agency and strong-arm operation for the mobsters. The organization had so efficient an intelligence service that it kept accurate tabs on every shipment, whether by rail or water, arriving in the city. Various loaders, operating through the agency, would go to the terminals, check on weights and names of truckers and consignees, and issue a loading ticket—whether any services were performed or not—setting forth the amount of the charge. Then the collectors made their rounds. If payment was refused, Varick, through its union contacts, could provoke a slowdown or threaten a reluctant shipper with a strike.

Varick Enterprises, which at one time helped elect a leader of Tammany Hall, dissolved in the mid-forties when the District Attorney's office began to investigate its operations. The boss loaders then reverted to the previous policy of controlling territories on an independent basis.

The career of John "Cockeye" Dunn illustrates the ripe rewards

* The shortest waterfront reign was that of Eddie McGuire who ruled for five minutes. When the leadership was vacant in 1928 the pier leaders met on the Colombian pier and shook dice for the leadership. Eddie won. Five minutes later everybody left the pier but Eddie. A watchman found him dead, with five bullets in his body.

and the casual murders that attended the growth of the loading racket. In 1936, Dunn, a man who had served time in two reformatories and a stretch in Sing Sing, turned to the waterfront. In short order, by murdering two men and wounding another, Dunn blasted his way into control of loading on Pier 59. In November, 1936, he and his lieutenants formed a "workers committee" and obtained from the ILA a charter for a union local known as the Terminal Checkers and Platform Men, Local 1346–2. With this local, Dunn planned to control loading not only at the piers but in the inland freight terminals as well. Dunn did not organize workers; he simply went to the employers, "negotiated" a contract, and then told the freight handlers they belonged to his union. The following year, Dunn extended his activities. He dropped his ILA charter and obtained from the national AFL three federal charters under the name of Motor and Bus Terminal Checkers, Platform and Office Workers. The charters were for New York, New Jersey, and Pennsylvania, and Dunn made himself business agent and vice-president of the New York local, while his hired slugger, Andrew "Squint" Sheridan, became organizer for the Jersey local. Through these locals, Dunn became a power in the trucking industry, at the same time maintaining control over a number of piers.

Shortly after the war, in May, 1946, a man named Anthony Hintz was designated as hiring boss on Pier 51. Hintz refused to play ball with Dunn and held out for months, despite efforts at intimidation. On January 8, 1947, as Hintz started down the stairway of his house to go to the dock, three men came up, and one pumped six bullets into him. For three days Hintz wavered on the edge of death; then, while his life was ebbing away, he told police, "Dunn shot me." The reason was simple. As Squint Sheridan, Dunn's partner, told the police: "To control a pier you've got to control the loading . . . Andy [Hintz] was a boss loader"—and he stood in the way. The profits of loading from one pier alone, said Sheridan, were about $900 a week.

For a while it seemed as if Dunn would talk and name others connected with the loading racket. In the end, however, he remained silent, and Dunn and Sheridan went to the chair in July, 1949.

In the postwar years, public loading was grudgingly given a garb of legality and became institutionalized. The process started incongruously when loading shakedowns began to reach outrageous heights. In the fall of 1948, tough, barrel-chested Joseph Adelezzi, managing director of the Motor Carriers Association, was ready to declare war. "We had a belly full of it," he said. "There was no uniformity as to loading rates. . . . There was no system, no regulation, no control of any kind. We told them we had gone as far as we could, and we would go no further, regardless of their guns."

The truckers demanded that the shipping lines, who were the pier lessees, or their stevedoring agents, take over the loading. This would have meant the establishment of regular charges by the shipping companies, and the end of the racket. But the shipping companies refused. Their interest was in a quick turn-around of their ships, and to get it they needed a large labor supply and a tractable labor force. For this, they needed a "cooperative" union local; and by this time, the locals were controlled by the racketeers. Moreover, by the ability to create delay, by slowdown or strike, the pier cliques were able to exert crippling leverage upon the companies. For this reason, it paid the shipping companies to cooperate and buy off the mobsters.

The shipping companies, therefore, refused to handle the loading. Actually, the truckers did not want to handle loading either. What they objected to was the arbitrary and eratic setting of rates which made it difficult to rationalize the extra charges to their customers. All they wanted was stability and order.

ILA president, Joe Ryan, hastily called a conference between the public loaders and truckers. The truckers agreed, in return for a contract setting uniform loading rates, that they would surrender the right to do the loading themselves. The contract was signed, but the abuses continued. Following renewed complaints, Commissioner of Investigation Murtagh asked the steamship companies to take over the loading themselves or to designate in writing the names of *the* public loaders authorized to operate on their piers. Hitherto, even the official identity of the loaders had been unknown; payments were made in cash, no books or records were kept. The steamship companies, mindful of the power of the loaders, refused to take over the job themselves, and proceeded to name the same persons, many of them men with criminal records, who were already in control of the piers, as the legal designees for the job. The effect of the city's feeble gesture was to give official stamp and recognition to the public loaders on the dock. The public loaders, though in effect independent contractors, became officially members of the longshore union, in the Port Loaders Council of the ILA. As a union, the loaders negotiated loading rates with the truckmen's association. Loading in New York had become "legitimatized."

The beauty of "loading" was that is provided a bland legal mask for extraordinary gain on almost no investment, other than muscle-men for intimidation, and that it provided a lucrative income, as regular as death and taxes, and subject only to the normal vagaries of the business cycle.

The real significance of the racket, for sociological investigation, is that "loading" is to be found *only* on the New York waterfront. There has never been a loading racket in San Francisco, in New Orleans, in Baltimore or Philadelphia—the other major maritime ports in the U.S. There are many indigenous or historical factors to account for this lack, but the key fact is that the *spatial* arrangements of these other ports is such that loading never had a "functional" significance. In all these ports, other than New York, there are direct railroad connections to the piers, so that transfer of cargoes is easily and quickly accomplished; nor is there in these ports the congested and choking narrow-street patterns which in New York forced the trucks to wait, piled up "time charges," or made for off-pier loading. Here is where a difference in the "economic matrix" helps in part to explain the presence or absence of racketeering.

the history of the ILA

What in the background or nature of the union led it to its parlous state?

The politics and the tactics of "immigrant" unions can be more readily understood if seen against the complicated background of competing ethnic groups in urban politics. Just as the "Jewish" unions in New York—the Ladies' Garment Workers, the Amalgamated Clothing Workers, and the Hatters—were intertwined at birth and at early growth with the Socialist party, so the "Irish" unions in New York—the longshoremen, the teamsters, and the building trades—were inextricably linked with Tammany Hall and its system of privilege. Many of the early builders, contractors, and stevedores were union men who struck out for themselves. They prospered by obtaining city contracts for paving, hauling, construction, etc. In these efforts they were often aided by the union leaders with political pull. Out of these collusive arrangements a complex web of friendships and political alliances arose. Except for a brief period in its early abortive days, the longshoremen's union has been part of this web.

Longshore organization has had a sporadic history on the East Coast. In the 1870's and 1880's a group of workers formed the Longshoremen's Union Protective Association, which sought to stabilize conditions on the docks. A more determined effort was made in the mid-1880's by an Englishman, Edward McHugh, who came to New York as an emissary from the dockworkers of London and Glasgow to organize a longshoremen's union so that simultaneous union action on both sides of the Atlantic would be possible against recalcitrant employers. McHugh organized the American Longshoremen's Union, but like many other unionists at the time, his interest soon turned to politics. In 1886, McHugh and the fledgling longshoremen's union took an active part in the Henry George mayoralty campaign, but in the following year, when the coalition United Labor party fell apart, the union faded and McHugh returned to London.

Longshore organization in New York was revived after the turn of the century by a fabulous West Side character named Dick Butler, who took over the old name and started anew the unaffiliated Longshoremen's Union Protective Association. A longshoreman and construction worker in his youth, Butler soon found the primrose path of politics and the *bon vivant* life of a Broadway blade and saloon keeper more to his taste. But through all these peregrinations, he retained a significant role in the union. A follower of former New York police chief and Tammany insurgent Big Bill Devery, Butler realized that a union was a convenient base for making political deals and getting out—and protecting—the vote during roughhouse Tammany primaries. His method of collective bargaining was primitive. Soon after the LUPA was revived, he won for the men a three cents an hour raise in wages. "I managed this," he recalled later, "by going down and having a heart-to-heart talk with P. A. S. Franklin who is now the head of the International Mercantile Marine." The personal touch was to dominate ILA bargain methods to this day.

Meanwhile, in 1892, a "Lumber Handlers of the Great Lakes" was started in Buffalo, which affiliated with the AFL. A year later, its jurisdiction was extended to all longshore work, and the following year, in 1894, it took the name of the International Longshoremen's Association. The union began its growth in the Great Lakes area under the leadership of T. V. O'Connor, who had started as a dockhand on a Great Lakes tugboat. In 1906, O'Connor became head of the Licensed Tugmen's Protective Association of the Great Lakes, and later, head of the ILA.

In 1912, O'Connor threatened to "muscle in" on the East Coast. To avoid fratricidal warfare, Dick Butler merged his LUPA with the International Longshoremen's Union and became the first Atlantic District president of the ILA. A third man rounded out the triumvirate of early ILA leaders. This was an Italian prize fighter, Paul Vacarelli, who was known better by his *nom de guerre* of Paul Kelly. Vacarelli started out his work career on a garbage scow and soon organized the scow trimmers' union. He stepped ashore and, like Butler, went into the saloon business while retaining union office. Politics was the next natural calling and, under the tutelage of Big Tim Sullivan, Vacarelli became the political *padrone* of the lower East Side. His saloon in Great Jones Street, called "Little Naples," was the hangout for such famous characters of New York lore as Monk Eastman, Six-fingered Murphy, Nine-eyed Donnigan, Yaky Yaky Brady, and Big Jack Zelig.

A triumvirate in power is an unstable combination. In 1917, Dick Butler set out to challenge O'Connor. Naturally he needed some sinews of war, and Butler appealed to his political and underworld friends. All the big gamblers up and down Broadway contributed to Butler's war chest. (Arnold Rothstein, the financier of the underworld, gave fifteen hundred dollars.) Said Butler simply: "The gamblers were grateful because I protected them during the Gaynor regime." Butler also had the support of the Atlantic District and two of its rising powers, Joseph P. Ryan and Al Marinelli. Butler also had the backing of the other member of the *troika,* Paul Vacarelli, but, in classic fashion, Vacarelli double-crossed Butler at the last moment and swung his support to O'Connor. Butler lost in a close fight.

Two years later, at Galveston, in 1919, Butler made another try. He sought to persuade Joe Ryan to run for the presidency, but the latter refused. When Big Dick came to the convention, he found to his surprise that he and confrere Marinelli had been denied seats. Butler attacked O'Connor as a strikebreaker. The latter retorted that Butler and Marinelli had organized a private detective agency which had "shaken down" the workers for "protection." Said Butler, in protest to these allegations: "To support this good work we collected a dollar a year from each man, which is a common enough practice in organized labor. O'Connor knew all about this but he elected to use it for propaganda against us."

In spectacular fashion, Butler made his big bid for power in the famous general port strike of 1919. During the war, living costs had skyrocketed, but longshore wages were kept at 65 cents an hour by the government's National Adjustment Commission. The men demanded a dollar an hour straight time and two dollars for overtime; they got instead a "Woolworth raise"—five cents straight time and ten cents overtime. The rank and file ignored the leaders, and 25,000 longshoremen walked out, completely paralyzing the port. Unable to control the men, O'Connor declared that the port had been taken over by an "irresponsible mob of longshoremen who have been stampeded into an unauthorized strike by I.W.W. and Bolshevik influences." But the leader of the "subversives" was none other than Dick Butler, supported strangely, or perhaps not so strangely, by New York's Mayor Hylan, a puppet of William Randolph Hearst, and Jersey City's Mayor Hague. In fact, when the shipping companies sought to bring scabs into the Jersey docks, Hague's cops stood firm against them. Violence flared throughout the port. For four weeks the men held out firmly. Finally, through the intervention of Secretary of Labor Wilson, a conciliation commission, composed of Mayor Hylan, Vacarelli, and James Hughes, was named. On the promise of a new award, Hylan and Butler brought the striking longshoremen back.

As a reward for his role in the 1919 strike, O'Connor was appointed by President Harding a member of the Shipping Board; made chairman of it by Coolidge; reappointed by Hoover; and ousted by Franklin D. Roosevelt. Butler returned to Tammany politics and was named by Jimmy Walker as superintendent of the "white-elephant" Bronx Terminal. Joe Ryan, who had replaced Vacarelli as vice-president of the union, finally became president of the ILA. Said Butler, lightheartedly: "[Joe Ryan] broke in under me in 1913 and if he hasn't forgotten the tricks I taught him, he ought to get along." He did.

For a quarter of a century Joe Ryan was the paladin of the ILA. At the hale and hearty age of sixty-eight, before the sorrows of a criminal indictment, he looked like the cartoonist's caricature of a Tammany Hall gent: well-tailored clothes draped over a hulking frame, a large diamond glittered from a thick finger of his ham-shaped hands, and a bulbous nose limned a fleshy face. Ryan mixed with the Broadway sporting crowd, lived well, and ate well at a favorite Chelsea restaurant, where he occasionally indulged his taste for caviar—a taste, as he admits, that was developed in the days when boxes of the Russian delicacy often broke open on the docks during unloading.

Life was not always so easy for Joseph Patrick Ryan. He was born in 1884, the son of a landscape gardener who died when young Joe was a few years old. Shortly after, his mother passed away too, and Joe was raised in the tough West Side neighborhood abutting the Hudson. In good Chelsea tradition, he left school at the age of twelve, after completing six grades, and after some sundry jobs he settled down as a streetcar conductor for five and a half years and a car inspector for another two years. Bored with the routine, Joe, in 1912, turned to the casual work of the waterfront, and, soon after, his jovial manner, heavy fists, and lush oratorical manner made him a leader in the union. In his first year on the waterfront, Ryan was partially incapacitated when a heavy sling-weight broke and showered him with dense bits of iron. Ryan's local, Local 791, came to his aid by making him part-time financial secretary. Ryan never did any longshore work after that. In three years, the post had become converted to a full-time job. Ryan, proving himself to be a deft labor politician, became an International vice-president in 1918, and president of the union in 1927. In 1943, a grateful convention elected him president of the union for life. Ten years later, in maudlin sorrow, he left the office under fire.

While Joe Ryan symbolized the "Irish" rule of the longshoremen, actually the union has always had an Italian majority. Ryan remained at the top because he had strong political influence with the Irish leadership of Tammany Hall—and political support was necessary to keep the police from interfering with the pier rackets—because he had "front" and could talk to the shipowners, whereas the Italians, mostly immigrants, had few individuals who could present a public appearance, and because Joe Ryan left the Italians strictly alone.

A rough geographical separation underlay this political division. Almost all the West Side piers, along the Hudson, were controlled by the Irish. These were the first piers that were built, and the Irish, as the earlier immigrants, congregated in these areas. The West Side was a community, with the men living near the piers, in Chelsea and in the brownstone strip between the Tenderloin and the river. The saloons and the parish houses bounded their lives. They rarely moved away. They lived as an isolated mass against other ethnic masses in the city.

When shipping expanded after World War I, the congested Hudson piers were unable to carry the traffic, and new piers and bulkheads were established in Brooklyn, Staten Island, and Hoboken, where the Italian communities, living in the slum areas adjacent to these piers, claimed the jobs. And the Italian mobs, deeply entrenched in bootlegging, gambling, and narcotics, quickly moved onto the piers.

The heart of mob control in Brooklyn was the six so-called Italian locals of the ILA, whose four thousand members worked the South Brooklyn piers from Brooklyn Bridge to Twentieth Street. For twenty years these locals were ruled by the notorious Camarda family and their underworld associates. These included, over the years, Albert Anastasia, Joe Adonis, and other notorious members of Italian gangsterdom. When, in 1939, a rank-and-file leader named Peter Panto protested the extortions and depredations along the waterfront, he was cruelly murdered and his body found, two years later, in a lime pit in New Jersey. Albert Anastasia, the chief executioner for "Murder Inc.," was arrested for the murder, and although a former killer for the mob, Allie Tannenbaun, testified that Anastasia had personally supervised the killing, District Attorney William O'Dwyer unaccountably failed to press the indictments. (It was a case that was to haunt O'Dwyer many years later when he was mayor of New York. The release of Anastasia was a question, raised by the Kefauver Committee, which O'Dwyer was never able to answer satisfactorily.) In the investigations that followed the Panto murder, the Brooklyn Grand Jury revealed, in 1940, that the treasuries of the six locals had been looted of serveral hundred thousand dollars; but, quite mysteriously, the books disappeared or were found burned. Although, after the murder, the ILA announced a reform in Brooklyn locals, the Camarda family effectively retained control of the six locals, gradually to be replaced by Tony Anastasia, brother of Albert, who, despite the fact that in 1946 he had led a group of strikebreakers for the Phelps-Dodge corporation, became boss of the

Erie Basin group of docks and, soon after, of the entire Brooklyn waterfront.

the pattern of political accommodation

Central to any understanding of crime is the political setup of a city. For more than forty years, through reform as well as Tammany administrations, the waterfront was a protected political enclave. It was so because of the singular relationships of the business community, which wanted to keep the waterfront as it was, and of the political machines to which it paid tribute.

Doing business in the Port of New York are 155 steamship lines, a dozen large (and twenty small) stevedoring concerns, a half-dozen major railroad lines, a fleet of tugboat operators, etc. In learning the ropes, the "savvy" businessman had to learn to untie knots, and the biggest knot was the political one. Since the port is a municipal enterprise, a businessman had to negotiate pier leases from the city, get various licenses, and learn his way around the Office of Marine and Aviation. Without some political know-how and political support, he is, literally, sunk.

The exploitative possibilities of pier contracts were developed almost fifty years ago by Charles F. Murphy, the famed leader of Tammany Hall. A contemporary account in the New York *World* of October 1, 1905, reported: "During Mr. Murphy's short career as leader of Tammany Hall his contracting firm has acquired, mainly through manipulation of the Dock Department, contracts aggregating $30,000,000. . . ."

In the early thirties, the Seabury investigation showed that the North German Lloyd line paid the president of the National Democratic Club $50,000 in order to bid for a new pier the city had just acquired; the pier itself, assessed at $633,000, was offered to the city, through the law firm of George Olvany, the leader of Tammany Hall, for $3,000,000. Such history repeats itself in every generation; in 1947, during the O'Dwyer regime, an ex-bootlegger who sought to rent a pier was told to see Clarence Neal, a power in Tammany Hall, and to engage his services for $100,000. As a result of these disclosures, Mr. O'Dwyer's Commissioner of Marine and Aviation and his two chief deputies retired, but in quiet.

Since Tammany has always loomed so important, one of the sources of ILA power in New York has been it influence in Tammany Hall. From 1928 to 1938, Joe Ryan was chairman of the AFL Central Trades and Labor Council, and in that post spoke for "labor" in the political campaigns. Thus, official political endorsement by labor came, in effect, from Joe Ryan. More tangibly, the longshoremen have long been allied with the teamsters, forming a powerful political bloc which supplies manpower—and money—for Tammany campaigns. Ryan was long a figure in the "West Side" Tammany bloc, largely of Irish leaders, and was instrumental in electing the late Michael J. Kennedy to Congress in 1938. Later, Kennedy was elected leader of Tammany Hall.

Another, and for many years, hidden source of ILA influence was the strange but potent friendship between Joe Ryan and a prominent New York businessman with diverse port and business interests, named William J. McCormack. For a period of thirty years, McCormack was one of the silent powers in Democratic politics. He was one of the organizers and, for many years, executive vice-president of the powerful U.S. Trucking Corporation, whose board chairman was Alfred E. Smith. He was a partner with politically hefty Sam Rosoff in a number of contracting and bus ventures.* He is the owner of Transit-Mix Concrete Company, which has held a number of city contracts and supplies building materials to builders who do. His Morania Oil Company supplies fuel oil to the city. His largest enterprise, Penn Stevedore Company, unloads all the freight brought into the city by the Pennsylvania Railroad, principally all the fruit and vegetables freighted daily into the metropolis. For many years, in effect, McCormack acted as the agent of the Pennsylvania Railroad in New York politics.

McCormack's entente cordiale with Joe Ryan was of long standing. In fact, McCormack was the veteran chairman of the reception committee of the annual dinner-dance of the Joseph P. Ryan Association, a fraternal club whose yearly affairs used to bring together the weirdest collection of city notables, steamship company officials, and waterfront denizens that ever stepped out of a Damon Runyon story.

* The story is told—and perhaps it is apocryphal—that McCormack and Rosoff got their starts in a unique partnership. Rosoff had a New York contract to remove all cinders and ashes from city buildings, including schools. McCormack won a New York City contract to pave city streets. Rosoff would dump the cinders on an empty lot on the West Side, where they would be picked up by McCormack's trucks and used to pave the city's streets.

Because of his influence in union circles,* teamster as well as longshoreman, and because of his standing in business and his power in politics, silent William McCormack was long regarded as the virtual czar or "Mr. Big" of the port. McCormack's friendship with Ryan seems to have weighed heavily in his own favor in the ILA's dealing with the Penn Stevedore firm, which unloads all the freight cars of the Pennsylvania Railroad that are floated across the harbor. Although the ILA rate for longshore work in 1951 was $2.10 an hour, the men working on McCormack's piers, members of a separate ILA local, received only $1.54 an hour (a saving of 56 cents an hour on 2,000 or more men employed on the piers!). The reason given was that these men were railway "freight handlers" and not longshoremen. But when the question arose as to the eligibility of these men for the multiple welfare benefits under the Railway Retirement Act, it was said that they were longshoremen.

The results of the political accommodation were most evident in the throttling of needed reforms on the waterfront. In 1948, the New York Port Authority† submitted to the city a comprehensive plan for putting the port on a businesslike, non-political basis under Port Authority rule. Its blueprint called for $114 million capital investment for a huge produce terminal to be built over the water (to replace the shoddy and sprawling Washington market area), as well as consolidated railroad car floats, new piers, and a plan for traffic control. Its designs would have allowed greater mechanization of work, the reduction of waiting time, flexible planning to regularize employment—in short, those factors which could "rationalize" a chaotic and crumbling industry and bring the port back to prominence and use. But it also would have spoiled McCormack's control of some piers. The offer was rejected by the city. The excuse was that the financial return guaranteed the city was inadequate. But the more important reason was glaringly apparent: the entrenched interests would have been upset.

Across the Hudson River, in Jersey City, where life is more simple and direct, and politics more brutal and unadorned, the

* So fraternal are Mr. McCormack's ties with the ILA that, according to the *New Yorker* profile of restaurateur Toots Shor, McCormack presented the latter's first-born with a silver cargo hook and a lifetime membership card in the ILA!

† An independent agency chartered by the States of New York and New Jersey, which runs the Hudson River bridges and tunnels, the airports in the metropolitan area, and several harbor facilities.

relationship of the ILA to the political setup produced a clear mirror of the meaning of political accommodation. In Jersey City the piers still form one of the chief sources of job patronage for those faithful to the machine, and the loading concessions are one of the plums of political victory. In turn, the kickbacks from jobs, and the assessments from these prizes, finance the political machine.

A period of change is always an excellent sociological laboratory, and the period following the downfall of the Hague machine in Jersey City provides a good look at the intricate and corrupt ties of a racket-ridden union and a corrupt city machine. In 1948, the rotting Hague machine was overthrown by an insurgent chieftain, John V. Kenny. Naturally, followers of newly-elected Mayor Kenny wanted the spoils. The "old guard" was backed by Joe Ryan, who had maintained excellent relations with Hague. After a month-long strike, a compromise was effected, whereby the Kenny people took over Pier D, while the Hague-Ryan loaders kept control of nearby Pier F.

But tranquility was hard to achieve. A new mob from New York, led by an old associate of Lucky Luciano named Tony Strollo, alias Bender, assumed control of the U.S. Army's Linden Avenue pier. Jersey City's City Hall could find no jobs on Linden Avenue for its faithful. Mayor Kenny stepped in, publicly branded Bender a "New York mobster," and barred his brother, Dominic, the night hiring boss, from the pier. Finally, Mayor Kenny sued for peace. Hat in hand, he crossed the river and met Bender secretly at midnight in a New York hotel. New York District Attorney Hogan exposed the meeting and called it "an appalling demonstration of underworld domination of the waterfront."

The steamship companies didn't care, because they lost little by this control. In fact, by negotiating with a pliable union, they gained considerably.

the pattern of economic accommodation

From 1919, the close of World War I, when the men walked out in protest against the government's *ad hoc* wage award, until 1945, at the close of World War II, when a flash wildcat strike shut down the New York docks, a pattern of economic accommodation existed which worked to the benefit of the shipowners and the union barons and against the interests of the men. Collective-bargaining agreements were reached regularly without strike, but these agreements brought few benefits other than miniscule hourly wage increases for the men. The system of the open shape and tight control over hiring kept the men in line. Even during the 1930's, when labor was organizing aggressively over the country and pushing for new gains, the ILA—though it lost the West Coast to Harry Bridges, who took his newly organized longshoremen out of the ILA into the CIO—was able to maintain an iron hand over the disorganized New York docks. The few rebellions, principally on the Brooklyn docks, where the Communists sought to gain a foothold among the Italian workers, were dealt with summarily.

For twenty-five years, through the protective atmosphere of the New Deal, the aggressive spirit of the CIO, the unity of World War II, the shipowners were able to hold unchallenged sway. In 1945, the pattern of economic accommodation abruptly broke down. Why?

One answer was the new-found cohesiveness of the men. During World War II, for the first time, steady work gangs were employed at the same dock, and work was regularized. The men had a vital stake in the continuation of this new system. Locals grew stronger, and new leadership arose to challenge Ryan. A second reason, less apparent, but of significance, was the entry of new criminal elements on the docks. During the war, the Navy had kept a tight rein on the rackets; at the same time, the old West Side mobsters had lost the direct protection of the police during the LaGuardia reform administration, although LaGuardia himself never took any direct steps to clean up the docks. The ripe opportunities for theft, the postwar expansion of shipping and the quickened need for fast turn-arounds (which made the shipowners more vulnerable to strikes and delays), the opportunities for revenues for loading, tempted new elements to move onto the docks. And in almost every instance where the rank and file revolted against Ryan, some mobster elements were backing them. As Murray Kempton said, somewhat elegantly: "There were hoods on both sides, but some hoods were with the men, and some against them." A third reason was the push of the Italian groups, under Anastasia, to extend their power along the Brooklyn and Jersey docks. The Italians had long chafed under the old Irish rule, and wanted a larger share of the spoils. The only way they could hit at Ryan was through the shipowners, and they did. The combination of these elements made the postwar period a volatile one indeed. In the years from 1946 to

1951, almost every major agreement reached by Ryan and the shipowners was followed by a wildcat strike which tied up the port. It was the only way open to the dissidents.

Over the years Ryan had worked out a technique to control bargaining. The employers represented only Port of New York shippers and their New York stevedoring contractors. The union group, however, consisted of coastwise delegations, not only of longshoremen but of checkers, cargo repairmen, etc. Each local in the four ILA Atlantic Coast districts from Newfoundland to Cape Hatteras, no matter how small (and many had fewer than fifty members), had one vote, plus additional votes in proportion to their membership. The effect was to discriminate against the large longshore locals in New York. And although the agreement was with the New York shippers, the entire Atlantic Coast district voted on contract provisions which applied principally to New York.

In October, 1945, when contract talks had just concluded, longshoremen working the Grace Line piers, along the lower Hudson, walked off because the union negotiators had failed to press the demand for a limitation of slingloads to two tons. Ryan denounced the walkout as the work of "hotheads." A day later, the Atlantic wage conference voted unanimously to accept the new contract. Despite the "unanimous" conference vote, however, the leading dissident in the port, Local 791, which manned a number of the Hudson River piers, voted not to go back, and 30,000 longshoremen followed its lead.

Ryan sought to drive the men back to work by announcing that he had reopened negotiations with the shipowners and that 75 per cent of the men voting in a referendum favored returning to work. The leadership of Local 791 wavered, but a new element entered the waterfront, a rank-and-file committee in Brooklyn headed by a man named William E. Warren, but guided, actually, by the Communists. There was little question of the Communist role. Strategy was being planned by a Communist party functionary named John Steuben; Harold Cammer of the law firm of Witt and Cammer, which handled chiefly party-line unions, became the legal adviser for the rank-and-file committee. But the grievances were genuine, and the men were motivated by a hatred of Ryan.

On the promise of arbitration, the rank-and-file revolt caved in. The arbitration award, by William H. Davis, confirmed the rank and file. The men won a 25-cent-an-hour wage increase as against the original 10 cents; the elimination of the third shape; and a vacation plan with one week's pay for a man with 1,350 hours of work credit.

Seeking to tighten his control, Ryan moved to "clean house." Warren, the leader of the Brooklyn locals, was expelled from the union (for "nonpayment of dues"). Asked if he would be allowed to work, an ILA official said: "Sure he can report, but if he falls and hurts himself it'll be no one's fault." The day after, Warren reported for work at the Columbia Street piers and "fell and hurt himself." Shortly after, Warren announced that he had been duped by the Communists and repudiated the role of Witt and Cammer.

In the next years, restlessness on the docks continued. In 1946 and 1947, Local 791 took the lead in a number of wildcat strikes. Steam was building up, and the boiler finally exploded in 1948. The issue, presumably, was wages. But what scared the steamship operators was an economic issue which subsequently became known as "overtime-on-overtime." Complicated as the issue is, it is the dollars-and-cents problems such as these that are the heart of union problems. And this one, therefore, is worth following in some detail.

Until 1945, the ILA and the New York Shipping Association had designated forty-four hours as the straight-time workweek, and overtime was paid from that point on. However, longshore work which was "out-of-hours"—that is, at night or on Sunday—commanded premium or extra pay. Sometimes a man worked more than forty-four hours, but some portion of those original forty-four hours were evening or Sunday, hours which commanded time-and-a-half premium pay. Was the "overtime" wage (the hours beyond forty-four) to be time-and-a-half of the straight-time wage, or was the time-and-a-half to be based on the average of the straight-time *and* premium pay? In principle: Should overtime only be paid as a function of the straight-time *rate*, or, as time-and-a-half of the *actual earned* (including premium pay) rate? To complicate matters further, the Federal Wage and Hour Law, passed in 1940, set *forty* hours as the regular workweek. The federal law specified overtime as beginning after forty hours, while the longshore contract had set it at forty-four. Were the longshoremen now entitled to back pay for the overtime between forty and forty-four hours?

In 1941, a number of ILA workers filed a legal suit charging that true overtime had not been paid. Their claim was upheld by the Wage and Hour Administrator, by seven different courts (including three U.S. Circuit Courts of Appeals), and finally, in 1948, by the U.S. Supreme Court, which held that the longshore contracts violated the Wage and Hour Law.* The shippers feared that as a result of the decision they would be liable for millions of dollars in back pay. More than that, they would face the further embarrassment of opening their books for the wartime period to determine who was entitled to how much back pay, a procedure which might reveal the extent of payroll padding, duplicate hiring, and other practices which, since the government was paying all bills during this period on a cost-plus basis, could only have been conducted on a collusive basis. The shipping companies demanded, therefore, that the union waive all claims for overtime pay. This became one of the issues in dispute.

In August, 1948, when the parties could not reach an agreement, President Truman stepped in and slapped down an eighty-day Taft-Hartley injunction. The day before the injunction expired, Ryan and the shippers came to an agreement. The union agreed to petition Congress jointly with the steamship companies to exempt the longshore industry from the Wage and Hour Law on premium pay and to wipe out all back suits! Ryan also obtained a ten-cent-an-hour increase, a minimum guarantee of four hours "call-in" work, and the reduction in the eligibility requirement for vacation pay from 1,350 to 1,250 hours. Ryan called it a "good deal" and a "fine agreement." The men thought otherwise. Again they walked off. This time, Ryan turned *volte-face* and accepted the walkout and made the strike legal. *This was the first regularly called strike in the history of the union.* Ryan was sent back to negotiate, and the operators suffered what they themselves called "an old-fashioned shellacking." Still, the "shellacking" was not so bad. Pressure from the union and the shippers resulted in a congressional bill in March, 1949, reversing the Supreme Court. By classifying premium pay as overtime pay, the bill exempted the longshore industry from the Wage and Hour act and wiped out all claims to back pay during the 1940 to 1948 period. It was a rare act of "sacrifice" on the part of a union: abandoning several millions of dollars of legally entitled back pay for the workers in order to assure labor-management "harmony."

* The Court's reasoning: the "out of hours" pay was not overtime, but regular pay, and overtime should therefore be calculated on that basis.

Restlessness on the waterfront increased in the years following the 1948 strike. The case of "Cockeye" Dunn added to the tension. Sitting in the death house at Sing Sing, he sent word to the District Attorney that he wanted to "talk." Rumors of a statement implicating some "Mr. Big," a higher-up power on the waterfront, circulated freely. Although Dunn went to the chair without making a public statement, the affair itself spurred public curiosity. The waterfront exposés in the New York *Sun* by Malcolm Johnson, which later won the Pulitzer Prize, increased the heat. A valiant crusade by a Jesuit priest, Father John Corridan of the Xavier Labor School, raised embarrassing questions for Ryan. Father Corridan made an economic analysis of the plight of the longshoremen and, for the first time, obtained the release of data indicating the extent of casual employment and low pay. Investigators for the Kefauver Committee asked embarrassing questions, particularly regarding the large financial worth of union officials who earned moderate salaries. A series of biting exposés by New York *Post* columnist Murray Kempton got under Ryan's skin. Finally, the establishment of the New York Anti-Crime Committee, with a division headed by William J. Keating, a former assistant district attorney who had specialized on the waterfront, brought together in one place a vast amount of data which was freely used by journalists to spotlight poor labor conditions.

In such an explosive atmosphere, any spark could ignite the harbor. The spark was the 1951 negotiations. The ILA won a ten-cent-an-hour wage increase, the amount permissible then under Wage Stabilization Board rules; one shape a day; and welfare benefits. Paradoxically, it was a good contract, as good as could be gotten—the first good one that Ryan had negotiated. Yet a wildcat strike erupted. Realistically, within the wartime Wage Stabilization Board framework there was little more that the strikers could have obtained. But the impulse behind the walkout was no longer economic; it was purely the reaction of a fed-up group "voting with their feet."

The lead was taken by Local 791 and its business agent, "Gene" Sampson. But this time other elements appeared in the leadership as well. A number of local mobsters, seeing an opportunity to dump Ryan, moved in for the kill. For the first time, Ryan's regime was really in danger. The shipowners, fearing that the ouster of Ryan might lead to a new ferocious war for power, decided to stand by the aging ILA leader and take a long strike. For twenty-five days the strike rolled on. Finally, a face-saving maneuver was worked out by the New York State Board of Mediation. The rank and file had charged that the contract had been signed illegally. Now a fact-finding board would decide whether the contract had been duly ratified. After hearing thirty witnesses fill two thousand pages of testimony, the Board, in Solomon-like judgment, found most of the rank-and-file charges to be true, yet certified the contract as valid.

intervention

For more than a year the waterfront simmered. Rumors of investigation flew thick and fast. The feuding for control of the Jersey waterfront made news as sluggings, bombings, and beatings continued on the Jersey City docks. In November, 1952, the whole pot slopped over. The waterfront story that hitherto had been spelled out in bits and pieces blazed into headlines as the New York State Crime Commission opened public hearings in December, 1952, and paraded a number of witnesses to the stand to describe the seamy side of waterfront life. In the broad picture, there was little new. But what the Crime Commission did, backed by the data seized by subpoena, was to dot every "i" and cross every "t"—the payoffs of the stevedoring concerns to the union officials, the parceling out of crime concessions, the income from loading, and the like.

Once the documented picture of waterfront corruption was on the record, the American Federation of Labor and the New York State authorities were forced to begin a clean-up. The action was a remarkable tribute to the force of public opinion. Clearly, the shipping industry had wanted the pattern of accommodation to continue. The ILA obviously desired no change. The American Federation of Labor, hobbled by a tradition of non-interference in the internal affairs of its affiliates, had pursued a hands-off policy. And the City of New York, even through the reform administration of Fiorello H. LaGuardia, as well as during the lax regimes of O'Dwyer and Impelliteri, feared to tangle with the entrenched powers. But the situation was too volatile. The intermittent wildcat strikes, the lucrative racket prizes which attracted new gangster elements who used the contract grievances to keep the pot boiling, and the constant drumfire of press and magazine criticism finally forced the authorities to act. Governor Dewey, harassed by concurrent scandals in harness-track trotting which involved high Republican officials, saw the waterfront situation as a providential means of gaining favorable publicity and hurting the Democrats as well. George Meany, more mindful than his predecessor of the harm to the Federation in the continuing publicity about labor corruption, felt compelled to move too.

The mobs sought desperately to hold on. Representatives of the loaders approached state officials and proposed various legal dodges which would have left them effectively in control of the piers; the names of the respectable banking officials who were prepared to "front" for the mobs left the state leaders almost stunned. Tony Anastasia privately approached the AFL and indicated that he would dump the West Side "Irish" mobs if the AFL would leave his barony untouched; the Irish mobs made the same proposals regarding Anastasia. But the situation had gone too far. The point of no return had been reached. In September, 1953, the AFL expelled the ILA and chartered a new union in its stead. And the states of New York and New Jersey set up a bi-state waterfront commission with broad regulatory powers over the longshoremen, the loaders, and the stevedoring concerns. In effect, the harbor was declared a quasi-utility, and a set of controls, as stringent as any imposed on an industry, was established. All pier superintendents and hiring bosses had to obtain licenses, and no ex-convict could be employed in these jobs unless he could prove good conduct over the previous five years. All longshoremen had to register. To maintain registration, a longshoreman had to work steadily or, failing to work nine months, lose his registration. In this fashion, the commission sought to cut the supply of casual or "weekend" laborers, who, by bribing hiring bosses for the lucrative evening and weekend premium-pay hours, had contributed to waterfront disorganization. Ex-convicts were barred from registration unless they obtained clearance from the commission. The shape-up, as such, was abolished, and replaced by employment centers. The stevedoring concerns still maintained control over hiring, however, but they could only employ registered longshoremen. Compulsory public loading was outlawed. Either the steamship companies could provide loaders, or the teamsters could employ their own men. Apart from the licensing and registration provisions, the New York State waterfront act also stipulated that union locals whose officers included convicted felons could not collect dues from registered longshoremen. About 30 per cent of the

ILA officers in the New York port, it was estimated, had criminal records.

While these moves were taking place, the collective-bargaining contract between the shippers and the old ILA had expired. The two parties sought to come to a new long-term agreement which would give the ILA exclusive control of the waterfront. But this situation was a difficult one. The old ILA had to make substantial demands to show the longshoremen that it was no longer a tool of the shippers. The steamship companies were unwilling to pay the price. On September 30, 1953, the old ILA, desperately striving to win a new contract, called a strike which effectively shut down the East Coast ports. The fact that it was able to do so against adverse odds testified to its grip on the docks.

In response to various pressures, President Eisenhower set up a Board of Inquiry preliminary to obtaining a Taft-Hartley injunction. The board skirted the issue which it had been called upon to judge. In effect, the question of the injunction was left squarely up to the Administration. And the Administration, guided by Governor Dewey's office, in turn left the issue up to the AFL! So close was the co-operation between the AFL and the state officials that if the AFL had opposed a Taft-Hartley injunction, none would have been issued.

The Administration applied to the federal court for an eighty-day injunction. Under the injunction, the ILA would be unable to strike, while presumably the nascent AFL union would be free to exert pressure on the shippers. It was clearly a political move intended to help the AFL. Caught between fires, the shippers appealed to the National Labor Relations Board to hold a representation election, promising to refrain from signing any contract with the ILA until the Board had determined who was the legal bargaining agent. The NLRB, fearful that the expiration of the Taft-Hartley injunction would mean a ruinous waterfront war for which they would be blamed, ordered an election for December 22. When the results were in, the ILA had won. It had received 9,060 votes to 7,568 for the AFL, while 4,399 votes were challenged, principally by the AFL.

How can one explain the victory of the old union in such an obviously rotten and exploitative situation? When the ILA was first expelled from the AFL, many observers felt that the old union would crumble and that the longshoremen, "emancipated" finally from the grip of the racketeers, would rush joyfully into the ranks of the new union. But they did not. A list of factors indicate the complexity of the problem:

(1) While many of the longshoremen were cowed and exploited, a sizeable core, roughly one-third of the work force, did have considerable privileges because of the system of favoritism. This group worked hard for the ILA.

(2) A number of the wildcat walkouts over the collective-bargaining agreements were not as "spontaneous" as they seemed, but were inspired by dissident racketeer elements who sought to use these walkouts either for shakedowns of shipping concerns or to pry control of some piers from entrenched groups. Hence, the depth of the "spontaneous" support the AFL would get was exaggerated.

(3) Politics is primarily a matter of organization; and organization, particularly in such a rough-and-ready place as the waterfront, is built on the informal and "natural" leaders of the group. Years of racket control, however, had eliminated the independent leadership among the men.

(4) Ethnic considerations were important. The Italians in Brooklyn feared Anastasia, but they knew him as one of their own. The AFL was never able to obtain a foothold in the closely-knit Italian community.

(5) The AFL union imprudently accepted into its ranks several old ILA officials who had mob connections, principally Tony (Cheese) Marchitto of Jersey City. This confirmed a latent cynicism of many longshoremen that both sides were no good.

(6) The ILA itself put on a "reform" face. At a special convention in Philadelphia in mid-November, Joe Ryan, who had been acclaimed president "for life," stepped down with a pension "for life," and Captain William J. Bradley, head of a small tugboat local, was named president. John L. Lewis, for reasons of power or of pique at the AFL, thereupon announced his backing of the "new" ILA and pledged a loan of $200,000 to aid the union in its fight against the AFL.

(7) The longshoremen resented the close ties of the AFL to the Dewey administration and feared that the AFL support for the licensing and registration features of the Waterfront Act would lead to government hiring-halls.

A second NLRB election, held after Governor Dewey had "twisted the arm" of the Board, was again won by the ILA, by a count of 9,110 to 8,977, with 1,797 pro-ILA votes challenged. Again the ILA held its ranks and rode out the storm.

For the next three years, from 1953 to 1956, the ILA sought some cover of respectability in the labor movement. In the "public morality" of American society, corruption can be tolerated, if clothed, but naked corruption is unsettling. At first the ILA, under the new "reform" leadership of William Bradley, a former tugboat captain, sought to affiliate with the Miners. But this was not feasible, since the Miners, because Lewis had refused to sign the non-Communist affidavit of the Taft-Hartley Act, could not participate in the NLRB elections. Bradley then worked out a "mutual-aid pact" with Jimmy Hoffa, the fast-moving boss of the Midwest teamsters, who was then seeking to extend his power in the union. There seem to have been private negotiations, too, with Harry Bridges' West Coast longshoremen, a move privately favored by Hoffa, which would have set up a bi-coast teamster-longshore combination; but this did not materialize.

In October, 1956, the AFL made its last challenge to the ILA. But it was obvious that its chances were slim. Maritime union leader Joe Curran, mindful of the need for longshoremen co-operation on the docks, came out publicly in support of the ILA. When the votes were announced, the ILA had won by 11,827 to 7,428.

After all the strenuous efforts at clean-up, the old crowd was still in control. Some changes for the better had been made. The Waterfront Commission, by reducing the number of longshoremen eligible for work, had helped to regularize employment. The union itself had begun to set up orderly records and to organize welfare benefits. But the mob control was secure. Tough Tony Anastasia had extended his power over the Brooklyn docks. Ed Florio, after fourteen months in Atlanta prison, was again the power in Hoboken. The Bowers group that had organized the loading on the West Side were still entrenched. And the ILA itself had won a union shop which gave it even greater power over jobs on the waterfront.

the cycle resumes

Looking back at the four decades, how could such a corrupt and fetid state of affairs have continued for so long? One simple answer is that most of the individuals concerned found it difficult to recognize the face of evil. Joe Ryan was not a vicious man. A morose and sentimental individual, he came to success through the "freight entrance" and knew the seamy side of life the way a well-worn *douanier* knows the little vices and hypocrisies of the great travelers. The waterfront is tough, and he accepted life that way. Like many self-made men, he scorned—and feared—"do-gooders" and reformers who have never known hard knocks.

In the union Ryan was a captive. Each little local around a pier or neighborhood was a molecular world of its own with its own traditions, prerogatives, cliques, and jealousies. Each warlord knew his particular work and felt at home there; the larger society, the complexities of the skyscraper world over the "shadow line," were beyond his ken. Joe Ryan was the emissary to this world. He was the "waxer" who, despite the rough manner, could talk and hold his own. That is why he reigned but did not rule.

The steamship companies also accepted the "tough world." It was easier to make a "deal." Besides, "the men are undisciplined, and need a strong hand." So, on loading and other lucrative concessions, the companies looked the other way—in exchange for the promise of the hiring boss that he would keep the men in line and get the ships in and out fast. Besides, many of the costs of doing business were met by government maritime subsidies—so what was the point of getting excited?

For the loaders, tough punks from the tough West Side world, the waterfront was a place where everybody was out to make a buck, so why not they? "The steamship companies couldn't complain; it cost them nothing to have loaders on the pier. The truckers? They objected to loading only because they wanted to do the job themselves so they could make the buck out of the customer rather than us. The consignee? Why should they object; they could pass the costs along to the customers easily. The public? What's that? Everybody is out to make a buck; some pay, some don't; that's life."

Underneath all three, bearing the load, were the longshoremen. Fifty years ago, the Irish were the dominant group. Many of the West Side Hudson piers are still manned by the Irish, but the majority of longshoremen today are Italians and "Austrians"—a vague waterfront term that covers all Slavs and East Europeans. Traditionally, most of the longshoremen have lived close to the docks, forming a homogeneous, self-contained community. Along with the house, there is the bar, the social club, and occasionally the parish house as the center of community life. St. Veronica's Parish on the West Side is typical longshore slum. The men live in a narrow band of tenements between Houston and the Federal Home of Detention. Slashed across the center is Pig Alley, a block-long cobblestoned, junk-strewn thoroughfare where in the daytime the boys play stickball and at night the souses lurch along until they slide down into the street to sleep off their drunk. In the summer, the street is the living-room. There are the usual number of brawls, and on Sunday the little girls walk self-consciously in their white organdies to communion. Most of the people live in the houses where they were born, and die there. There are the usual feuds and fights. But withal, it is a community, and no one is a "cop-hollerer." In recent years some longshoremen have sought to break away from the docks. They moved to Queens, the Bronx, and Washington Heights. The reason usually is "the kids." The world is a jungle, and they want to give their children a better start. On the docks, only the mobsters are successful, and they are a poor model for the devout.

As the Irish have moved out, the Italians have moved in, and the old patterns of exploitation in its many vicious forms appear once more. Many of the men are illegal aliens, smuggled into the country like cattle. Most of the aliens came from the hometowns of the ILA organizers. The dock is an anonymous place to work; subject to arrest and deportation, the men are unusually docile. Hence, it is easy to arrange "short gangs." Fifteen men do the work of the regular twenty-two whose "names" are entered on the books, and the difference is split between the hiring boss and the stevedore. The steamship companies don't mind; the men work fast and efficiently.

How can one break this vicious cycle? One answer is the "regularization" of work. The action of the Waterfront Commission is a step in that direction. But this is not enough. The matrix of the problem is the dilapidated physical condition of the port. The New York waterfront remains, aging, chipping, cracking, and congested by traffic. With everyone crowded by space, they became also crowded by "time" and sought to cut corners. And the fulcrum is still time. Ships still require a fast turn-around to equalize mounting dock costs. Trucks still wait long hours to load or discharge consignments. The pier facilities are still inadequate to speed the flow of cargo; the narrow, fringe-like piers still have little radial space to permit trucks to maneuver and unload. Forced into the narrow, gridiron-patterned streets built to accommodate the horse and wagon, the trucks force all traffic to back up behind them. And astride the ports stand the mobs; at this vantage point between trucker and steamship company, like medieval robber barons, they erected their sluice gates and exacted their tolls. The barriers may have been torn down. But the dilapidation remains.

EDMUND WILSON

the national winter garden

There is a rumor that the National Winter Garden Burlesque has fallen a victim to the current purity wave and been obliged to abate the Aristophanic license for which it was formerly celebrated. The management of the National Winter Garden (not the Broadway Winter Garden, of course, but the one at Second Avenue and Houston Street) has been kind enough to supply the *New Republic* with a season pass, and, as the result of a recent visit, the writer of these notes is happy to announce that this report is entirely without foundation and to recommend the Minsky Brothers' Follies as still among the most satisfactory shows in town. The great thing about the National Winter Garden is that, though admittedly as vulgar as possible, it has nothing of the peculiar smartness and hardness one is accustomed to elsewhere in New York. It is refreshing because it lies quite outside the mechanical routine of Broadway. Though more ribald, it is more honest and less self-conscious than the ordinary risqué farce and, though crude, on the whole more attractive than most of the hideous comic-supplement humors of uptown revue and vaudeville. Nor is it to be confounded with the uptown burlesque show of the type of the Columbia, which is now as wholesome and as boring as any expensive musical comedy. The National Winter Garden has a tradition and a vein of its own.

For one thing, the Minsky Brothers go in for a kind of beauty which has long passed out of fashion elsewhere. The National Winter Garden has no use for the slim legs and shallow breasts the modern American taste for which has been so successfully exploited by Ziegfeld and the other uptown producers. Save for their bobbed hair and modern shoes, the chorus at the National Winter Garden might have come out of the pictures of Casino girls in old *Munsey's Magazines* of the nineties. And the humor of the National Winter Garden differs, also, from the humor of other shows. It mainly consists of gags, to be sure, but they are not the gags you are used to. For all their violence, the comic interludes have a certain freshness and wit. In the current version of *Anthony and Cleopatra,* a perennial Minsky classic, Julius Caesar, in a tin helmet and smoking a big cigar, catches Anthony (the Jewish comic) on a divan with Cleopatra (the principal strip-tease girl) and wallops him over the bottom with the flat of an enormous sword. "I'm dying! I'm dying!," groans Anthony, as he staggers around in a circle; and Caesar and Cleopatra, the Roman soldiers and the Egyptian slave-girls break into a rousing shimmy to the refrain of "He's dying! He's dying!" "I hear de voices of de angels!" says Anthony. "What do they say?" asks Caesar. "I don't know: I don't speak Polish." He is groggy; he totters; he faints. "I hear de cockroaches calling me!" he cries; and from the orchestra sounds, acrid and sinister, the cry of the expectant roaches. "Bring me the wassup," says Cleopatra, and her slave-girl, kneeling, presents a box, from which Cleopatra takes a huge property phallus. (At some point in the development of the ancient act, the word *asp* was evidently confused with *wasp.*) It is impossible to report in these pages all the incidents of the scenes that follow. Cleopatra falls prone on her lover's body, and Caesar, with pathetic reverence, places on her posterior a wreath, which he waters with a watering-pot. Charmian and Britannicus, after some play of their own with the wassup, finally fall lifeless, too, the girl as she flops on the soldier exploding a toy balloon which he has been wearing as a false chest. This curious piece of East Side folk-drama has been popular at Minsky's for years, and it is always a little different. Sometimes Caesar makes his entrance on a bicycle, blowing his own bugle; sometimes his entrance is heralded by a flourish of trumpets from the orchestra, as the company lines up and looks out the wings: Caesar enters from the other direction and gooses the last man, so that the whole row falls down like dominoes. There is also a remarkable gallows skit, which begins as an affecting piece of realism and ends as a low joke.

The orchestra at the National Winter Garden is energetic even in summer. The girls are not only robust but take a certain jolly interest in the show and sometimes betray their roles by laughing inappropriately at the jokes. The audience are keenly appreciative, and the house peals with easy thunder more infectious than the punctual crashes uptown. The theater, at the top of an office building, is very well ventilated; and just now you can see through an open exit the foothills of the downtown buildings against a pale lilac-gray sky. After the show, you can walk down the fire-escape.

The most celebrated performer of the National Winter Garden was a Yiddish comedian named Jack Shargel, who has now retired from the stage. To these raw buffooneries he is said to have brought a touch of the wistfulness of a Lew Fields or a Charlie Chaplin. A connoisseur of the theater in its best days has described to me a scene in which Jack Shargel received a rose from a beautiful lady just going off the stage. He kissed it, he smelt it in ecstasy, then, with a graceful and infinitely tender gesture, he stretched out his hand and tossed it away: it fell with a crash of glass.

HART CRANE

national winter garden

Outspoken buttocks in pink beads
Invite the necessary cloudy clinch
Of bandy eyes. . . . No extra mufflings here:
The world's one flagrant, sweating cinch.

And while legs waken salads in the brain
You pick your blonde out neatly through the smoke.
Always you wait for someone else though, always—
(Then rush the nearest exit through the smoke).

Always and last, before the final ring
When all the fireworks blare, begins
A tom-tom scrimmage with a somewhere violin,
Some cheapest echo of them all—begins.

And shall we call her whiter than the snow?
Sprayed first with ruby, then with emerald sheen—
Least tearful and least glad (who knows her smile?)
A caught slide shows her sandstone grey between.

Her eyes exist in swivellings of her teats,
Pearls whip her hips, a drench of whirling strands.
Her silly snake rings begin to mount, surmount
Each other—turquoise fakes on tinselled hands.

We wait that writhing pool, her pearls collapsed,
—All but her belly buried in the floor;
And the lewd trounce of a final muted beat!
We flee her spasm through a fleshless door. . . .

Yet, to the empty trapeze of your flesh,
O Magdalene, each comes back to die alone.
Then you, the burlesque of our lust—and faith,
Lug us back lifeward—bone by infant bone.

WILLIAM CARLOS WILLIAMS

the pure products of america

The pure products of America
go crazy—
mountain folk from Kentucky

or the ribbed north end of
Jersey
with its isolate lakes and

valleys, its deaf-mutes, thieves
old names
and promiscuity between

devil-may-care men who have taken
to railroading
out of sheer lust of adventure—

and young slatterns, bathed
in filth
from Monday to Saturday

to be tricked out that night
with gauds
from imaginations which have no

peasant traditions to give them
character
but flutter and flaunt

sheer rags—succumbing without
emotion
save numbed terror

under some hedge of choke-cherry
or viburnum—
which they cannot express—

Unless it be that marriage
perhaps
with a dash of Indian blood

will throw up a girl so desolate
so hemmed round
with disease or murder

that she'll be rescued by an
agent—
reared by the state and

sent out at fifteen to work in
some hard pressed
house in the suburbs—

some doctor's family, some Elsie—
voluptuous water
expressing with broken

brain the truth about us—
her great
ungainly hips and flopping breasts

addressed to cheap
jewelry
and rich young men with fine eyes

as if the earth under our feet
were
an excrement of some sky

and we degraded prisoners
destined
to hunger until we eat filth

while the imagination strains
after deer
going by fields of goldenrod in

the stifling heat of September
Somehow
it seems to destroy us

It is only in isolate flecks that
something
is given off

No one
to witness
and adjust, no one to drive the car

dedication for a plot of ground

This plot of ground
facing the waters of this inlet
is dedicated to the living presence of
Emily Dickinson Wellcome
who was born in England; married;
lost her husband and with
her five year old son
sailed for New York in a two-master;
was driven to the Azores;
ran adrift on Fire Island shoal,
met her second husband
in a Brooklyn boarding house,
went with him to Puerto Rico
bore three more children, lost
her second husband, lived hard
for eight years in St. Thomas,
Puerto Rico, San Domingo, followed
the oldest son to New York,
lost her daughter, lost her "baby,"
seized the two boys of
the oldest son by the second marriage
mothered them—they being
motherless—fought for them
against the other grandmother
and the aunts, brought them here
summer after summer, defended
herself here against thieves,
storms, sun, fire,
against flies, against girls
that came smelling about, against
drought, against weeds, storm-tides,
neighbors, weasels that stole her chickens,
against the weakness of her own hands,
against the growing strength of
the boys, against wind, against

the stones, against trespassers,
against rents, against her own mind.

She grubbed this earth with her own hands,
domineered over this grass plot,
blackguarded her oldest son
into buying it, lived here fifteen years,
attained a final loneliness and—

If you can bring nothing to this place
but your carcass, keep out.

WILLIAM BLAKE

london

I wander thro' each charter'd street,
Near where the charter'd Thames does flow,
And mark in every face I meet
Marks of weakness, marks of woe.

In every cry of every Man,
In every Infant's cry of fear,
In every voice, in every ban,
The mind-forg'd manacles I hear.

How the Chimney-sweeper's cry
Every black'ning Church appalls;
And the hapless Soldier's sigh
Runs in blood down Palace walls.

But most thro' midnight streets I hear
How the youthful Harlot's curse
Blasts the new born Infant's tear,
And blights with plagues the Marriage hearse.

ALLEN GINSBERG

america

America I've given you all and now I'm nothing.
America two dollars and twentyseven cents January 17, 1956.
I can't stand my own mind.
America when will we end the human war?
Go fuck yourself with your atom bomb.
I don't feel good don't bother me.
I won't write my poem till I'm in my right mind.
America when will you be angelic?
When will you take off your clothes?
When will you look at yourself through the grave?
When will you be worthy of your million Trotskyites?
America why are your libraries full of tears?
America when will you send your eggs to India?
I'm sick of your insane demands.
When can I go into the supermarket and buy what I need with my good looks?
America after all it is you and I who are perfect not the next world.
Your machinery is too much for me.
You made me want to be a saint.
There must be some other way to settle this argument.
Burroughs is in Tangiers I don't think he'll come back it's sinister.
Are you being sinister or is this some form of practical joke?
I'm trying to come to the point.
I refuse to give up my obsession.
America stop pushing I know what I'm doing.
America the plum blossoms are falling.
I haven't read the newspapers for months, everyday somebody goes on trial for murder.
America I feel sentimental about the Wobblies.
America I used to be a communist when I was a kid I'm not sorry.
I smoke marijuana every chance I get.
I sit in my house for days on end and stare at the roses in the closet.
When I go to Chinatown I get drunk and never get laid.

My mind is made up there's going to be trouble.
You should have seen me reading Marx.
My psychoanalyst thinks I'm perfectly right.
I won't say the Lord's Prayer.
I have mystical visions and cosmic vibrations.
America I still haven't told you what you did to Uncle Max
after he came over from Russia.

I'm addressing you.
Are you going to let your emotional life be run by Time
Magazine?
I'm obsessed by Time Magazine.
I read it every week.
Its cover stares at me every time I slink past the corner
candystore.
I read it in the basement of the Berkeley Public Library.
It's always telling me about responsibility. Businessmen are
serious. Movie producers are serious. Everybody's serious
but me.
It occurs to me that I am America.
I am talking to myself again.

Asia is rising against me.
I haven't got a chinaman's chance.
I'd better consider my national resources.
My national resources consist of two joints of marijuana
millions of genitals an unpublishable private literature that
goes 1400 miles an hour and twentyfive-thousand mental
institutions.
I say nothing about my prisons nor the millions of under-
privileged who live in my flowerpots under the light of
five hundred suns.
I have abolished the whorehouses of France, Tangiers is
the next to go.
My ambition is to be President despite the fact that I'm a
Catholic.

America how can I write a holy litany in your silly mood?
I will continue like Henry Ford my strophes are as individual
as his automobiles more so they're all different sexes.

America I will sell you strophes $2500 apiece $500 down
on your old strophe.
America free Tom Mooney
America save the Spanish Loyalists
America Sacco & Vanzetti must not die
America I am the Scottsboro boys.
America when I was seven momma took me to Communist
Cell meetings they sold us garbanzos a handful per ticket
a ticket costs a nickel and the speeches were free
everybody was angelic and sentimental about the workers
it was all so sincere you have no idea what a good thing
the party was in 1835 Scott Nearing was a grand old man
a real mensch Mother Bloor made me cry I once saw
Israel Amter plain. Everybody must have been a spy.
America you don't really want to go to war.
America it's them bad Russians.
Them Russians them Russians and them Chinamen. And
them Russians.
The Russia wants to eat us alive. The Russia's power mad. She
wants to take our cars from out our garages.
Her wants to grab Chicago. Her needs a Red Readers' Digest.
Her wants our auto plants in Siberia. Him big bureaucracy
running our fillingstations.
That no good. Ugh. Him make Indians learn read. Him need
big black niggers. Hah. Her make us all work sixteen
hours a day. Help.
America this is quite serious.
America this is the impression I get from looking in the
television set.
America is this correct?
I'd better get right down to the job.
It's true I don't want to join the Army or turn lathes in
precision parts factories, I'm nearsighted and psychopathic
anyway.
America I'm putting my queer shoulder to the wheel.

LOUIS SIMPSON

landscape with barns

The barns like scarlet lungs are breathing in
Pneumonia. The North wind smells of iron.
It's winter on the farm. The Hupmobile
That broke its back is dying at the fence.
At night in a thin house we watch TV
While moonlight falls in silence, drop by drop.

The country that Columbus thought he found
Is called America. It looks unreal,
Unreal in winter and unreal in summer.
When movies spread their giants on the air
The boys drive to the next town, drunk on nothing.
Youth has the secret. Only death looks real.

We never die. When we are old we vanish
Into the basement where we have our hobbies.
Enough, when something breaks, that widows mourn
"He would have fixed it. He knew what to do."
And life is always borrowing and lending
Like a good neighbor. How can we refuse?

LOUIS SIMPSON

the inner part

When they had won the war
And for the first time in history
Americans were the most important people—

When the leading citizens no longer lived in
their shirt sleeves,
And their wives did not scratch in public;
Just when they'd stopped saying "Gosh!"—

When their daughters seemed as sensitive
As the tip of a fly rod,
And their sons were as smooth as a V–8 engine—

Priests, examining the entrails of birds,
Found the heart misplaced, and seeds
As black as death, emitting a strange odor.

WELDON KEES

robinson

The dog stops barking after Robinson has gone.
His act is over. The world is a gray world,
Not without violence, and he kicks under the grand piano,
The nightmare chase well under way.

The mirror from Mexico, stuck to the wall,
Reflects nothing at all. The glass is black.
Robinson alone provides the image Robinsonian.

Which is all of the room—walls, curtains,
Shelves, bed, the tinted photograph of Robinson's first wife,
Rugs, vases, panatellas in a humidor.
They would fill the room if Robinson came in.

The pages in the books are blank,
The books that Robinson has read. That is his favorite chair,
Or where the chair would be if Robinson were here.

All day the phone rings. It could be Robinson
Calling. It never rings when he is here.

Outside, white buildings yellow in the sun.
Outside, the birds circle continuously
Where trees are actual and take no holiday.

robinson at home

Curtains drawn back, the door ajar.
All winter long, it seemed, a darkening
Began. But now the moonlight and the odors of the street
Conspire and combine toward one community.

These are the rooms of Robinson.
Bleached, wan, and colorless this light, as though
All the blurred daybreaks of the spring
Found an asylum here, perhaps for Robinson alone,

Who sleeps. Were there more music sifted through the floors
And moonlight of a different kind,
He might awake to hear the news at ten,
Which will be shocking, moderately.

This sleep is from exhaustion, but his old desire
To die like this has known a lessening
Now there is only this coldness that he has to wear.
But not in sleep.—Observant scholar, traveller,

Or uncouth bearded figure squatting in a cave,
A keen-eyed sniper on the barricades,
A heretic in catacombs, a famed roué,
A beggar on the streets, the confidant of Popes—

All these are Robinson in sleep, who mumbles as he turns,
"There is something in this madhouse that I symbolize—
This city—nightmare—black—"
He wakes in sweat
To the terrible moonlight and what might be
Silence. It drones like wires far beyond the roofs,
And the long curtains blow into the room.

relating to robinson

Somewhere in Chelsea, early summer;
And, walking in the twilight toward the docks,
I thought I made out Robinson ahead of me.

From an uncurtained second-story room, a radio
Was playing *There's A Small Hotel*; a kite
Twisted above dark rooftops and slow drifting birds.
We were alone there, he and I,
Inhabiting the empty street.

Under a sign for Natural Bloom Cigars,
While lights clicked softly in the dusk from red to green,
He stopped and gazed into a window
Where a plaster Venus, modeling a truss,
Looked out at Eastbound traffic. (But Robinson,
I knew, was out of town: he summers at a place in Maine,
Sometimes on Fire Island, sometimes the Cape,
Leaves town in June and comes back after Labor Day.)
And yet, I almost called out, "Robinson!"

There was no chance. Just as I passed,
Turning my head to search his face,
His own head turned with mine
And fixed me with dilated, terrifying eyes
That stopped my blood. His voice
Came at me like an echo in the dark.

"I thought I saw the whirlpool opening.
Kicked all night at a bolted door.
You must have followed me from Astor Place.
An empty paper floats down at the last.
And then a day as huge as yesterday in pairs
Unrolled its horror on my face
Until it blocked—" Running in sweat
To reach the docks, I turned back
For a second glance. I had no certainty,

There in the dark, that it was Robinson
Or someone else.
The block was bare. The Venus,
Bathed in blue fluorescent light,
Stared toward the river. As I hurried West,
The lights across the bay were coming on.
The boats moved silently and the low whistles blew.

WELDON KEES

aspects of robinson

Robinson at cards at the Algonquin; a thin
Blue light comes down once more outside the blinds.
Gray men in overcoats are ghosts blown past the door.
The taxis streak the avenues with yellow, orange, and red.
This is Grand Central, Mr. Robinson.

Robinson on a roof above the Heights; the boats
Mourn like the lost. Water is slate, far down.
Through sounds of ice cubes dropped in glass, an osteopath,
Dressed for the links, describes an old Intourist tour.
—Here's where old Gibbons jumped from, Robinson.

Robinson walking in the Park, admiring the elephant.
Robinson buying the *Tribune*, Robinson buying the *Times*. Robinson
Saying, "Hello. Yes, this is Robinson. Sunday
At five? I'd love to. Pretty well. And you?"
Robinson alone at Longchamps, staring at the wall.

Robinson afraid, drunk, sobbing. Robinson
In bed with a Mrs. Morse. Robinson at home;
Decisions: Toynbee or luminol? Where the sun

Shines, Robinson in flowered trunks, eyes toward
The breakers. Where the night ends, Robinson in East
Side bars.

Robinson in Glen plaid jacket, Scotch-grain shoes,
Black four-in-hand and oxford button-down,
The jeweled and silent watch that winds itself, the brief-
Case, covert topcoat, clothes for spring, all covering
His sad and usual heart, dry as a winter leaf.

SAUL BELLOW

the wrecker

cast

A HUSBAND
A WIFE
A MOTHER-IN-LAW
A CITY EMPLOYEE

scene

The living-room of a railroad flat on the East Side. Chesterfield suite, ribbon plants, rubber plants, all the cherished objects of the woman's temple, the man's asylum. At curtain wife and mother-in-law are discovered packing fragile articles into a barrel, wrapping them in paper.

Suddenly, a huge crash backstage.

MOTHER-IN-LAW (*Gives a shriek, suppresses it, asks angrily*) How can you stand it!

WIFE (*Looks concerned; she leans forward slightly against the barrel, not daring to look in the direction of the noise*) I've been standing it since yesterday. I'll probably get used to it. They say you get used to any kind of noise.

MOTHER-IN-LAW You should never have let him start.

WIFE I held him back till yesterday, when the people downstairs moved. They were the last.

MOTHER-IN-LAW The place is spooky. An empty building, and you on the third floor. They all left their trash on the stairs. It shows how inconsiderate people are. As long as there's a single tenant in the house they shouldn't have cluttered the staircase. I could hardly pass by.

WIFE (*sorrowfully patient with her mother*) I'm sorry mother, but it's the last time you'll be visiting me here anyway.

MOTHER-IN-LAW (*another rumbling noise offstage rear: she turns towards it*) I suppose he fought with all the neighbors enough. You shouldn't be sorry to leave this . . . this dump. It ought to have been condemned years ago.

WIFE Oh, I'm not exactly sorry. After fifteen years in the same place, though, you stop criticizing it. You never think whether it's a bad place or a good one.

MOTHER-IN-LAW Nonsense. You ought to be happy to move into an elevator building. And get rid of the old dumbwaiter. And have white woodwork. And a toilet where you don't have to pull the chain. Things a person needs for her self-respect.

WIFE It was good enough when I was a bride. (*Teary, thinking deep into the past.*) I was proud of it. And Albert used to be so kind about it. He helped me paper the walls. . . .

MOTHER-IN-LAW Sarah, he's a neurotic.

WIFE Oh, mother! You don't have to sound like a doctor. (*Terrible crash offstage*)

MOTHER-IN-LAW Would any person in his right mind be doing that? Have you moved out the breakables?

WIFE I took a lot of things over to the new apartment yesterday.

MOTHER-IN-LAW I suppose you're trying to save money by doing the moving yourself. I'm positively disgusted. Why, on the bonus the City is offering you could have it all done for you while you went to Atlantic City or even Virginia Beach and took a rest. You'd come back to a clean house. He turns down the bonus the City's giving for moving a few days before the lease is up so they can start their work. He keeps you here, and you let him. Oh, it's maddening. A husband like that is maddening. I predict that on this very spot, in this very space, when the school is built they'll be teaching about men like him in the abnormal psychology course! Why, think what you could do with a thousand dollars. You could get a new coat.

WIFE We could pay our debts.

MOTHER-IN-LAW And last year he let his insurance policy lapse because of a hundred-dollar premium. He's of unsound mind. Don't try to tell me he's not.

WIFE (*mildly*) He doesn't believe in life insurance.

MOTHER-IN-LAW I don't know where he gets his thoughts. (*Husband enters pulling a mirror on casters, an oval mirror. He is wearing dusty overalls, a painter's cap and carries a hammer on his hip, a hatchet on the other side. He holds a short crowbar*)

HUSBAND I thought I'd better get this out of the way.

MOTHER-IN-LAW (*sarcastic*) Why not smash it. Break all the furniture too, while you're at it. It would be good for your temperament.

HUSBAND (*turning*) Oh, it's you. For once I'm glad to see you. Last night I dreamed you were here—like the bird at the battle. Welcome to the last of my house! (*He is very enthusiastic*) (*To* WIFE) Baby, I knocked out the pantry wall, and do you know what? now you can go from the kitchen to the dining-room without turning corners. It was thrilling to knock a hole in that wall. Oh! Wow, what excitement!

MOTHER-IN-LAW Pretty expensive amusement.

HUSBAND What do you mean, amusement!

MOTHER-IN-LAW A thousand dollar amusement. Do you give any thought to what you could do with that money? Have you taken even five minutes off to sit down quietly in a corner and concentrate on what you could do? Your thoughts are always on the move, like the bottom of the sea.

HUSBAND I have thought. With a thousand dollars I could pay off a lot of people who have never done anything except make me unhappy, and strengthen their hand so they make me and others like me still more unhappy. Installments! For a lot of stuff I never really needed!

MOTHER-IN-LAW Like meat.

HUSBAND Food I pay for. Those are debts of honor. But the other stuff. Huh!

MOTHER-IN-LAW Like insurance.

HUSBAND If I have to die, what will happen? The less secure Sarah is the more she'll feel my death. You want to be able to mourn for me, don't you, darling?

WIFE Of course.

HUSBAND There. And if I leave her too comfortable she won't feel my death acutely enough. Why should things be better when I die? The city is full of unhappy old women whose husbands left them well-off. It is like revenge from the grave. There lies the husband in the earth. With probably a telephone beside him . . . they say there is one beside Mary Baker Eddy. A monument to his wife's security. And now she goes shopping—she doesn't need anything. She goes to Schrafft's. She pesters the elevator starter to find her an Irish Sweepstakes ticket. She buys magazines and doesn't know what to do with herself.

MOTHER-IN-LAW (*snaps her fingers*) That! for you and your philosophy. A man who has no respect for a thousand dollars isn't intelligent. You're a scared to do better in life.

HUSBAND I'm getting a thousand dollars' worth out of it. More. (*Shakes his crowbar like a spear*) Oh, what am I wasting words on you for! Today I'm a man of deeds, like a hero out of Homer, like a man who does something for civilization.

WIFE This is what he keeps saying.

HUSBAND Where there's no demolition there's no advancement. The old must go down. You only see what is built. You forget what had to be taken away, and yet it is the same process. Man does not wait for time to do his work for him. He makes an end; he begins again. (*Pounds the floor with the butt of his crowbar. A picture falls from the wall*)

WIFE Look what you've done!

MOTHER-IN-LAW If you have to tear down walls, why don't you go downstairs and do it. They've moved out and nobody'll care. Then you'd have the bonus and your fun.

HUSBAND It shows how little you understand. The neighbor's walls do not interest me. It was right here that everything happened to me. Here I was out of work, and looked at the walls. And here I was sick, and looked at the walls. And here I was blue, and here I cursed the world. And here maybe I learned my own limitations—oh, yes, that realization that I wasn't all I thought I was. It all took place within these walls. It went into them. And you ask me what I've got against them? *Plenty!* I *know* them. Oh, I've made a long study of them. There's a long history between us. And now that they have to come down why shouldn't I put my hand to the work? Who has a better right—a more sacred right? Why should I leave it to anyone? I will do it. Myself, I'll tear holes out. I'll see the East River through the dining-room. I'll have the satisfaction myself, and get my revenge for all those terrible times. What good will the walls downstairs do me? I want to take it out on my own walls. I know every lump, every blister, every face in the cracks of the ceiling. Now I'm going to see what this place is made of, what the walls are like inside. I'm going to tear out the laths and get behind all the swellings—like the brows, eyes, landscapes and so on. I'll find all the rats' nests and see if there are any treasures or bones. You can never tell what you'll find in an old building.

WIFE (*To* MOTHER) You see how overexcited he is?

MOTHER-IN-LAW I see he's passing up an opportunity to make your life easier because he wants to play like a boy. Treasures! People ought to be forced to be their age. What if he put on a sailor suit and told you he was going to sail his little boat in Central Park pond? What a sex the males are! It's a miracle how anything ever works out.

HUSBAND I am excited! I feel like Samson in the Temple of Gaza! (*So poses in the doorway*) Take cover, ye Philistines, your oppression is ended. My strength has come back to me. Though you took my hair and put out my eyes and bound me in your mill your walls are doomed! Doomed!

MOTHER-IN-LAW (*a little frightened*) He's off his rock.

HUSBAND (*rousing himself*) I am not. (*Points at her with the crowbar; says seriously*) Beware of diagnosing those near to you. You should never do that. Not even when it's true. At your age you should know better. What you think is lunacy is just happiness. You aren't used to it, probably haven't seen it in a long time. You've forgotten what it looks like.

WIFE You are happy?

HUSBAND Tremendously. Can't you see how happy I am? I'm a new man. And that's why I snap my fingers at the thousand dollar bonus. If I were as usual I'd need that thousand to help me bear it.

WIFE Is it as bad as that to be as usual? (*She is wounded*)

HUSBAND My dear, don't you take the blame for that. A daily life is a strange thing, and what are a husband and wife to do? They must live it together. Nobody is to blame. But these last two days I have carried a marvelous feeling in my heart. Like a poet. I have welcomed each night's sleep and blessed every morning's rising. I have been like a young boy reading a wonderful book who must put it down at night and says to himself, "Just close your eyes a while and when you open them again it will be morning and you can go on with it." And in the morning, which comes soon, it's very sweet; his book is still wonderful; it doesn't disappoint him. This is how my days have been since I started wrecking this apartment.

WIFE (*pathetic*) I didn't know you hated it so.

MOTHER-IN-LAW All I can say is that I hope it will pass over before it gets to the Bellevue stage.

(*A ring at the door.* WIFE *answers and admits the* CITY EMPLOYEE. *He has a portfolio under his arm—cardboard—and his double-breasted suit is chalkstriped. An eater of clams and drinker of beer. Seeing ladies he takes the toothpick from his mouth and with same hand removes his hat*)

CITY EMPLOYEE It gets kind of peculiar in a building when everybody leaves it.

WIFE Oh, it's the man from the City.

MOTHER-IN-LAW (*Best manners*) How do you do.

WIFE It is spooky, isn't it. Yesterday as I was cooking supper it was the first time I could remember that there was no radio program downstairs at Pellegrini's, and nobody playing the piano. It was just like the last days of some poor old widow.

CITY EMPLOYEE I come to open this bonus situation again. You understand, there's people waiting to start operations, the wrecking crew, the excavators, contractors. It's not exactly playing the game when everybody else has taken the bonus and moved out.

HUSBAND My lease runs for three weeks yet.

CITY EMPLOYEE You could be evicted with eminent domain.

HUSBAND It still would take weeks. Try it.

CITY EMPLOYEE It's no good trying to hold the City up for more dough, if that's your idea.

HUSBAND So, you think I have an idea to get dough out of you?

MOTHER-IN-LAW I wish I thought he was that smart.

CITY EMPLOYEE Well, you don't want to put the City on the spot like this.

HUSBAND What do I care about the City? It never did me a favor in all my life.

CITY EMPLOYEE What are you talkin'. There's invisible benefits all over. The sidewalks, the sewers, the water, the bridges, the garbage, the police. . . .

HUSBAND The police are no invisible benefit. (*Swings his crowbar over his shoulder, turns about limberly and marches away*)

(CITY EMPLOYEE *stands amazed. A great crash is heard. Staggering.*)

CITY EMPLOYEE What's that—what's he doin'?

MOTHER-IN-LAW Can't you guess?

WIFE Mother!

MOTHER-IN-LAW Do you think you can keep it a secret? He's wrecking the house.

WIFE Mother, that's downright disloyal.

CITY EMPLOYEE Is he nuts or something? (*Slams hat against thigh*) Who said he could? This is bought by the City. He's on m'nicipal property. Why, it ain't legal anyhow. (*Another crash.* CITY EMPLOYEE *shouts down corridor*) Hey! (*No answer.* CITY EMPLOYEE *exits, rear*)

MOTHER-IN-LAW Now maybe we'll get somewhere with that stubborn man.

WIFE Now he's in trouble.

MOTHER-IN-LAW He deserves it.

WIFE No he doesn't. You don't understand him.

MOTHER-IN-LAW If I had to live with him fifteen years to understand him it wouldn't be worth it.

(CITY EMPLOYEE *re-enters covered with white dust, quivering with anger. He shouts down corridor, rear*)

CITY EMPLOYEE Who the hell do you think *you* are! (*Another crash*) Who gave you the right? (*Sound of chopping*) Lady, your husband better not carry this any further. I'm tellin' you for your own good. He's poundin' chunks out of the walls with a sledge hammer. This just is not allowed, and that's all.

WIFE Why not? It's his right. Isn't a man's home his castle?

CITY EMPLOYEE (*Startled, wiping his face*) He can have it for his castle, but not for his loony bin. Besides, it ain't his. The City bought it and they can get him for damaging municipal property.

WIFE They've got their nerve. We paid enough rent before the City even heard of it.

MOTHER-IN-LAW The way you stand up for him!

WIFE Of course I do. Ain't I the man's wife? I know what he's been through if you don't, and if he wants his revenge on the place it's his by right.

CITY EMPLOYEE (*Feels his ear*) Do I understand, lady, that he's passin' up the bonus just to do the wreckin' job on this place himself? (*Hears the husband hammering within. His face passes through wonder, outrage, envy and finally stops at an expression of law violated*) It's not only crazy but illegal. It's real bad. For this he can go to jail. (*Draws forth notebook, looks about, makes notes*) He don't even have a permit.

MOTHER-IN-LAW I knew all along it was something fundamental.

WIFE I don't understand why.

CITY EMPLOYEE Lady, for one thing wrecking is a licensed occupation. You can't just go wreck. You have to know how. You must realize it's a profession like any other and you have to qualify for it. How does he know what to do about electricity, gas, water? Can he take out the bathtub or the toilet, any fixtures? He'd be shocked, suffocated or drowned. And what about the street? You have to protect your pedestrians. Where's your scaffold? Where's your dumping? He can get the book thrown at him.

(*Thunderous crash.* HUSBAND *enters carrying framed wedding picture*)

HUSBAND I think this wedding picture got jarred, dear. No real harm. Better put it away.

WIFE (*Catches breath*) You're starting on the bedroom! (*She takes picture from him, holds it tightly*)

HUSBAND I thought I might do a little work in there later today.

WIFE The bedroom.

CITY EMPLOYEE Listen bud, you're heading into all kinds of trouble.

WIFE (*From a different viewpoint*) Yes, Albert, you are.

HUSBAND The City wants to have this place torn down, doesn't it? It wants a school built here, doesn't it? Suppose I volunteered my help in tearing down my own apartment? They'd never accept it. I'd have to see people and fill forms and answer questions and in the end I wouldn't get in on it. So I'm independently contributing my labor. What's wrong with that? (*Hooks crowbar into mantelpiece and wrenches off top. Bric-a-brac goes flying*)

WIFE (*Wildly*) Oh, my things! The sea-shells! The little jug from Vermont! The little cups! (*Goes on hands and knees.* MOTHER-IN-LAW, *muttering, helps*)

HUSBAND Oh, it's nothing, Sarah. I'll get you new knick-knacks. These are about worn out. Look at that grand cockroach. If it isn't the oldest resident in person! He's not even disturbed. What presence. This is what you call aristocracy. Fifteen years we've been his vassals. He's never done a lick of work, I'll bet. Why should he?

MOTHER-IN-LAW (*To* CITY EMPLOYEE) You see what's happening? But it's probably just temporary. You ought to give him till tomorrow to decide. He'll most likely come back to his senses.

CITY EMPLOYEE He's off his control, all right, I can see that.

HUSBAND See what a difference the point of view makes. I never was better. I am a magician. This joint is enchanted, you see. I'm getting rid of a lot of past life, dangerous to the soul. The past, you understand, is very dangerous if you don't deal with it. If I had a warehouse I could put this harmful past life into, or if I could take it to sea in a scow and dump it, let the seagulls have it, I'd be satisfied. You can't drag your heavy, heavy history around with you. Suppose the humming bird had to keep remembering that in the ancient past it was a snake?

CITY EMPLOYEE (*Touching his forehead*) Oh, man! (*He goes out*)

MOTHER-IN-LAW I'd better talk to him. Maybe I can make him hold off a while. You'd better reason with *him* meanwhile and please God his mentality will return. (*Exit*)

WIFE (*Broken cup in hand*) Albert. . . .

HUSBAND Yes, darling?

WIFE Isn't there anything—anything here you don't hold a grudge against?

HUSBAND (*Speculative*) I suppose there is.

WIFE You suffered in every room?

HUSBAND Well, you carry it around from room to room, you see.

WIFE The bedroom, too.

HUSBAND (*Uneasy*) No more than the others, probably.

WIFE Isn't there anything you'd like to save instead of wreck? You might remember something that made your life worth-while.

HUSBAND Of course. You want to be fair about it.

WIFE (*With light irony*) The kitchen, perhaps, in memory of good meals. (*He shrugs. Wife changes tone*) Albert, I have tried to make you a home. We've had many bad times, that's true. But didn't I comfort you? That time you came in and said your paycheck was stolen?

HUSBAND (*Feebly*) It was, too.

WIFE The time you were knocked down by the cab on Lexington Avenue and I brought you home from the hospital in a taxi, and when you woke up at night I'd go and make tea for you and stay awake with you. And what about the time the furniture company wanted to repossess the living-room suite . . . ?

HUSBAND Yes, I remember.

WIFE And what about the time we came back from Jones Beach that afternoon, and. . . .

HUSBAND Sure, sure, that was great. That was a wonderful afternoon, wasn't it.

WIFE What about all those good things?

HUSBAND We haven't forgotten. Did I say we should? But let's not get sentimental, old girl. Because when you come right down to it, you can't check off every grievance against a happy time. You can't have happy times if you have to swallow all the grievances. Anyhow, this is too much like bookkeeping. Why do you have to pretend to me that you're not sore at this joint, too? It never bored you? Didn't it ever make you want to yell? Didn't you ever feel here that you were in a cage? Didn't these walls ever look at you with yellow foreheads and their lousy, dull eyes? Don't kid me.

WIFE (*Hesitant*) Sometimes, of course.

HUSBAND (*Hands her a hatchet*) What are you waiting for, then? Be honest. Pitch in.

WIFE (*Decisively rejects hatchet*) No, I'm not going to. I papered and painted these walls myself, and washed the floors and the woodwork.

HUSBAND And swore at the landlord.

WIFE Never mind the landlord. We lived here.

HUSBAND We suffered here.

WIFE That would have happened to you anywhere.

HUSBAND Sometimes you ought to give in to your violent feelings, Sarah. It's great to be angry. Anger is beautiful. It gives you a sense of honor. It brings back your self-respect.

WIFE All right, then. I am angry.

HUSBAND About what?

WIFE It's the bedroom I'm angry about. You haven't been happy, and this is your way of saying it.

HUSBAND (*Without enough emphasis*) Yes, I have been. Well, look here, Sarah old girl. Let's not act in bad faith. I mean—you know. If it isn't always what it should be, at least you don't have to think you're protecting the home by pretending. Most likely it all clears up in the end. . . .

WIFE You don't love me.

HUSBAND (*Indignant*) Of course I love you. Do you think I'm wrecking this joint for myself? Every other hole I pound in the wall is for you. I say, "This is for Sarah. This is where she bowed her head. This is where she heard bad news. This is where she scalded her foot. Where we argued. . . ."

WIFE But the bedroom, Albert, the bedroom.

HUSBAND Well, come and help me bust up the dining-room and we can discuss the bedroom later. It's only another room.

WIFE It isn't. And if you touch it. . . .

HUSBAND Threats?

WIFE You can't expect me to be overjoyed.

HUSBAND And you can't expect me to be superhuman like you. If you can forgive everything, that's your good luck. But if I did it I'd be acting in bad faith. Things always should be nice, that's for sure. But tell me, why is it so glorious to tear this house down? Why is it ecstasy to see the ceilings fall, and chopping I feel like dancing, and the smell of dust makes my heart float with joy, like the smell of flowers, and I never feel tired?

WIFE Have I tried to stop you? Did I insist about the thousand dollars? Did I complain at having to pack all the things myself?

HUSBAND All that is true. Still, you should be glad I have found something that cries aloud to be done, an object. . . .

WIFE Yes, I should be delighted that you don't knock me down; I should be pleased you don't batter me on the head with your axe, like the pantry shelves.

HUSBAND Sweetheart, please understand. An object. . . .

WIFE . . . is a substitute for me. Because I've had you in a trap. Was this your home or was it the Bastille? Did it mean nothing to you? Did you have to lie down each night worried that animals might bite you in your sleep, or people run in to attack you? You have no gratitude in your make-up. I often go back to where I used to live when I was a girl. The lot is vacant and nobody I know is there. I ask myself, "Where is everything that meant so much to me?" I'd bring it back if I could. Next year there'll be a school here, and children sitting where we used to. . . .

HUSBAND They'll be studying history.

WIFE And where will we be?

HUSBAND In the new apartment.

WIFE No, I'm speaking of the lives we used to lead here. Where will they be?

HUSBAND And where will the lives the children will lead here be later on? You say this was the Bastille for me. Don't you mean that you want it to be a museum?

WIFE Albert, I don't think I've made you a bad wife.

HUSBAND Of course not.

WIFE I've given in to your impulses and you always had my first consideration. I've never stood in your way. You want to wreck the house? Go ahead, wreck it!

HUSBAND Angel!

WIFE Only, if you wreck the bedroom, you'll be moving into the new apartment by yourself.

HUSBAND You don't mean it!

WIFE I'll leave you. It was you who told me anger was wonderful.

HUSBAND You wouldn't do that.

WIFE I will. And what else can I do? You force me into it.

HUSBAND I am convinced now. Only the most ordinary men should become husbands. Whatever they may dream of, when you come right down to it women want their husbands to be ordinary and to make no trouble. Husbands are not heroes: heroes are not husbands. That's all there is to it.

WIFE Do you call what you're doing heroism? (*She laughs*)

HUSBAND Amuse yourself if you like. It shows you never applied your mind to this subject. Does it say anywhere that Achilles ever built anything? Or Ulysses? They tore down Troy and killed everyone in it. Who were the heroes of the war? The fellows who dropped bombs on cities. A hero destroys the links with the past when they bother him. He frees himself from what other men have done before him.

WIFE (*Indignant*) Other men before him? Are you trying to say. . . . What other men have ever been in that bedroom? Accusing me!

HUSBAND No, no, no. Why do you have to be so damned literal? Besides . . . you don't have to protest so much. You'll make me think I'm missing up on something. Is it some other bedroom I should be thinking of tearing down? Is that it?

WIFE (*Startled at first, then reproachful*) How can such things ever enter your mind? Oh, Albert!

HUSBAND I always mean well, but my mind betrays me. Ah, Sarah, come along. (*Active again*) Try it. When you've tried it you'll understand what I've been driving at. You have to prime yourself sometimes. Take one sock at a wall. Just one. See how different you'll feel. (*Hands her his hatchet*) You don't realize what you'll get out of it.

WIFE No. I've already told you what I'd do.

HUSBAND Come, free yourself, Sarah.

WIFE No, that's not what I call freeing myself. It's ingratitude.

HUSBAND You're not big, but you sure are obstinate. And also because it was *your* house it was wonderful. That's how vain you are.

WIFE Now I will leave. It's a lucky thing I thought of opening a bank account of my own.

HUSBAND You're far too rigid—far, far. You have to learn to be more flexible. It's a practical matter. For the sake of your health.

WIFE (*Sighs and shakes her head*) How many ideas you have. Do you want me to believe that what you're doing you're doing for your health's sake?

HUSBAND Of course it's for my health. (*To audience*) I'm dead serious. (*To* WIFE) Now why else do you think I'm being so truthful? It's risky. If I say too much you'll get sore. But if I don't do it I feel sick. (*Puts backs of hands to eyes and brings hands away with a whisking motion*) Let's wipe out some of the falsehood. Let's admit what our souls tell us is true and stop denying it for the sake of keeping the peace or preserving the marriage and the home. Yes, just because of health. So the old bedroom will be destroyed, but maybe then the new one will be fit for princes and queens. Maybe it will make the roses bloom from the plaster and daisies from the rug.

WIFE (*Half swayed*) Oh, Albert, do you really think so?

HUSBAND Yes, yes. So come. We'll take some of the doors off the hinges and set them up. Have you noticed how pretty it is when the wreckers are working, with blue doors and pink doors standing outside? And you know how the plaster was always falling into the bath-tub, well now we can fill the tub with plaster. Rip up the old linoleum. Tear up the floors. Go through the place like a hurricane. Come on.

WIFE (*Steels herself*) No.

HUSBAND (*Turning*) You won't?

WIFE I told you what I'd do.

HUSBAND It's the bedroom?

WIFE Yes, I'll leave.

HUSBAND (*Furious*) All right, go then. Go. Damn! Take your shells and your damn precious female breakables, your Vermont jugs and your slave-chains of china, and get out of here. I'll wreck the joint myself. I'll demolish it; I'll raze it; I'll tear it to pieces; I'll level it down to the ground. (*Smites ceiling with crowbar. Chandelier falls and hits him on the head. He drops to floor*)

WIFE (*Rushing to him*) Oh, he's fractured his skull. Albert, Baby. Oh, sweetheart, what have you done? Mother! Mama! Oh, help. (*Kisses him, rubs his hands, examines his head, listens to his heart*) It must be a concussion. I'll never forgive myself if it is. If he had to do it, at least I could have stuck by him and made him do it in a safer way. Oh, my little sweetheart. Little bright-thoughts. (*As he revives*) My spunky one. You stood right up to me. Oh, honey, you were so right. Let's never quarrel. How does it feel? (*He groans, holds his head, starts to sit up*)

HUSBAND If it was any heavier it would have killed me. I bit my tongue.

WIFE Albert, darling; Albert, look at me! (*She takes the hatchet and starts delicately to chip at the walls*) Albert, you see, I've got the idea. It's just as you said. It really is glorious. (*Finds bulb and throws it down. Is slighty shocked by noise and own daring*) Oh, Albert, how slow I am to learn anything. If I didn't have you to show me the way I'd be just a timid, conservative, pokey little creature worrying like a mole. Imagine how it would be to live a whole life without doing anything big. (*Chips away at the fireplace*)

HUSBAND Just about knocked my brains out. What are you doing? (*Watches*)

WIFE Doing? Why, what you tried to convince me to do, for my own good. And I couldn't agree with you more.

HUSBAND (*Doesn't look happy about it*) Wait a minute.

WIFE (*Still chipping*) Why, what's the matter? Is it the noise?

HUSBAND Now hold on a minute.

WIFE But you've convinced me. . . .

HUSBAND Yes, but I'm not so sure . . . On you it doesn't look so good.

WIFE Why not, I'd like to know. Now you want to stop me? Just as I've discovered what you meant? I know you didn't expect me to, but I have found out and you (*shakes her head*) don't want me to?

HUSBAND (*Rising. Uncomfortable*) It's not that exactly.

WIFE How's your head?

HUSBAND All right, I guess.

WIFE You don't feel dizzy?

HUSBAND Not very. It's a miracle.

WIFE (*Hands him crowbar*) Then you can go back to work. (*Kisses him*)

HUSBAND I do think I need a little rest first.

WIFE But not for long. I suddenly feel such strength in me. As soon as I picked up the hatchet it just poured into my hands. An hour ago they felt so feeble I couldn't have peeled a potato. Rest, dear, and then we can start on the bedroom together.

HUSBAND The bedroom?

WIFE Of course, the bedroom.

HUSBAND (*Thinking*) You. . . .

WIFE Of course. I. Now that I understand what you meant.

HUSBAND Well, Sarah, (*Haltingly*) is it really—I mean from your standpoint—such a good idea?

WIFE You don't want to wreck it? I do, now. When I think of some of the things that happened, all of a sudden I want to express what I never dared. . . .

HUSBAND (*Reprovingly*) Sarah!

WIFE Well, I want to admit what's true, too. You have nothing against that, have you? There are a few places on the ceiling that just burn me up when I think of them. I've only now become conscious of it all.

HUSBAND Sarah, don't you feel . . . ? Are you sure?

WIFE Why, darling, you surprise me. Have you changed your mind about the bedroom? Why, silly, didn't you tell me a daily life was a strange thing, and what were husband and wife to do about it . . . they have to live it together?

HUSBAND Yes, yes, of course. But. . . .

WIFE And don't you want to wreck the house?

HUSBAND Yes, but all at once you want to start with the bedroom. Tell me something. . . .

WIFE What is there to tell? Do I have to draw pictures?

HUSBAND Please, Sarah.

WIFE (*Once more offers him the crowbar*) Are you with me or not? Are you going to back down or will you come alone?

HUSBAND All right. (*He is very reluctant*)

WIFE Better fetch a stepladder. I'm mad to get at that ceiling. (*Grips hatchet, and laughs exultantly*) Something has just entered my mind.

HUSBAND What?

WIFE That maybe the best way to preserve the marriage is to destroy the home. (*Embraces him*)

HUSBAND (*Mildly*) It may well be.

(Curtain. After which, a thunderous crash)

JEAN-PAUL SARTRE

individualism and conformism in the united states

How is one to talk about 135 million Americans when we have only six weeks to spend here? It would require a ten-year stay. We are set down in a city where we pick up a few details. Yesterday it was Baltimore, today it is Knoxville, the day after tomorrow it will be

New Orleans, and then, after admiring the biggest factory or the biggest bridge or the biggest dam in the world, we fly with our heads full of figures and statistics.

We shall have seen more steel and aluminum than human beings. But can one talk about steel? As to "impressions," they come as they please.

"Stick to facts!" some people tell us.

But what facts? The length of a certain shipyard, or the electric blue of the oxyhydrogen blowpipe in the pale light of a shed? In choosing, I am already making a decision as to what America is.

On the other hand, some people say, "Get some perspective!" But I distrust those perspectives that are already generalizations. I have therefore decided to set forth my personal impressions and interpretations, on my own responsibility. This America may be something I've dreamed up. In any case, I will be honest with my dream: I shall set it forth just as it came to me.

And today I should like to tell you my impressions of two contradictory slogans that are current in Paris: "Americans are conformists" and "Americans are individualists."

Like everyone else, I had heard of the famous American "melting pot" that transforms, at different temperatures, Poles, Italians and Finns into United States citizens. But I did not quite know what the term really meant.

Now, the day after my arrival I met a European who was in the process of being melted down. I was introduced, in the big lobby of the Plaza Hotel, to a dark man of rather medium height who, like everyone here, talked with a somewhat nasal twang, without seeming to move his lips or cheeks, who would burst out laughing with his mouth, but who didn't laugh with his eyes, and who expressed himself in good French, with a heavy accent, though his speech was sprinkled with Americanisms and barbarisms.

When I congratulated him on his knowledge of our language, he replied with astonishment, "But I'm a Frenchman!" He had been born in Paris, had been living in America for only fifteen years and, before the war, had returned to France every six months. Nevertheless, America already half-possessed him. His mother had never left Paris. When he talked, with a deliberately vulgar accent, about "Paname," he seemed much more like a Yankee bent on displaying his knowledge of Europe than an exiled Frenchman recalling his native land. He felt obliged every now and then to throw a roguish wink in my direction and exclaim: "Aha! New Orleans, pretty girls!" But what he was really doing was living up to the American image of the Frenchman rather than trying to be obliging to a fellow-countryman. "Pretty girls," he said with a forced laugh; I felt Puritanism just round the corner, and a chill ran through me.

I felt as if I were witnessing an Ovidian metamorphosis. The man's face was still too expressive. It had retained the slightly irritating mimicry of intelligence which makes a French face recognizable anywhere. But he will soon be a tree or a rock. I speculated curiously as to the powerful forces that had to be brought into play in order to achieve these disintegrations and reintegrations so surely and rapidly.

But these forces are mild and persuasive. You have only to walk about in the streets, enter a shop or turn on a radio to meet them and feel their effect upon you, like a warm breath.

In America—at least the America with which I'm familiar—you are never alone in the street. The walls talk to you. To left and right of you there are advertisement hoardings, illuminated signs and immense display windows which contain only a big placard with a photographic montage or some statistics. You see a distressed-looking woman offering her lips to an American soldier, or an aeroplane bombing a town and, under the picture, the words, "Bibles, not bombs." The nation walks about with you, giving you advice and orders. But it does so in an undertone and is careful to explain its admonition in minute detail. There is not a single command, whether in a cosmetic advertisement ("Today, more than ever, it is your duty to be beautiful. Take care of your face for *his* return. Buy X . . . Cream") or in a piece of War Bond propaganda, which is not accompanied by a brief comment or explanatory picture.

Yesterday I lunched at a restaurant in Fontana, an artificial town built about a great dam in Tennessee.

Along the busy highway leading to the dam is a big hoarding with a parable, in cartoon form, on the subject of teamwork. Two donkeys tied to each other are trying to reach two hay-stacks which are a certain distance apart. Each donkey is tugging on the halter in an opposite direction. They half-strangle each other. But finally they understand. They come together and start working on the first haystack. When they have eaten it, we see them biting together into the second one.

Obviously the commentary has been deliberately avoided. The

passer-by *must* draw the conclusion *himself*. There is no pressure put on him. On the contrary, the cartoon is an appeal to his intelligence. He is obliged to interpret and understand it; he is not bludgeoned with it as with the loud Nazi propaganda posters. It remains in half-tone. It requires his cooperation in order to be deciphered. Once he has understood, it is as though he himself has conceived the idea. He is more than half convinced.

Loudspeakers have been installed in factories everywhere. They are meant to combat the worker's isolation in the presence of matter. At first, when you go through the immense navy yard near Baltimore, you find the human dispersion, that great solitude of the worker, with which we are familiar in Europe. All day long, masked men, bending over steel plates, manipulate their oxyhydrogen blow-pipes. But as soon as they put on their helmets they can hear music. And even the music is a kind of guidance that stealthily insinuates itself into them; even the music is a directed dream. And then the music stops, and they are given information about the war or their work.

When we were leaving Fontana, the engineer who had so kindly escorted us all about led us into a little glass-enclosed room in which a new wax disc, already prepared to record our voices, was revolving on a turntable. He explained that all the foreigners who had visited the dam had, on leaving, summed up their impressions before the microphone. Far be it from us to refuse such a kind host; those of us who spoke English said something and the speeches were recorded. The following day they would be broadcast in the yard, the cafeteria and in every house in town, and the workers would be pleased to learn of the excellent impression they had made upon the foreigners and would work with an even greater will.

Add to this the advice given on the radio, the letters to the newspapers, and, above all, the activities of the innumerable organizations whose aims are almost always educational, and you will see that the American citizen is quite hedged in.

But it would be a mistake to regard this as an oppressive tactic on the part of the government or the big American capitalists.

Of course, the present government is at war; it has to use methods like these for war propaganda. In addition, one of the government's principal concerns is education.

In Tennessee, for example, where the farmers had been ruining the soil by planting corn every year, it is trying hard to teach them gradually to let the soil rest by varying the crops from year to year. And in order to achieve its purpose, it has mingled gifts (low-priced electricity, free irrigation) with rational arguments. But there is a much more spontaneous and diffuse phenomenon involved here.

This educative tendency really springs from the heart of the community. Every American is educated by other Americans and educates others in turn. All through New York, in the schools and elsewhere, there are courses in Americanization.

Everything is taught: sewing, cooking, and even flirting. A school in New York gives a course for girls on how to get their boy-friends to propose to them. All of this is directed at forming pure Americans rather than men. But the American makes no distinction between American reason and ordinary reason. All the advice with which his path is marked is so perfectly motivated, so penetrating, that he feels lulled by an immense solicitude that never leaves him helpless or abandoned.

I have known modern mothers who never ordered their children to do anything without first persuading them to obey. In this way they acquired a more complete and perhaps more formidable authority over their children than if they had threatened or beaten them. In the same way, the American, whose reason and freedom are called upon at every hour of the day, makes it a point of honour to do as he is asked. It is when he is acting like everyone else that he feels most reasonable and most American; it is in displaying his conformism that he feels freest.

As far as I can judge, the American nation's characteristic traits are the opposite of those which Hitler imposed upon Germany and which Maurras wanted to impose upon France.

To Hitler (or Maurras), an argument was good for Germany if it was, first of all, German. If it had the slightest whiff of universality, it was always suspect.

The peculiarity of the American, on the other hand, is the fact that he regards his thought as universal. One can discern in this a Puritan influence which I need not go into here. But above all, there is that concrete, daily presence of a flesh and blood Reason, a visible Reason. Thus, most of the people I spoke with seemed to have a naïve and passionate faith in the virtues of Reason. An American said to me one evening, "After all, if international politics were in the hands of well-balanced and reasonable men, wouldn't war be abolished for ever?" Some French people present said that this did not necesarily follow, and he got angry. "All right," he said in scornful indignation, "go and build cemeteries!" I, for my part, said nothing; discussion between us was impossible. I believe in the existence of evil and he does not.

It is this Rousseau-like optimism which, where Nazi Germany is concerned, cuts him off from our point of view. In order to admit the existence of such atrocities, he would have to admit that men can be wholly bad. "Do you think there are two Germanys?" an American doctor asked me. I replied that I didn't.

"I understand," he said. "France has suffered so much that you are unable to think otherwise. It's too bad."

And then there is the machine, which also acts as a universalizing factor. There is generally only one way of using a mechanical object, namely, the one indicated in the accompanying leaflet. The American uses his mechanical corkscrew, his refrigerator or his automobile in the same way and at the same time as all other Americans. Besides, this object is not made to order. It is meant for anyone and will obey anyone, provided he knows how to use it correctly.

Thus, when the American puts a nickel into the slot in the tram or in the underground, he feels just like everyone else. Not like an anonymous unit, but like a man who has divested himself of his individuality and raised himself to the impersonality of the Universal.

It was this complete freedom in conformism that struck me at the very beginning. There is no freer city than New York. You can do as you please there. It is public opinion that plays the role of the policeman. The few Americans I met seemed to me at first to conform through freedom, to be depersonalized through rationalism. They seemed to identify Universal Reason with their own particular nation, within the framework of the same creed.

But almost immediately I discovered their profound individualism. This combination of social conformism and individualism is, perhaps, what a Frenchman will have most difficulty in understanding. For us, individualism has retained the old, classical form of "the individual's struggle against society and, more particularly, against the State." There is no question of this in America. In the first place, for a long time the State was only an administrative body. In recent years it has tended to play another role, but this has not changed the American's attitude towards it. It is "their" State, the expression of "their" nation; they have both a profound respect for it and a proprietary love.*

If you merely walk about in New York for a few days you cannot fail to notice the deep link between American conformism and American individuality. Seen flat on the ground from the point of length and width, New York is the most conformist city in the world. From Washington Square north, there is not a single oblique or curving street, with the exception of old Broadway. A dozen long, parallel furrows go straight from the tip of Manhattan to the Harlem River. These are the avenues, which are intersected by hundreds of smaller furrows rigorously perpendicular to them.

This chequerboard is New York. The streets look so much alike that they have not been named. They have merely been given registration numbers, like soldiers.

But if you look up, everything changes. Seen in its height, New York is the triumph of individualism. The tops of the buildings defy all the rules of town planning. They have twenty-seven, fifty-five and a hundred storeys. They are grey, brown or white, Moorish, medieval, renaissance or modern. On lower Broadway, they press against each other, dwarfing the tiny black churches, and then, suddenly, they separate, leaving between them a gaping hole of light. Seen from Brooklyn they seem to have the nobility and solitude of bouquets of palm trees on the banks of rivers in Moroccan Susa—bouquets of skyscrapers which the eye is always trying to assemble and which are always coming undone.

Thus, at first, American individualism seemed like a third dimension. It is not incompatible with conformism, but, on the contrary, implies it. It represents, however, a new direction, both in height and depth, within conformism.

First, there is the struggle for existence, which is extremely harsh. Every individual wants to succeed, that is, to make money. But this is not to be regarded as greed or merely a taste for luxury. In the States, money is, I think, the necessary but symbolic token of

* An R.P.F. gang tried to disrupt a political meeting in which I happened to be participating, and the affair ended in a brawl. An American who shared our ideas was amazed that we did not call in the police. I explained our reluctance, but he remained upset. "Back home," he told me, "the police force belongs to all the citizens. We find it *natural* to turn to them for help."

success. You must succeed because success is a proof of virtue and intelligence and also because it shows that you enjoy divine protection.

And you must also succeed because only then can you face the crowd as a person. Take the American newspapers. So long as you have not achieved success, you cannot expect your articles to appear in the form in which you have submitted them. They will be cut and pruned. But if you have a money-making name, then everything changes; what you write will go through without cuts. You have acquired the right to be yourself.

The same situation holds in the theatre. A lady very well versed in French literature and known in publishing circles asked me if I should like to have a play of mine done in the States. I replied that I should be delighted were it not for the fact that producers were in the habit of modifying the texts submitted to them. She seemed highly surprised and said: "If they don't, who will? What you have written is meant to be read. But they have to work on it to make understandable."*

Thus, in the struggle for life, American individuality is, above all, each person's passionate aspiration toward the state of the individual. There are individuals in America, just as there are skyscrapers. There are Ford and Rockefeller, and Hemingway and Roosevelt. They are models and examples.

The buildings are, in this sense, votive offerings to success. Behind the Statue of Liberty, they are like the statues of a man or an undertaking which has risen above the rest. They are immense publicity ventures, constructed in large part to demonstrate the financial triumph of individuals or groups. The owner occupies only a small part of the premises and rents out the rest. Thus, I was not mistaken in taking them for symbols of New York individualism. They simply demonstrate that, in the United States, individuality is something to be won. That is probably the reason why New York seemed so passionately attached to a liberal economy.

Yet everyone knows of the power of trusts in the United States, a power which represents another form of controlled economy. But

* This is the source of the misunderstanding in the Kravchenko case. Since re-writing is an accepted practice in America, Kravchenko is regarded by Americans as the author of his book. We, on the contrary, have some difficulty in considering him as such.

the New Yorker has not forgotten the period when a man could win a fortune by his personal initiative. What he dislikes about the controlled economy is the red tape. Thus, paradoxically enough, the same man who so obediently submits to guidance in public and private life is intransigent where his job is concerned. The reason is that this is the area of his independence, his initiative and his personal dignity.

As for the rest, there are the "associations." In 1930 it was estimated that in Washington there were more than five hundred group and association headquarters. I shall mention only one, the Foreign Policy Association.

On the seventeenth floor of the building we met, "over a cup of tea," a few of those tall, grey-haired, pleasant, but somewhat cold women, intelligent as men, who, ever since the beginning of the war, represent the majority of members of these associations. They told us how, in 1917, a certain number of people, firmly convinced that the United States was entering the war with no knowledge of foreign affairs, had decided to devote their free time to supplying the country with the knowledge it lacked.

The Association now has 26,000 members, with 300 branches in the various states. Its bulletin is sent to more than 500 newspapers. Its publications are consulted by political leaders. It has, moreover, given up the idea of informing the general public; it informs the informers (scholars, teachers, clergymen and journalists). It publishes a weekly bulletin containing a study of an international question and an analysis of happenings in Washington. Every fortnight it issues a bulletin to the newspapers which then reprint it in whole or in part.

Try to imagine an association of this kind in the France of 1939 providing information for Bonnet or Daladier and sending its periodicals to Maurras for *Action Française* and to Cachin for *l'Humanité*.

But I was particularly struck with our hostess' last words. "What we do," she said, "is to protect the individual. Outside the clubs, a man is alone. Inside, he is a person. By belonging to several of them he protects himself against any particular one." The meaning of this individualism is plain to see. The citizen must, first of all, fit himself into a framework and protect himself; he must enter into a social contract with other citizens of his own kind. And it is this small community which confers upon him his individual function and personal worth. Within the association, he can take the initiative, can advocate his personal political views and influence, if he is able to, the line of the group.

Just as the solitary person arouses suspicion in the States, so this controlled, hedged-in individualism is encouraged. This is demonstrated, on quite another level, by industrialists' attempts to encourage self-criticism among their personnel.

When the worker is organized, when the propaganda of government and management has sufficiently integrated him into the community, he is *then* asked to distinguish himself from others and to prove his initiative. More than once near factory entrances we came upon brightly coloured booths in which improvements suggested by employees and snapshots of their inventors, who were frequently rewarded, were displayed behind glass.

I have said enough, I hope, to give some idea of how the American is subjected, from the cradle to the grave, to an intense drive to organize and Americanize him, of how he is first depersonalized by means of a constant appeal to his reason, civic sense and freedom, and how, once he has been duly fitted into the national life by professional associations and educational and other edifying organizations, he suddenly regains consciousness of himself and his personal autonomy. He is then free to escape into an almost Nietzschean individualism, the kind symbolized by the skyscrapers in the bright sky of New York. In any event, it is not based on our kind of individualism, but on conformism. Personality must be won. It is a social function or the affirmation of society.

JEAN-PAUL SARTRE

american cities

For the first few days I was lost. My eyes were not accustomed to the skyscrapers and they did not surprise me; they did not seem like man-made, man-inhabited constructions, but rather like rocks and hills, dead parts of the urban landscape one finds in cities built on a turbulent soil and which you pass without even noticing. At the same time, I was continually and vainly looking for something to catch my attention for a moment—a detail, a square, perhaps, or a public building. I did not yet know that these houses and streets should be seen in the mass.

In order to learn to live in these cities and to like them as Americans do, I had to fly over the immense deserts of the west and south. Our European cities, submerged in human countrysides that have been worked over mile by mile, are continuous. And then we are vaguely aware that far away, across the sea, there is the desert, a myth. For the American, this myth is an everyday reality. We flew for hours between New Orleans and San Francisco, over an earth that was dry and red, clotted with verdigris bushes. Suddenly, a city, a little checkerboard flush with the ground, arose and then, again, the red earth, the Savannah, the twisted rocks of the Grand Canyon, and the snows of the Rocky Mountains.

After a few days of this diet, I came to understand that the American city was, originally, a camp in the desert. People from far away, attracted by a mine, a petroleum field or fertile land, arrived one fine day and settled as quickly as possible in a clearing, near a river. They built the vital parts of the town, the bank, the town hall, the church, and then hundreds of one-storey frame houses. The road, if there was one, served as a kind of spinal column to the town, and then streets were marked out like vertebrae, perpendicular to the road. It would be hard to count the American cities that have that kind of parting in the middle.

Nothing has changed since the time of the covered wagons; every year towns are founded in the United States, and they are founded according to the same methods.

Take Fontana, Tennessee, which is situated near one of the great T.V.A. dams. Twelve years ago there were pine-trees growing in the mountain's red soil. As soon as the contruction of the dam began, the pines were felled and three towns—two white ones of 3000 and 5000 inhabitants each, and one Negro town—sprang from the soil. The workers live there with their families; four or five years ago, when work was in full swing, one birth was recorded each day. Half of the village looks like a pile-dwellers' community: the houses are of wood, with green roofs, and have been built on piles to avoid dampness. The other half is made of collapsible dwellings, "prefabricated houses." They too are of wood; they are constructed about 500 miles away and loaded onto trucks: a single team of men can set one up within four hours after its arrival. The smallest costs the employer two thousand dollars, and he rents them to his workers for nineteen dollars a month (thirty-one dollars if they are furnished). The interiors, with their mass-produced furniture, central heating, electric lamps, and refrigerators, remind one of ship cabins. Every square inch of these antiseptic little rooms has been utilized; the walls have clothes-presses and under the beds there are chests of drawers.

One leaves with a slightly depressed feeling, with the feeling of having seen the careful, small-scale reconstruction of a 1944 flat in the year 3000. The moment one steps outside one sees hundreds of houses, all alike, piled up, squashed against the earth, but retaining in their very form some sort of nomadic look. It looks like a caravan graveyard. The pile-dweller community and the caravan cemetery face one another. Between them a wide road climbs toward the pines. There you have a city, or rather the nucleus of an American city, with all its essential parts. Below is the Woolworth's, higher up the hospital, and at the top, a "mixed" church in which what might be called a minimum service—that is, one valid for all creeds—is conducted.

The striking thing is the lightness, the fragility of these buildings. The village has no weight, it seems barely to rest on the soil; it has not managed to leave a human imprint on the reddish earth and the dark forest; it is a temporary thing. And besides, it will soon take to the road; in two years the dam will be finished, the workers will leave, and the prefabricated houses will be taken down and sent to a Texas oil well or a Georgia cotton plantation, to reconstitute another Fontana, under other skies, with new inhabitants.

This roving village is no exception; in the United States, communities are born as they die—in a day. The Americans have no complaint to make; the main thing is to be able to carry their homes with them. These homes are the collections of objects, furnishings, photographs, and souvenirs belonging to them, that reflect their own image and constitute the inner, living landscape of their dwellings. These are their penates. Like Aeneas, they haul them about everywhere.

The "house" is the shell; it is abandoned on the slightest pretext.

We have workers' communities in France. But they are

sedentary, and then they never become real cities; on the contrary, they are the artificial product of neighbouring cities. In America, just as any citizen can theoretically become President, so each Fontana can become Detroit or Minneapolis; all that is needed is a bit of luck. And conversely, Detroit and Minneapolis are Fontanas which have had luck. To take only one example: in 1905 Detroit had a population of 300,000. Its population is now 1,000,000.

The inhabitants of this city are perfectly aware of this luck; they like to recall in their books and films the time when their community was only an outpost. And that is why they pass so easily from city to outpost; they make no distinction between the two. Detroit and Minneapolis, Knoxville and Memphis were *born temporary* and have stayed that way. They will never, of course, take to the road again on the back of a truck. But they remain at the meeting point; they have never reached an internal temperature of solidification.

Things that would not constitute a change of situation for us are, for the American, occasions for real breaks with his past. There are many who, on going off to war, have sold their apartments and everything else, including their suits. What is the point of keeping something that will be outmoded upon their return? Soldiers' wives often reduce their scale of living and go to live more modestly in other neighbourhoods. Thus, sadness and faithfulness to the absent are marked by a removal.

The removals also indicate fluctuations in American fortunes.

It is customary, in the United States, for the fashionable neighbourhoods to slide from the centre to the outskirts of the city; after five years the centre of town is "polluted." If you walk about there, you come upon tumble-down houses that retain a pretentious look beneath their filth; you find a complicated kind of architecture, one-storey frame houses with entrances formed by peristyles supported by columns, gothic chalets, "Colonial houses," etc. These were formerly aristocratic homes, now inhabited by the poor. Chicago's lurid Negro section contains some of these Greco-Roman temples; from the outside they still look well. But inside, twelve rat- and louse-plagued Negro families are crowded together in five or six rooms.

At the same time, changes are continually made within the same place. An apartment house is bought to be demolished, and a larger apartment house is built on the same plot. After five years, the new house is sold to a contractor who tears it down to build a third one. The result is that in the States a city is a moving landscape for its inhabitants, whereas our cities are our shells.

In France, one hears only from very old people what a forty-year-old American said to me in Chicago. "When I was young, this whole neighbourhood was taken up by a lake. But this part of the lake was filled in and built over." And a thirty-five-year-old lawyer who was showing me the Negro section said: "I was born here. Then it was a white section and, apart from servants, you would not have seen a Negro in the streets. Now the white people have left and 250,000 Negroes are crowded into their houses."

M. Verdier, the owner of the "City of Paris" department store in San Francisco, witnessed the earthquake and fire that destroyed three quarters of the city. At that time he was a young man; he remembers the disaster perfectly. He watched the reconstruction of the city which still had an Asiatic look around 1913, and then its rapid Americanization. Thus, he has superimposed memories of three San Franciscos.

We Europeans change within changeless cities, and our houses and neighbourhoods outlive us; American cities change faster than their inhabitants do, and it is the inhabitants who outlive the cities.

I am really visiting the United States in wartime; the vast life of the American city has suddenly become petrified; people hardly change their residences any more. But this stagnation is entirely temporary; the cities have been immobilized like the dancer on the film-screen who stays with his foot suspended in air when the film is stopped; one feels all about one the rising of the sap which will burst open the cities as soon as the war is ended.

First, there are immediate problems; Chicago's Negro section will have to be rebuilt, for instance. The government had begun this before Pearl Harbor. But the government-built apartment houses barely managed to shelter 7000 people. Now, there are 250,000 to be housed. Then the industrialists want to enlarge and transform their factories; the famous abattoirs of Chicago are going to be completely modernized.

Finally, the average American is obsessed by the image of the "modern house" which is considerably publicized and which will be, so we are told, a hundred times more comfortable than the present dwellings and whose construction in huge quantities certainly has its place in the plans for "industrial conversion" which are now springing up almost everywhere.

When the war is over, America will certainly be seized with a real construction fever. Today the American sees his city objectively; he does not dream of finding it ugly, but thinks it really old. If it were even older, like ours, he could find a social past, a tradition in it. We generally live in our grandfathers' houses. Our streets reflect the customs and ways of past centuries; they tend to filter the present; none of what goes on in the Rue Montorgueil or the Rue Pot-de-Fer is completely of the present. But the thirty-year-old American lives in a house that was built when he was twenty.

The houses that are too young to seem *old* seem merely outdated to them; they lag behind the other tools, the car that can be traded in every two years, the refrigerator or the wireless set. That is why they see their cities without vain sentimentality. They have grown slightly attached to them, as one becomes attached to one's car, but they consider them as instruments, rather than anything else, instruments to be exchanged for more convenient ones.

For us a city is, above all, a past; for them it is mainly a future; what they like in the city is everything it has not yet become and everything it can be.

What are the impressions of a European who arrives in an American city? First, he thinks he has been taken in. He has heard only about skyscrapers; New York and Chicago have been described to him as "upright cities." Now his first feeling is, on the contrary, that the average height of an American city is noticeably smaller than that of a French one. The immense majority of houses have only two storeys. Even in the very large cities, the five-storey apartment house is an exception.

Then he is struck by the lightness of the materials used. In the United States stone is less frequently used than in Europe. The skyscraper consists of a coating of concrete applied to a metal framework, and the other buildings are made of brick or wood. Even in the richest cities and the smartest sections, one often finds frame houses. New Orleans' lovely colonial houses are of wood; many of the pretty chalets belonging to the Hollywood stars and film-directors are made of wood; so are the "California style" cottages in San Francisco. Everywhere you find groups of frame houses crushed between two twenty-storeyed buildings.

The brick houses are the colour of dried blood, or, on the contrary, daubed and smeared with bright yellow, green or raw white.* In most of the cities, they are roofless cubes or rectangular parallelepipeds, with severely flat façades. All these houses, hastily constructed and made expressly to be hastily demolished, obviously bear a strange resemblance to Fontana's "prefabricated houses."

The lightness of these jerry-built houses, their loud colours alternating with the sombre red of the bricks, the extraordinary variety of their decorations which does not manage to conceal the uniformity of their patterns, all give one the feeling, when in the middle of the city, of walking through the suburbs of a watering town, like Trouville or Cabourg or La Baule. Only those ephemeral seaside chalets with their pretentious architectural style and their fragility can convey to those of my French readers who have never seen the States an idea of the American apartment house.

To complete the impression, I should also like to add that sometimes one also thinks of an exposition-city, but an obsolescent, dirty one, like those that ten years later, in some park, survive the celebration that occasioned them. For these shanties quickly grow dirty, particularly in industrial sections.

Chicago, blackened by its smoke, clouded by the Lake Michigan fog, is a dark and gloomy red. Pittsburgh is more gloomy still. And there is nothing more immediately striking than the contrast between the formidable power, the inexhaustible abundance of what is called the "American Colossus" and the puny insignificance of those little houses that line the widest roads in the world. But on second thought, there is no clearer indication that America is not finished, that her ideas and plans, her social structure and her cities have only a strictly temporary reality.

These perfectly straight cities bear no trace of organization. Many of them have the rudimentary structure of a polypary. Los Angeles, in particular, is rather like a big earthworm that might be chopped into twenty pieces without being killed. If you go through this enormous urban cluster, probably the largest in the world, you

* Kisling and Masson have often complained of the fact that the urban landscape of the United States is not very stimulating to painting. I believe this is partly due to the fact that the cities have already been painted. They do not have the hesitant colours of our own cities. What is one to do with these tones which already are art, or artifice at least? All one can do is leave them alone.

come upon twenty juxtaposed cities, strictly identical, each with its poor section, its business streets, night-clubs and smart suburb, and you get the impression that a medium-sized urban centre has schizogenetically reproduced itself twenty times.*

In America, where the neighbourhoods are added on to each other as the region's prosperity attracts new immigrants, this juxtaposition is the rule. You pass without any transition from a poor street into an aristocratic avenue; a promenade lined with skyscrapers, museums and public monuments and adorned with lawns and trees, suddenly stops short above a smoky station; one frequently discovers at the feet of the largest buildings, along an aristocratic avenue, a "zone" of miserable little kitchen-gardens.

This is due to the fact that these cities that move at a rapid rate are not constructed in order to grow old, but move forward like modern armies, encircling the islands of resistance they are unable to destroy; the past does not mainfest itself in them as it does in Europe, through public monuments, but through survivals. The wooden bridge in Chicago which spans a canal two steps away from the world's highest skyscrapers is a survival. The elevated railways, rolling noisily through the central streets of New York and Chicago, supported by great iron pillars and cross-girders, nearly touching the façades of houses on either side, are survivals. They are there simply because no one has taken the time to tear them down, and as a kind of indication of work to be done.

You find this disorder in each individual vista. Nowhere have I seen so many empty lots. Of course they do have a definite function; they are used as car parks. But they break the alignment of the street nonetheless sharply for all that. Suddenly it seems as if a bomb had fallen on three or four houses, reducing them to powder, and as if they had just been swept out; this is a "parking space," two hundred square metres of bare earth with its sole ornament, perhaps, a poster on a big hoarding. Suddenly the city seems unfinished, badly assembled; suddenly you rediscover the desert and the big empty site: noticeable at Fontana. I remember this Los Angeles landscape in the middle of the city, two modern apartment houses, two white cubes framing an empty lot with the ground torn up—a parking space. A few abandoned-looking cars were parked there.

* To convey an idea of this city to the reader, I suggest that he try to imagine, not one Cote d'Azur city, but the entire region between Cannes and Menton.

A palm tree grew like a weed between the cars. Down at the bottom there was a steep grassy hill, rather like the fortification mounds we use for garbage disposal. On top of the mound was a frame house, and a little below this a string stretched between two little trees, with multi-coloured washing hanging out to dry. When one turned around the block of houses, the hill disappeared; its other side had been built up, covered with asphalt, streaked with tar roads, and pierced with a magnificent tunnel.

The most striking aspect of the American city is the vertical disorder. These brick shanties are of varying heights; I noted at random during a walk in Detroit the following successive proportions: one storey, two storeys, one storey, one storey, three storeys. You find the same proportions in Albuquerque or San Antonio, at the other end of the country. In depth, above this irregular crenellation, you see apartment houses of all shapes and dimensions, long cases, thick thirty-storeyed boxes with forty windows to a storey. As soon as there is a bit of fog the colours fade away, and only volumes remain—every variety of polyhedron. Between them, you have enormous empty spaces, empty lots cut out in the sky.

In New York, and even in Chicago, the skyscraper is on home ground, and imposes a new order upon the city. But everywhere else it is out of place; the eye is unable to establish any unity between these tall, gawky things and the little houses that run close to the ground; in spite of itself it looks for that line so familiar in European cities, the sky-line, and cannot find it. That is why the European feels at first as though he were travelling through a rocky chaos that resembles a city—something like Montpellier-le-Vieux—rather than a city.

But the European makes a mistake in visiting American cities as one does Paris or Venice; they are not meant to be seen that way. The streets here do not have the same meaning as our streets. In Europe, a street is half-way between the path of communication and the sheltered "public place." It is on a footing with the cafés, as proved by the use of the "terrasses" that spring up on the sidewalks of the cafés in fine weather. Thus it changes its aspect more than a hundred times a day, for the crowd that throngs the European street changes, and men are its primary element. The American street is a piece of highway. It sometimes stretches over many miles. It does no stimulate one to walk. Ours are oblique and twisting, full of bends and secrets. The American street is a straight line that gives itself away immediately. It contains no mystery. You see the street straight through, from one end to the other no matter what your location in it. And the distances in American cities are too great to permit moving about on foot; in most of them one gets about almost exclusively in cars, on buses and by underground. Sometimes, while going from one appointment to another, I have been carried like a parcel from underground to escalator, from escalator to elevator, from elevator to taxi, from taxi to bus and, again, by metro and elevator, without walking a step.

In certain cities I noticed a real atrophy of the sidewalk. In Los Angeles, for example, on La Cienega, which is lined with bars, theatres, restaurants, antique dealers and private residences, the sidewalks are scarcely more than side-streets that lead customers and guests from the roadway into the house. Lawns have been planted from the façades to the roadway of this luxurious avenue. I followed a narrow path between the lawns for a long time without meeting a living soul, while to my right, cars streaked by on the road; all animation in the street had taken refuge on the high road.

New York and Chicago do not have neighbourhoods, but they do have a neighbourhood life; the American is not familiar with his city; once he is ten "blocks" away from his home, he is lost. This does not mean that there are no crowds in the business streets, but they are crowds that do not linger; people shop or emerge from the Underground to go to their offices.

I rarely saw an occasional Negro day-dreaming before a shop.

Yet one quickly begins to like American cities. Of course they all look alike. And when you arrive at Wichita, Saint Louis or Albuquerque, it is disappointing to realize that, hidden behind these magnificent and promising names, is the same standard checkerboard city with the same red and green traffic lights and the same provincial look. But one gradually learns to tell them apart. Chicago, the noble, lurid city, red as the blood that trickles through its abattoirs, with its canals, the grey water of Lake Michigan and its streets crushed between clumsy and powerful buildings, in no way resembles San Francisco, city of air, salt and sea, built in the shape of an amphitheatre.

And then one finally comes to like their common element, that temporary look. Our beautiful closed cities, full as eggs, are a bit stifling. Our slanting, winding streets run head on against walls and houses; once you are inside the city, you can no longer see beyond it. In America, these long, straight unobstructed streets carry one's glance, like canals, outside the city. You always see mountains or fields or the sea at the end of them, no matter where you may be.

Frail and temporary, formless and unfinished, they are haunted by the presence of the immense geographical space surrounding them. And precisely because their boulevards are highways, they always seem to be stopping places on the roads. They are not oppressive, they do not close you in; nothing in them is definitive, nothing is arrested. You feel, from your first glance, that your contact with these places is a temporary one; either you will leave them or they will change around you.

Let us beware of exaggerating; I have spent Sundays in the American provinces that were more depressing than Sundays anywhere else; I have seen those suburban "colonial style" inns where, at two dollars a head, middle-class families go to eat shrimp cocktails and turkey with cranberry sauce in silence while listening to the electric organ. One must not forget the heavy boredom that weighs over America.

But these slight cities, still so similar to Fontana and the outposts of the Far West, reveal the other side of the United States: their freedom. Here everyone is free—not to criticize or to reform their customs—but to flee them, to leave for the desert or another city. The cities are open, open to the world, and to the future. This is what gives them their adventurous look and, even in their ugliness and disorder, a touching beauty.

JEAN-PAUL SARTRE

new york, the colonial city

I really knew I would like New York, but I thought I'd be able to like it immediately, as I had liked the red brick of Venice and London's massive, sombre houses. I didn't know that, for the newly arrived European, there was a "New York sickness," like sea-sickness, air-sickness and mountain-sickness.

At midnight, an official bus took me from La Guardia Field to the Plaza Hotel. I had pressed my forehead against the window, but had been able to see only red and green lights and dark buildings. The next day, without any transition, I found myself at the corner of 58th Street and Fifth Avenue. I walked for a long time under the icy sky. It was a Sunday in January, 1945, a deserted Sunday. I was looking for New York and couldn't find it. The further I progressed along an avenue that seemed coldly mediocre and banal, the further the city seemed to retreat before me, like a ghost town. What I was looking for was probably a European city.

We Europeans live on the myth of the big city that we forged during the nineteenth century. American myths are not ours, and the American city is not our city; it has neither the same character nor the same functions. In Spain, Italy, Germany and France we find circular cities that were originally surrounded by ramparts meant not only to protect the inhabitants against enemy invasion, but also to conceal the inexorable presence of Nature. These cities are, moreover, divided into sections that are similarly round and closed. The piled-up tangle of houses weighs heavily on the soil. They seem to have a natural tendency to draw together, so much so that now and then we have to clear a way through with an axe, as in a virgin forest. Streets run into other streets. Closed at both ends, they do not look as though they lead outside the city. Inside them, you go around in circles. They are more than mere arteries; each one constitutes a social milieu.

You stop along these streets, meet people, drink, eat and linger. On Sundays, you get dressed and take a stroll for the sole pleasure of greeting friends, to see and be seen. These are the streets that inspired Jules Romains' "unanisme." They are filled with a communal spirit that changes from hour to hour.

Thus, my near-sighted European eyes, slowly venturing out, on the watch for everything, vainly tried to find something to arrest them. Anything at all—a row of houses suddenly barring the way, a street corner, or some old, time-mellowed house. But it was no use. New York is a city for far-sighted people, a city in which you can only "adjust" to infinity. My glance met nothing but space. It slid over blocks of identical houses, with nothing to arrest it; it was about to lose itself in empty space, at the horizon.

Céline has remarked of New York that "it is a vertical city." This is true, but it seemed to me, at first, like a length-wise city. The traffic that comes to a standstill in the side streets is all-privileged and flows tirelessly down the avenues. How often the taxi-drivers, willing to take passengers from north to south, flatly refuse to take any for the east and west! The side streets have hardly any function other than to mark off the limits of the apartment houses between the avenues. They are cut by the avenues, spread and thrown toward the north. That was why I, a naïve tourist, vainly tried for a long time to find *quartiers*. In France we are surrounded and protected by urban centres; the prosperous districts protect the rich from the poor, and the poor districts protect us from the disdain of the rich, and similarly, the entire city protects us against Nature.

In New York, where the major axes are parallel avenues, I was unable to discover *quartiers* except on Lower Broadway. I could only find filmy atmospheres, longitudinally stretched masses with nothing to mark a beginning or end. I gradually learned to recognize the atmosphere of Third Avenue where, under the shadow of the noisy elevated railway, people meet, smile and chat without even knowing each other; and that Irish bar in which a German, passing by my table, stopped for a minute to say: "Are you French? I'm a Jerry"; the reassuring comfort of the Lexington Avenue shops; the dreary elegance of Park Avenue; the cold luxury and stucco impassiveness of Fifth Avenue; the gay frivolity of Sixth and Seventh Avenues; the food markets on Ninth Avenue; and the No Man's Land of Tenth Avenue. Each avenue wraps its neighbouring streets in its own atmosphere, but one street down, you're suddenly plunged into another world. Not far from the palpitating silence of Park Avenue where glide the cars of the lords and masters, I come to First Avenue where the earth is constantly trembling under the passing trucks. How am I to feel safe on one of those endless "north-south" highways when, a few steps away to east or west, other lengthwise worlds await me? Behind the Waldorf-Astoria and the blue and white canopies of "smart" buildings, I glimpse the "Elevated," which carries with it something of the Bowery's poverty.

All of New York is striped this way with parallel and non-communicating significances. These long, perfectly straight lines suddenly gave me the feeling of space. Our cities are constructed to protect us against it; the houses cluster like sheep. But space crosses through New York, quickening and expanding it. The space, the great, empty space of the steppes and pampas, flows through New York's arteries like a draught of cold air, separating one side from the other. An American friend who was showing me about the smart sections of Boston pointed to the left of a boulevard and said, "The 'nice' people live there." And then, pointing to the right side, he added ironically, "No one has ever been able to find out who lives here." The same is true of New York; between the two sides of a given street, you have all the space.

New York is half-way between a pedestrian's and a driver's city. You do not go for walks in New York; you fly through it; it is a city in motion. I feel at ease if I walk quickly; if I stop, I get flustered and wonder, "Why am I in this street rather than in one of the hundreds of others like it?" Why am I standing in front of this drug-store, or this Schrafft's or Woolworth branch, rather than in front of any other of these thousands of identical ones?

And suddenly pure space looms into view. I imagine that if a triangle could become conscious of its position in space, it would be terrified at the realization of the rigorousness of its defining co-ordinates, but that it would also be terrified to discover that it is merely any triangle, any place. You never lose your way in New York; one glance is enough for you to get your bearings; you are on the East Side, at the corner of 52nd Street and Lexington Avenue. But this spacial precision is not accompanied by any precision of feeling. In the numerical anonymity of the streets and avenues, I am simply anybody, anywhere. No matter where I may be, my position is marked out in longitude and latitude. But no valid reason justifies my presence in this place rather than in any other, since this one is so like another. You never lose your way, and you are always lost.

Is it a city I am lost in, or is it Nature? New York is no protection against Nature's violence. It is an open-skied city. Storms flood its wide streets that take so long to cross when it rains. Hurricanes shake the brick houses and rock the skyscrapers. They are announced formally over the radio, like declarations of war. In summer, the air vibrates between the houses; in winter, the city is flooded, so that you might think yourself in some Parisian suburb flooded by the Seine, but in America, it is only melting snow.

Nature weighs so heavily on New York that this most modern of cities is also the dirtiest. From my window I see thick, muddy papers, tossed by the wind, flitting over the pavement. When I go out, I walk in a blackish snow, a sort of puffy crust the same colour as the sidewalk, so that it looks as if the sidewalk itself is buckling. From the first of May, the heat crashes down on the city like an atomic bomb. The heat is Evil. People go up to one another and say, "It's murder!" The trains carry off millions of fleeing city-dwellers who, on descending from the train, leave damp marks on the seat, like snails. It is not the city they are fleeing, but Nature. Even in the depths of my apartment, I am open to attack from a mysterious and secretly hostile Nature. I feel as though I were camping in the heart of a jungle crawling with insects. There is the wailing of the wind, the electric shocks I get each time I touch a doorbell or shake a friend's hand, the cockroaches that scoot across my kitchen, the elevators that make me nauseous and the inextinguishable thirst that rages in me from morning till night. New York is a colonial city, an outpost. All the hostility and cruelty of Nature are present in this city, the most prodigious monument man has ever erected to himself. It is a light city; its apparent lack of weight surprises most Europeans. In this immense and malevolent space, in this rocky desert that will tolerate no vegetation of any kind, millions of brick, wooden and reinforced concrete houses, that all look as it they are about to fly away, have been constructed.

I like New York. I learned to like it. I become accustomed to its massive groupings and its long vistas. My eyes no longer linger over the façades in quest of a house which might, by some remote chance, not be identical with the others. My eyes immediately slip by to the horizon to look for the buildings lost in fog, mere volumes, merely the sky's austere framework. One is rewarded when one has learned how to look at the two rows of apartment houses which, like cliffs, line a great artery; their mission is completed down there, at the avenue's end, in simple, harmonious lines; a scrap of sky floats between them.

New York reveals itself only at a certain height, a certain distance, and a certain speed; these are not the pedestrian's height, distance or speed. This city looks amazingly like the great plains of Andalusia—monotonous when travelled over on foot, magnificent and changing when seen from a car.

I learned to like New York's sky. In European cities where roofs are low, the sky crawls close to the earth and seems tamed. The New York sky is beautiful because the skyscrapers push it back, very far over our heads. Pure and lonely as a wild beast, it guards and watches over the city. And it is not only a local protection; one feels that it stretches out into the distance over all America; it is the whole world's sky.

I learned to like Manhattan's avenues. They are not sober little walks closed in between houses, but national highways. The moment you set foot on one of them, you understand that it has to go on to Boston or Chicago. It fades away outside the city and the eye can almost follow it into the country. A wild sky over parallel rails, that, more than anything else, is New York. When you are at the heart of this city, you are at the heart of Nature.

I had to get used to it, but now that I have, there is no place in which I feel more free than in the New York crowds. This light, ephemeral city that looks every morning and evening, under the sun's inquisitive rays, like a simple juxtaposition of rectangular parallelepipeds, is never oppressing or depressing. You can experience the anguish of solitude here, but never that of oppression.

In Europe, we become attached to a neighbourhood, to a cluster of houses or a street-corner, and we are no longer free. But hardly have you plunged into New York than your life is completely cut to New York's size. You can gaze down in the evening from the top of the Queensborough Bridge, in the morning from New Jersey, at noon from the seventy-seventh storey of Rockefeller Center, but you will never be captivated by any of the city's streets, because none of them has a distinctive beauty of its own. There is beauty in all of them, as all of America's nature and sky is present in them. Nowhere will you ever have a stronger feeling of the simultaneity of human lives.

New York moves Europeans in spite of its austerity. Of course, we have learned to love our old cities, but their touching quality for us lies in a Roman wall that forms part of an inn's façade, or a house that Cervantes lived in, or the Place des Vosges, or the town hall at Rouen. We like museum-cities, and all our cities are rather like museums in which we wander about amidst ancestral homes. New York is not a museum-city, yet, for Frenchmen of my generation, it already possesses a melancholy of the past. When we were twenty, around 1925, we heard about the skyscrapers. For us they symbolized America's fabulous prosperity. We discovered them with amazement in the films. They were the architecture of the future, just as the cinema was the art of the future and jazz the music of the future. Today we know what to think about jazz. We know that it has more of a past than a future. It is a music of popular, Negro inspiration, capable of limited development and in a process of slow decline. Jazz is outliving its day. The talking film has not fulfilled the promise of the silent one. Hollywood is making no headway in a well-worn rut.

The war has certainly taught the Americans that their country was the greatest power in the world. But the period of easy living is over; many economists fear a new depression. Thus, no more skyscrapers are being built. It seems they are too hard to rent.

The man who walked about in New York before 1930 saw in the big buildings that dominated the city the first signs of an architecture destined to radiate over the whole country. The skyscrapers were alive then. Today, for a Frenchman arriving from Europe, they are already mere historical monuments, relics of a bygone age. They still rear up against the sky, but my mind is no longer with them, and the New Yorkers pass by at their feet without even looking. I cannot think of them without a certain sadness; they tell of an age in which we thought that the very last war had just ended and when we believed in peace. They are already a bit rundown; tomorrow, perhaps, they will be torn down. In any case, their construction required a faith we no longer have.

I walk between the little brick houses the colour of dried blood. They are younger than Europe's houses, but their fragility makes them look much older. Far away I see the Empire State or the Chrysler Building reaching vainly toward the sky, and suddenly I think that New York is about to acquire a History and that it already possesses its ruins.

That is enough to lend a bit of softness to the world's harshest city.

NORMAN MAILER

the third presidential paper—the existential hero

superman comes to the supermarket

Not too much need to be said for this piece; it is possible it can stand by itself. But perhaps its title should have been "Filling the Holes in No Man's Land."

American politics is rarely interesting for its men, its ideas, or the style of its movements. It is usually more fascinating in its gaps, its absences, its uninvaded territories. We have used up our frontier, but the psychological frontier talked about in this piece is still alive with untouched possibilities and dire unhappy all-but-lost opportunities. In European politics the spaces are filled—the average politician, like the average European, knows what is possible and what is impossible for him. Their politics is like close trench warfare. But in America, one knows such close combat only for the more banal political activities. The play of political ideas is flaccid here in America because opposing armies never meet. The Right, the Center, and what there is of the Left have set up encampments on separate hills, they face one another across valleys, they send out small patrols to their front and vast communiqués to their rear. No Man's Land predominates. It is a situation which calls for guerrilla raiders. Any army which would dare to enter the valley in force might not only determine a few new political formations, but indeed could create more politics itself, even as the guerrilla raids of the Negro Left and Negro Right, the Freedom Riders and the Black Muslims, have discovered much of the secret nature of the American reality for us.

I wonder if I make myself clear. Conventional politics has had so little to do with the real subterranean life of America that none of us know much about the real—which is to say the *potential*—historic nature of America. That lies buried under apathy, platitudes, Rightist encomiums for the FBI, programmatic welfare from the liberal Center, and furious pips of protest from the Peace Movement's Left. The mass of Americans are not felt as a political reality. No one has any idea of how they would react to radically new sense. It is only when their heart-land, their no man's land, their valley is invaded, that one discovers the reality.

In Birmingham during the days of this writing, the jails are filled with Negro children, 2000 of them. The militancy of the Negroes in Birmingham is startling, so too is the stubbornness of the Southern white, so too and unbelievable is the procrastination of the Kennedy administration. Three new realities have been discovered. The potential Left and potential Right of America are more vigorous than one would have expected and the Center is more irresolute. An existential political act, the drive by Southern Negroes, led by Martin Luther King, to end segregation in restaurants in Birmingham, an act which is existential precisely because its end is unknown, has succeeded en route in discovering more of the American reality to us.

If a public speaker in a small Midwestern town were to say, "J. Edgar Hoover has done more harm to the freedoms of America than Joseph Stalin," the act would be existential. Depending on the occasion and the town, he would be manhandled physically or secretly applauded. But he would create a new reality which would displace the old psychological reality that such a remark could not be made, even as for example the old Southern psychological reality that you couldn't get two Negroes to do anything together, let alone two thousand has now been destroyed by a new and more accurate psychological reality: you *can* get two thousand Negroes to work in cooperation. The new psychological realities are closer to history and so closer to sanity and they exist because, and only because, the event has taken place.

It was Kennedy's potentiality to excite such activity which interested me most; that he was young, that he was physically handsome, and that his wife was attractive were not trifling accidental details but, rather, new major political facts. I knew if he became President, it would be an existential event: he would touch depths in American life which were uncharted. Regardless of his politics, and even then one could expect his politics would be as conventional as his personality was unconventional, indeed one could expect his politics to be pushed toward conventionality precisely to counteract his essential unconventionality, one knew nonetheless that regardless of his overt politics, America's tortured psychotic search for security would finally be torn loose from the feverish ghosts of its old generals, its MacArthurs and Eisenhowers —ghosts which Nixon could cling to—and we as a nation would

> finally be loose again in the historic seas of a national psyche which was willy-nilly and at last, again, adventurous. And that, I thought, that was the hope for America. So I swallowed my doubts, my disquiets, and my certain distastes for Kennedy's dullness of mind and prefabricated politics, and did my best to write a piece which would help him to get elected.

For once let us try to think about a political convention without losing ourselves in housing projects of fact and issue. Politics has its virtues, all too many of them—it would not rank with baseball as a topic of conversation if it did not satisfy a great many things—but one can suspect that its secret appeal is close to nicotine. Smoking cigarettes insulates one from one's life, one does not feel as much, often happily so, and politics quarantines one from history; most of the people who nourish themselves in the political life are in the game not to make history but to be diverted from the history which is being made.

If that Democratic Convention which has now receded behind the brow of the Summer of 1960 is only half-remembered in the excitements of moving toward the election, it may be exactly the time to consider it again, because the mountain of facts which concealed its features last July has been blown away in the winds of High Television, and the man-in-the-street (that peculiar political term which refers to the quixotic voter who will pull the lever for some reason so salient as: "I had a brown-nose lieutenant once with Nixon's looks," or "that Kennedy must have false teeth"), the not so easily estimated man-in-the-street has forgotten most of what happened and could no more tell you who Kennedy was fighting against than you or I could place a bet on who was leading the American League in batting during the month of June.

So to try to talk about what happened is easier now than in the days of the convention, one does not have to put everything in—an act of writing which calls for a bulldozer rather than a pen—one can try to make one's little point and dress it with a ribbon or two of metaphor. All to the good. Because mysteries are irritated by facts, and the 1960 Democratic Convention began as one mystery and ended as another.

Since mystery is an emotion which is repugnant to a political animal (why else lead a life of bad banquet dinners, cigar smoke, camp chairs, foul breath, and excruciatingly dull jargon if not to avoid the echoes of what is not known), the psychic separation between what was happening on the floor, in the caucus rooms, in the headquarters, and what was happening in parallel to the history of the nation was mystery enough to drown the proceedings in gloom. It was on the one hand a dull convention, one of the less interesting by general agreement, relieved by local bits of color, given two half hours of excitement by two demonstrations for Stevenson, buoyed up by the class of the Kennedy machine, turned by the surprise of Johnson's nomination as vice-president, but, all the same, dull, depressed in its over-all tone, the big fiestas subdued, the gossip flat, no real air of excitement, just moments—or as they say in bullfighting—details. Yet it was also, one could argue—and one may argue this yet—it was also one of the most important conventions in America's history, it could prove conceivably to be the most important. The man it nominated was unlike any politician who had ever run for President in the history of the land, and if elected he would come to power in a year when America was in danger of drifting into a profound decline.

a descriptive of the delegates: sons and daughters of the republic in a legitimate panic; small-time practitioners of small-town political judo in the big town and the big time

Depression obviously has its several roots: it is the doubtful protection which comes from not recognizing failure, it is the psychic burden of exhaustion, and it is also, and very often, that discipline of the will or the ego which enables one to continue working when one's unadmitted emotion is panic. And panic it was I think which sat as the largest single sentiment in the breast of the collective delegates as they came to convene in Los Angeles. Delegates are not the noblest sons and daughters of the Republic; a man of taste, arrived from Mars, would take one look at a convention floor and leave forever, convinced he had seen one of the drearier squats of Hell. If one still smells the faint living echo of a carnival wine, the pepper of a bullfight, the rag, drag, and panoply of a jousting tourney, it is all swallowed and regurgitated by the senses into the fouler cud of a death gas one must rid oneself of—a cigar-smoking, stale-aired, slack-jawed, butt-littered, foul, bleak, hard-working, bureaucratic death gas of language and faces ("Yes, those *faces*," says the man from Mars: lawyers, judges, ward heelers, *mafiosos*, Southern goons and grandees, grand old ladies, trade unionists and finks), of pompous words and long pauses which lay like a leaden pain over fever, the fever that one is in, over, or is it that one is just behind history? A legitimate panic for a delegate. America is a nation of experts without roots; we are always creating tacticians who are blind to strategy and strategists who cannot take a step, and when the culture has finished its work the institutions handcuff the infirmity. A delegate is a man who picks a candidate for the largest office in the land, a President who must live with problems whose borders are in ethics, metaphysics, and now ontology; the delegate is prepared for this office of selection by emptying wastebaskets, toting garbage and saying yes at the right time for twenty years in the small political machine of some small or large town; his reward, one of them anyway, is that he arrives at an invitation to the convention. An expert on local catch-as-catch-can, a small-time, often mediocre practitioner of small-town political judo, he comes to the big city with nine-tenths of his mind made up, he will follow the orders of the boss who brought him. Yet of course it is not altogether so mean as that: his opinion is listened to—the boss will consider what he has to say as one interesting factor among five hundred, and what is most important to the delegate, he has the illusion of partial freedom. He can, unless he is severely honest with himself—and if he is, why sweat out the low levels of a political machine?—he can have the illusion that he has helped to choose the candidate, he can even worry most sincerely about his choice, flirt with defection from the boss, work out his own small political gains by the road of loyalty or the way of hard bargain. But even if he is there for no more than the ride, his vote a certainty in the mind of the political boss, able to be thrown here or switched there as the boss decides, still in some peculiar sense he is reality to the boss, the delegate is the great American public, the bar he owns or the law practice, the piece of the union he represents, or the real-estate office, is a part of the political landscape which the boss uses as his own image of how the votes will go, and if the people will like the candidate. And if the boss is depressed by what he sees, if the candidate does not feel right to him, if he has a dull intimation that the candidate is not his sort (as, let us say, Harry Truman was his sort, or Symington might be his sort, or Lyndon Johnson), then vote for him the boss will if he must; he cannot be caught on the wrong side, but he does not feel the pleasure of a personal choice. Which is the center of the panic. Because if the boss is depressed, the delegate is doubly depressed, and the emotional fact is that Kennedy is not in focus, not in the old political focus, he is not comfortable; in fact it is a mystery to the boss how Kennedy got to where he is, not a mystery in its structures; Kennedy is rolling in money, Kennedy got the votes in primaries, and, most of all, Kennedy has a jewel of a political machine. It is as good as a crack Notre Dame team, all discipline and savvy and go-go-go, sound, drilled, never dull, quick as a knife, full of the salt of hipper-dipper, a beautiful machine; the boss could adore it if only a sensible candidate were driving it, a Truman, even a Stevenson, please God a Northern Lyndon Johnson, but it is run by a man who looks young enough to be coach of the Freshman team, and that is not comfortable at all. The boss knows political machines, he knows issues, farm parity, Forand health bill, Landrum-Griffin, but this is not all so adequate after all to revolutionaries in Cuba who look like beatniks, competitions in missiles, Negroes looting whites in the Congo, intricacies of nuclear fallout, and NAACP men one does well to call Sir. It is all out of hand, everything important is off the center, foreign affairs is now the lick of the heat, and senators are candidates instead of governors, a disaster to the old family style of political measure where a political boss knows his governor and knows who his governor knows. So the boss is depressed, profoundly depressed. He comes to this convention resigned to nominating a man he does not understand, or let us say that, so far as he understands the candidate who is to be nominated, he is not happy about the secrets of his appeal, not so far as he divines these secrets; they seem to have too little to do with politics and all too much to do with the private madnesses of the nation which had thousands—or was it hundreds of thousands—of people demonstrating in the long night before Chessman was killed, and a movie star, the greatest, Marlon the Brando out in the night with them. Yes, this candidate for all his record, his good, sound, conventional liberal record has a patina of that other life, the second American life, the long electric night with the fires of neon leading down the highway to the murmur of jazz.

an apparent digression: a vivid view of the "City of Lost Angels"; the Democrats defined; a pentagon of traveling salesmen; some pointed portraits of the politicians

> *I was seeing Pershing Square, Los Angeles, now for the first time . . . the nervous fruithustlers darting in and out of the shadows, fugitives from Times Square, Market Street SF, the French Quarter—masculine hustlers looking for lonely fruits to score from, anything from the legendary $20 to a pad at night and breakfast in the morning and whatever you can clinch or clip; and the heat in their holy cop uniforms, holy because of the Almighty Stick and the Almightier Vagrancy Law; the scattered junkies, the small-time pushers, the queens, the sad panhandlers, the lonely, exiled nymphs haunting the entrance to the men's head, the fruits with the hungry eyes and the jingling coins; the tough teen-age chicks—'dittybops'—making it with the lost hustlers . . . all amid the incongruous piped music and the flowers—twin fountains gushing rainbow colored: the world of Lonely America squeezed into Pershing Square, of the Cities of Terrible Night, downtown now trapped in the City of lost Angels . . . and the trees hang over it all like some type of apathetic fate.*
>
> JOHN RECHY: *Big Table 3*

Seeing Los Angeles after ten years away, one realizes all over again that America is an unhappy contract between the East (that Faustian thrust of a most determined human will which reaches up and out above the eye into the skyscrapers of New York) and those flat lands of compromise and mediocre self-expression, those endless half-pretty repetitive small towns of the Middle and the West, whose spirit is forever horizontal and whose marrow comes to rendezvous in the pastel monotonies of Los Angeles architecture.

So far as America has a history, one can see it in the severe heights of New York City, in the glare from the Pittsburgh mills, by the color in the brick of Louisburg Square, along the knotted greedy façades of the small mansions on Chicago's North Side, in Natchez' antebellum homes, the wrought-iron balconies off Bourbon Street, a captain's house in Nantucket, by the curve of Commercial Street in Provincetown. One can make a list; it is probably finite. What culture we have made and what history has collected to it can be found in those few hard examples of an architecture which came to its artistic term, was born, lived and so collected some history about it. Not all the roots of American life are uprooted, but almost all, and the spirit of the supermarket, that homogenous extension of stainless surfaces and psychoanalyzed people, packaged commodities and ranch homes, interchangeable, geographically unrecognizable, that essence of the new postwar SuperAmerica is found nowhere so perfectly as in Los Angeles' ubiquitous acres. One gets the impression that people come to Los Angeles in order to divorce themselves from the past, here to live or try to live in the rootless pleasure world of an adult child. One knows that if the cities of the world were destroyed by a new war, the architecture of the rebuilding would create a landscape which looked, subject to specifications of climate, exactly and entirely like the San Fernando Valley.

It is not that Los Angeles is altogether hideous, it is even by degrees pleasant, but for an Easterner there is never any salt in the wind; it is like Mexican cooking without chile, or Chinese egg rolls missing their mustard; as one travels through the endless repetitions of that city which is the capital of suburbia with its milky pinks, its washed-out oranges, its tainted lime-yellows of pastel on one pretty little architectural monstrosity after another, the colors not intense enough, the styles never pure, and never sufficiently impure to collide on the eye, one conceives the people who live here—they have come out to express themselves, Los Angeles is the home of self-expression, but the artists are middle-class and middling-minded; no passions will calcify here for years in the gloom to be revealed a decade later as the tessellations of a hard and fertile work, no, it is all open, promiscuous, borrowed, half bought, a city without iron, eschewing wood, a kingdom of stucco, the playground for mass men—one has the feeling it was built by television sets giving orders to men. And in this land of the pretty-pretty, the virility is in the barbarisms, the vulgarities, it is in the huge billboards, the screamers of the neon lighting, the shouting farm-utensil colors of the gas stations and the monster drugstores, it is in the swing of the sports cars, hot rods, convertibles, Los Angeles is a city to drive in, the boulevards are wide, the traffic is nervous and fast, the radio stations play bouncing, blooping, rippling tunes, one digs the pop in a pop tune, no one of character would make love by it but the sound is good for swinging a car, electronic guitars and Hawaiian harps.

So this is the town the Democrats came to, and with their

unerring instinct (after being with them a week, one thinks of this party as a crazy, half-rich family, loaded with poor cousins, traveling always in caravans with Cadillacs and Okie Fords, Lincolns and quarter-horse mules, putting up every night in tents to hear the chamber quartet of Great Cousin Eleanor invaded by the Texas-twanging steel-stringing geetarists of Bubber Lyndon, carrying its own mean high-school principal, Doc Symington, chided for its manners by good Uncle Adlai, told the route of march by Navigator Jack, cut off every six months from the rich will of Uncle Jim Farley, never listening to the mechanic of the caravan, Bald Sam Rayburn, who assures them they'll all break down unless Cousin Bubber gets the concession on the garage; it's the Snopes family married to Henry James, with the labor unions thrown in like a Yankee dollar, and yet it's true, in tranquility one recollects them with affection, their instinct is good, crazy family good) and this instinct now led the caravan to pick the Biltmore Hotel in downtown Los Angeles for their family get-together and reunion.

The Biltmore is one of the ugliest hotels in the world. Patterned after the flat roofs of an Italian Renaissance palace, it is eighty-eight times as large, and one-millionth as valuable to the continuation of man, and it would be intolerable if it were not for the presence of Pershing Square, that square block of park with cactus and palm trees, the three-hundred-and-sixty-five-day-a-year convention of every junkie, pot-head, pusher, queen (but you have read that good writing already). For years Pershing Square has been one of the three or four places in America famous to homosexuals, famous not for its posh, the chic is round-heeled here, but because it is one of the avatars of the good old masturbatory sex, dirty with the crusted sugars of smut, dirty rooming houses around the corner where the score is made, dirty book and photograph stores down the street, old-fashioned out-of-the-Thirties burlesque houses, cruising bars, jukeboxes, movie houses; Pershing Square is the town plaza for all those lonely, respectable, small-town homosexuals who lead a family life, make children, and have the Philbrick psychology (How I Joined the Communist Party and Led Three Lives). Yes, it is the open-air convention hall for the small-town inverts who live like spies, and it sits in the center of Los Angeles, facing the Biltmore, that hotel which is a mausoleum, that Pentagon of traveling salesmen the Party chose to house the headquarters of the Convention.

So here came that family, cursed before it began by the

thundering absence of Great-Uncle Truman, the delegates dispersed over a run of thirty miles and twenty-seven hotels: the Olympian Motor Hotel, the Ambassador, the Beverly Wilshire, the Santa Ynez Inn (where rumor has it the delegates from Louisiana had some midnight swim), the Mayan, the Commodore, the Mayfair, the Sheraton-West, the Huntington-Sheraton, the Green, the Hayward, the Gates, the Figueroa, the Statler Hilton, the Hollywood Knickerbocker—does one have to be a collector to list such names?—beauties all, with that up-from-the-farm Los Angeles décor, plate-glass windows, patio and terrace, foam-rubber mattress, pastel paints, all of them pretty as an ad in full-page color, all but the Biltmore where everybody gathered every day—the newsmen, the TV, radio, magazine, and foreign newspapermen, the delegates, the politicos, the tourists, the campaign managers, the runners, the flunkies, the cousins and aunts, the wives, the grandfathers, the eight-year-old girls, and the twenty-eight-year-old girls in the Kennedy costumes, red and white and blue, the Symingteeners, the Johnson Ladies, the Stevenson Ladies, everybody—and for three days before the convention and four days into it, everybody collected at the Biltmore, in the lobby, in the grill, in the Biltmore Bowl, in the elevators, along the corridors, three hundred deep always outside the Kennedy suite, milling everywhere, every dark-carpeted grey-brown hall of the hotel, but it was in the Gallery of the Biltmore where one first felt the mood which pervaded all proceedings until the convention was almost over, that heavy, thick, witless depression which was to dominate every move as the delegates wandered and gawked and paraded and set for a spell, there in the Gallery of the Biltmore, that huge depressing alley with its inimitable hotel color, that faded depth of chiaroscuro which unhappily has no depth, that brown which is not a brown, that grey which has no pearl in it, that color which can be described only as hotel-color because the beiges, the tans, the walnuts, the mahoganies, the dull blood rugs, the moaning yellows, the sick greens, the greys and all those dumb browns merge into that lack of color which is an over-large hotel at convention time, with all the small-towners wearing their set, starched faces, that look they get at carnival, all fever and suspicion, and proud to be there, eddying slowly back and forth in that high block-long tunnel of a room with its arched ceiling and square recesses filling every rib of the arch with art work, escutcheons and blazons and other art, pictures I think, I cannot even remember, there was such a hill of cigar smoke the eye had to travel on its way to the ceiling, and at one end there was galvanized-pipe scaffolding and workmen repairing some part of the ceiling, one of them touching up one of the endless squares of painted plaster in the arch, and another worker, passing by, yelled up to the one who was working on the ceiling: "Hey, Michelangelo!"

Later, of course, it began to emerge and there were portraits one could keep, Symington, dogged at a press conference, declaring with no conviction that he knew he had a good chance to win, the disappointment eating at his good looks so that he came off hard-faced, mean, and yet slack—a desperate dullness came off the best of his intentions. There was Johnson who had compromised too many contradictions and now the contradictions were in his face: when he smiled the corners of his mouth squeezed gloom; when he was pious, his eyes twinkled irony; when he spoke in a righteous tone, he looked corrupt; when he jested, the ham in his jowls looked to quiver. He was not convincing. He was a Southern politician, a Texas Democrat, a liberal Eisenhower; he would do no harm, he would do no good, he would react to the machine, good fellow, nice friend—the Russians would understand him better than his own.

Stevenson had the patina. He came into the room and the room was different, not stronger perhaps (which is why ultimately he did not win), but warmer. One knew why some adored him; he did not look like other people, not with press lights on his flesh; he looked like a lover, the simple truth, he had the sweet happiness of an adolescent who has just been given his first major kiss. And so he glowed, and one was reminded of Chaplin, not because they were the least alike in features, but because Charlie Chaplin was luminous when one met him and Stevenson had something of that light.

There was Eleanor Roosevelt, fine, precise, hand-worked like ivory. Her voice was almost attractive as she explained in the firm, sad tones of the first lady in this small town why she could not admit Mr. Kennedy, who was no doubt a gentleman, into her political house. One had the impression of a lady who was finally becoming a woman, which is to say that she was just a little bitchy about it all; nice bitchy, charming, it had a touch of art to it, but it made one wonder if she were not now satisfying the last passion of them all, which was to become physically attractive, for she was better-looking than she had ever been as she spurned the possibilities of a young suitor.

Jim Farley. Huge. Cold as a bishop. The hell he would consign you to was cold as ice.

Bobby Kennedy, that archetype Bobby Kennedy, looked like a West Point cadet, or, better, one of those unreconstructed Irishmen from Kirkland House one always used to have to face in the line in Harvard house football games. "Hello," you would say to the ones who looked like him as you lined up for the scrimmage after the kickoff, and his type would nod and look away, one rock glint of recognition your due for living across the hall from one another all through Freshman year, and then bang, as the ball was passed back, you'd get a bony king-hell knee in the crotch. He was the kind of man never to put on the gloves with if you wanted to do some social boxing, because after two minutes it would be a war, and ego-bastards last long in a war.

Carmine DeSapio and Kenneth Galbraith on the same part of the convention floor. DeSapio is bigger than one expects, keen and florid, great big smoked glasses, a suntan like Mantan—he is the kind of heavyweight Italian who could get by with a name like Romeo—and Galbraith is tall-tall, as actors say, six foot six it could be, terribly thin, enormously attentive, exquisitely polite, birdlike, he is sensitive to the stirring of reeds in a wind over the next hill. "Our grey eminence," whispered the intelligent observer next to me.

Bob Wagner, the mayor of New York, a little man, plump, groomed, blank. He had the blank, pomaded, slightly worried look of the first barber in a good barbershop, the kind who would go to the track on his day off and wear a green transparent stone in a gold ring.

And then there was Kennedy, the edge of the mystery. But a sketch will no longer suffice.

perspective from the Biltmore balcony: the colorful arrival of the hero with the orange-brown suntan and amazingly white teeth; revelation of the two rivers political theory

> *. . . it can be said with a fair amount of certainty that the essence of his political attractiveness is his extraordinary political*

intelligence. He has a mind quite unlike that of any other Democrat of this century. It is not literary, metaphysical and moral, as Adlai Stevenson's is. Kennedy is articulate and often witty, but he does not seek verbal polish. No one can doubt the seriousness of his concern with the most serious political matters, but one feels that whereas Mr. Stevenson's political views derive from a view of life that holds politics to be a mere fraction of existence, Senator Kennedy's primary interest is in politics. The easy way in which he disposes of the question of Church and State—as if he felt that any reasonable man could quite easily resolve any possible conflict of loyalties—suggests that the organization of society is the one thing that really engages his interest.

RICHARD ROVERE: *The New Yorker, July 23, 1960*

The afternoon he arrived at the convention from the airport, there was of course a large crowd on the street outside the Biltmore, and the best way to get a view was to get up on an outdoor balcony of the Biltmore, two flights above the street, and look down on the event. One waited thirty minutes, and then a honking of horns as wild as the getaway after an Italian wedding sounded around the corner, and the Kennedy cortege came into sight, circled Pershing Square, the men in the open and leading convertibles sitting backwards to look at their leader, and finally came to a halt in a space cleared for them by the police in the crowd. The television cameras were out, and a Kennedy band was playing some circus music. One saw him immediately. He had the deep orange-brown suntan of a ski instructor, and when he smiled at the crowd his teeth were amazingly white and clearly visible at a distance of fifty yards. For one moment he saluted Pershing Square, and Pershing Square saluted him back, the prince and the beggars of glamour staring at one another across a city street, one of those very special moments in the underground history of the world, and then with a quick move he was out of the car and by choice headed into the crowd instead of the lane cleared for him into the hotel by the police, so that he made his way inside surrounded by a mob, and one expected at any moment to see him lifted to its shoulders like a matador being carried back to the city after a triumph in the plaza. All the while the band kept playing the campaign tunes, sashaying circus music, and one had a moment of clarity, intense as a *déjà vu*, for the scene which had taken place had been glimpsed before in a dozen musical comedies; it was the scene where the hero, the matinee idol, the movie star comes to the palace to claim the princess, or what is the same, and more to our soil, the football hero, the campus king, arrives at the dean's home surrounded by a court of open-singing students to plead with the dean for his daughter's kiss and permission to put on the big musical that night. And suddenly I saw the convention, it came into focus for me, and I understood the mood of depression which had lain over the convention, because finally it was simple: the Democrats were going to nominate a man who, no matter how serious his political dedication might be, was indisputably and willy-nilly going to be seen as a great box-office actor, and the consequences of that were staggering and not at all easy to calculate.

Since the First World War Americans have been leading a double life, and our history has moved on two rivers, one visible, the other underground; there has been the history of politics which is concrete, factual, practical and unbelievably dull if not for the consequences of the actions of some of these men; and there is a subterranean river of untapped, ferocious, lonely and romantic desires, that concentration of ecstasy and violence which is the dream life of the nation.

The twentieth century may yet be seen as that era when civilized man and underprivileged man were melted together into mass man, the iron and steel of the nineteenth century giving way to electronic circuits which communicated their messages into men, the unmistakable tendency of the new century seeming to be the creation of men as interchangeable as commodities, their extremes of personality singed out of existence by the psychic fields of force the communicators would impose. This loss of personality was a catastrophe to the future of the imagination, but billions of people might first benefit from it by having enough to eat—one did not know—and there remained citadels of resistance in Europe where the culture was deep and roots were visible in the architecture of the past.

Nowhere, as in America, however, was this fall from individual man to mass man felt so acutely, for America was at once the first and most prolific creator of mass communications, and the most rootless of countries, since almost no American could lay claim to the line of a family which had not once at least severed its roots by migrating here. But, if rootless, it was then the most vulnerable of countries to its own homogenization. Yet America was also the country in which the dynamic myth of the Renaissance—that every man was potentially extraordinary—knew its most passionate persistence. Simply, America was the land where people still believed in heroes: George Washington; Billy the Kid; Lincoln, Jefferson; Mark Twain, Jack London, Hemingway; Joe Louis, Dempsey, Gentleman Jim; America believed in athletes, rum-runners, aviators; even lovers, by the time Valentino died. It was a country which had grown by the leap of one hero past another—is there a county in all of our ground which does not have its legendary figure? And when the West was filled, the expansion turned inward, became part of an agitated, overexcited, superheated dream life. The film studios threw up their searchlights as the frontier was finally sealed, and the romantic possibilities of the old conquest of land turned into a vertical myth, trapped within the skull, of a new kind of heroic life, each choosing his own archetype of a neo-renaissance man, be it Barrymore, Cagney, Flynn, Bogart, Brando or Sinatra, but it was almost as if there were no peace unless one could fight well, kill well (if always with honor), love well and love many, be cool, be daring, be dashing, be wild, be wily, be resourceful, be a brave gun. And this myth, that each of us was born to be free, to wander, to have adventure and to grow on the waves of the violent, the perfumed, and the unexpected, had a force which could not be tamed no matter how the nation's regulators—politicians, medicos, policemen, professors, priests, rabbis, ministers, *idéologues*, psychoanalysts, builders, executives and endless communicators—would brick-in the modern life with hygiene upon sanity, and middle-brow homily over platitude; the myth would not die. Indeed a quarter of the nation's business must have depended upon its existence. But it stayed alive for more than that—it was as if the message in the labyrinth of the genes would insist that violence was locked with creativity, and adventure was the secret of love.

Once, in the Second World War and in the year or two which followed, the underground river returned to earth, and the life of the nation was intense, of the present, electric; as a lady said, "That was the time when we gave parties which changed people's lives." The Forties was a decade when the speed with which one's own events occurred seemed as rapid as the history of the battlefields, and for the mass of people in America a forced march into a new jungle of emotion was the result. The surprises, the failures, and the dangers of that life must have terrified some nerve of awareness in the power and the mass, for, as if stricken by the orgiastic vistas the myth had carried up from underground, the retreat to a more conservative existence was disorderly, the fear of communism spread like an irrational hail of boils. To anyone who could see, the excessive hysteria of the Red wave was no preparation to face an enemy, but rather a terror of the national self: free-loving, lust-looting, atheistic, implacable—absurdity beyond absurdity to label communism so, for the moral products of Stalinism had been Victorian sex and a ponderous machine of material theology.

Forced underground again, deep beneath all *Reader's Digest* hospital dressings of Mental Health in Your Community, the myth continued to flow, fed by television and the film. The fissure in the national psyche widened to the danger point. The last large appearance of the myth was the vote which tricked the polls and gave Harry Truman his victory in '48. That was the last. Came the Korean War, the shadow of the H-bomb, and we were ready for the General. Uncle Harry gave way to Father, and security, regularity, order, and the life of no imagination were the command of the day. If one had any doubt of this, there was Joe McCarthy with his built-in treason detector, furnished by God, and the damage was done. In the totalitarian wind of those days, anyone who worked in Government formed the habit of being not too original, and many a mind atrophied from disuse and private shame. At the summit there was benevolence without leadership, regularity without vision, security without safety, rhetoric without life. The ship drifted on, that enormous warship of the United States, led by a Secretary of State whose cells were seceding to cancer, and as the world became more fantastic—Africa turning itself upside down, while some new kind of machine man was being made in China—two events occurred which stunned the confidence of America into a new night: the Russians put up their Sputnik, and Civil Rights—that reluctant gift to the American Negro, granted for its effect on foreign affairs—spewed into real life at Little Rock. The national Ego was in shock: the Russians were now in some ways our technological superiors, and we had an internal problem of subject populations equal conceivably in its difficulty to the Soviet and its satellites. The fatherly calm of the General began to seem like the uxorious mellifluences of the undertaker.

Underneath it all was a larger problem. The life of politics and the life of myth had diverged too far, and the energies of the people one knew everywhere had slowed down. Twenty years ago a post-Depression generation had gone to war and formed a lively, grousing, by times inefficient, carousing, pleasure-seeking, not altogether inadequate army. It did part of what it was supposed to do, and many, out of combat, picked up a kind of private life on the fly, and had their good time despite the yaws of the military system. But today in America the generation which respected the code of the myth was Beat, a horde of half-begotten Christs with scraggly beards, heroes none, saints all, weak before the strong, empty conformisms of the authority. The sanction for finding one's growth was no longer one's flag, one's career, one's sex, one's adventure, not even one's booze. Among the best in this newest of the generations, the myth had found its voice in marijuana, and the joke of the underground was that when the Russians came over they could never dare to occupy us for long because America was too Hip. Gallows humor. The poorer truth might be that America was too Beat, the instinct of the nation so separated from its public mind that apathy, schizophrenia, and private beatitudes might be the pride of the welcoming committee any underground could offer.

Yes, the life of politics and the life of the myth had diverged too far. There was nothing to return them to one another, no common danger, no cause, no desire, and, most essentially, no hero. It was a hero America needed, a hero central to his time, a man whose personality might suggest contradictions and mysteries which could reach into the alienated circuits of the underground, because only a hero can capture the secret imagination of a people, and so be good for the vitality of his nation; a hero embodies the fantasy and so allows each private mind the liberty to consider its fantasy and find a way to grow. Each mind can become more conscious of its desire and waste less strength in hiding from itself. Roosevelt was such a hero, and Churchill, Lenin and De Gaulle; even Hitler, to take the most odious example of this thesis, was a hero, the hero-as-monster, embodying what had become the monstrous fantasy of a people, but the horror upon which the radical mind and liberal temperament foundered was that he gave outlet to the energies of the Germans and so presented the twentieth century with an index of how horrible had become the secret heart of its desire. Roosevelt is of course a happier example of the hero; from his paralytic leg to the royal elegance of his geniality he seemed to contain the country within himself; everyone from the meanest starving cripple to an ambitious young man could expand into the optimism of an improving future because the man offered an unspoken promise of a future which would be rich. The sexual and the sex-starved, the poor, the hard-working and the imaginative well-to-do could see themselves in the President, could believe him to be like themselves. So a large part of the country was able to discover its energies because not as much was wasted in feeling that the country was a poisonous nutrient which stifled the day.

Too simple? No doubt. One tries to construct a simple model. The thesis is after all not so mysterious; it would merely nudge the notion that a hero embodies his time and is not so very much better than his time, but he is larger than life and so is capable of giving direction to the time, able to encourage a nation to discover the deepest colors of its character. At bottom the concept of the hero is antagonistic to impersonal social progress, to the belief that social ills can be solved by social legislating, for it sees a country as all-but-trapped in its character until it has a hero who reveals the character of the country to itself. The implication is that without such a hero the nation turns sluggish. Truman for example was not such a hero, he was not sufficiently larger than life, he inspired familiarity without excitement, he was a character but his proportions came from soap opera: Uncle Harry, full of salty common-sense and small-minded certainty, a storekeeping uncle.

Whereas Eisenhower has been the anti-Hero, the regulator. Nations do not necessarily and inevitably seek for heroes. In periods of dull anxiety, one is more likely to look for security than a dramatic confrontation, and Eisenhower could stand as a hero only for that large number of Americans who were most proud of their lack of imagination. In American life, the unspoken war of the century has taken place between the city and the small town: the city which is dynamic, orgiastic, unsettling, explosive and accelerating to the psyche; the small town which is rooted, narrow, cautious and planted in the life-logic of the family. The need of the city is to accelerate growth; the pride of the small town is to retard it. But since America has been passing through a period of enormous expansion since the war, the double-four years of Dwight Eisenhower could not retard the expansion, it could only denude it of color, character, and the development of novelty. The small-town mind is rooted—it is rooted in the small town—and when it attempts to direct history the results are disastrously colorless because the instrument of world power which is used by the small-town mind is the committee. Committees do not create, they merely proliferate, and the incredible dullness wreaked upon the American landscape in Eisenhower's eight years has been the triumph of the corporation. A tasteless, sexless, odorless sanctity in architecture, manners, modes, styles has been the result. Eisenhower embodied half the needs of the nation, the needs of the timid, the petrified, the sanctimonious, and the sluggish. What was even worse, he did not divide the nation as a hero might (with a dramatic dialogue as the result); he merely excluded one part of the nation from the other. The result was an alienation of the best minds and bravest impulses from the faltering history which was made. America's need in those years was to take an existential turn, to walk into the nightmare, to face into that terrible logic of history which demanded that the country and its people must become more extraordinary and more adventurous, or else perish, since the only alternative was to offer a false security in the power and the panacea of organized religion, family, and the FBI, a totalitarianization of the psyche by the stultifying techniques of the mass media which would seep into everyone's most private associations and so leave the country powerless against the Russians even if the denouement were to take fifty years, for in a competition between totalitarianisms the first maxim of the prizefight manager would doubtless apply: "Hungry fighters win fights."

the hipster as presidential candidate: thoughts on a public man's eighteenth-century wife; face-to-face with the hero; significance of a personal note, or the meaning of his having read an author's novel

Some part of these thoughts must have been in one's mind at the moment there was that first glimpse of Kennedy entering the Biltmore Hotel; and in the days which followed, the first mystery—the profound air of depression which hung over the convention—gave way to a second mystery which can be answered only by history. The depression of the delegates was understandable: no one had too much doubt that Kennedy would be nominated, but if elected he would be not only the youngest President ever to be chosen by voters, he would be the most conventionally attractive young man ever to sit in the White House, and his wife—some would claim it—might be the most beautiful first lady in our history. Of necessity the myth would emerge once more, because America's politics would now be also America's favorite movie, America's first soap opera, America's best-seller. One thinks of the talents of writers like Taylor Caldwell or Frank Yerby, or is it rather *The Fountainhead* which would contain such a fleshing of the romantic prescription? Or is it indeed one's own work which is called into question? "Well, there's your first hipster," says a writer one knows at the convention, "Sergius O'Shaugnessy born rich," and the temptation is to nod, for it could be true, a war hero, and the heroism is bona-fide, even exceptional, a man who has lived with death, who, crippled in the back, took on an operation which would kill him or restore him to power, who chose to marry a lady whose face might be too imaginative for the taste of a democracy which likes its first ladies to be executives of home-management, a man who courts political suicide by choosing to go all out for a nomination four, eight, or twelve years before his political elders think he is ready, a man who announces a week prior to the convention that the young are better fitted to direct history than the old. Yes, it captures the attention. This is no routine candidate calling every shot by safety's routine book ("Yes," Nixon said, naturally but terribly tired an hour after his nomination, the TV cameras and lights and microphones bringing out a sweat of fatigue on his face, the words coming very slowly from the tired brain, somber, modest, sober, slow, slow enough so that one could touch emphatically the cautions behind each word, "Yes, I want to say," said Nixon, "that whatever abilities I have, I got from my mother." A tired pause . . . dull moment of warning, ". . . and my father." The connection now made, the rest comes easy, ". . . and my school and my church." Such men are capable of anything.)

One had the opportunity to study Kennedy a bit in the days that followed. His style in the press conferences was interesting. Not terribly popular with the reporters (too much a contemporary, and yet too difficult to understand, he received nothing like the rounds of applause given to Eleanor Roosevelt, Stevenson, Humphrey, or even Johnson), he carried himself nonetheless with a cool grace which seemed indifferent to applause, his manner somehow similar to the poise of a fine boxer, quick with his hands, neat in his timing, and two feet away from his corner when the bell ended the round. There was a good lithe wit to his responses, a dry Harvard wit, a keen sense of proportion in disposing of difficult questions—invariably he gave enough of an answer to be formally satisfactory without ever opening himself to a new question which might go further than the first. Asked by a reporter, "Are you for Adlai as vice-president?" the grin came forth and the voice turned very dry, "No, I cannot say we have considered *Adlai* as a vice-president." Yet there was an elusive detachment to everything he did. One did not have the feeling of a man present in the room with all his weight and all his mind. Johnson gave you all of himself, he was a political animal, he breathed like an animal, sweated like one, you knew his mind was entirely absorbed with the compendium of political fact and maneuver; Kennedy seemed at times like a young professor whose manner was adequate for the classroom, but whose mind was off in some intricacy of the Ph.D. thesis he was writing. Perhaps one can give a sense of the discrepancy by saying that he was like an actor who had been cast as the candidate, a good actor, but not a great one—you were aware all the time that the role was one thing and the man another—they did not coincide, the actor seemed a touch too aloof (as, let us say, Gregory Peck is usually too aloof) to become the part. Yet one had little sense of whether to value this elusiveness, or to beware of it. One could be witnessing the fortitude of a superior sensitivity or the detachment of a man who was not quite real to himself. And his voice gave no clue. When Johnson spoke, one could separate what was fraudulent from what was felt, he would have been satisfying as an actor the way Broderick Crawford or Paul Douglas are satisfying; one saw into his emotions, or at least had the illusion that one did. Kennedy's voice, however, was only a fair voice, too reedy, near to strident, it had the metallic snap of a cricket in it somewhere, it was more impersonal than the man, and so became the least-impressive quality in a face, a body, a selection of language, and a style of movement which made up a better-than-decent presentation, better than one had expected.

With all of that, it would not do to pass over the quality in Kennedy which is most difficult to describe. And in fact some touches should be added to his hint of a portrait, for later (after the convention), one had a short session alone with him, and the next day, another. As one had suspected in advance the interviews were not altogether satisfactory, they hardly could have been. A man running for President is altogether different from a man elected President: the hazards of the campaign make it impossible for a candidate to be as interesting as he might like to be (assuming he has such a desire). One kept advancing the argument that this campaign would be a contest of personalities, and Kennedy kept returning the discussion to politics. After a while one recognized this was an inevitable caution for him. So there would be not too much point to reconstructing the dialogue since Kennedy is hardly inarticulate about his political attitudes and there will be a library vault of text devoted to it in the newspapers. What struck me most about the interview was a passing remark whose importance was invisible on the scale of politics, but was altogether meaningful to my particular competence. As we sat down for the first time, Kennedy smiled nicely and said that he had read my books. One muttered one's pleasure. "Yes," he said, "I've read . . ." and then there was a short pause which did not last long enough to be embarrassing in which it was yet obvious no title came instantly to his mind, an omission one was not ready to mind altogether since a man in such a position must be obliged to carry a hundred thousand facts and names in his head, but the hesitation lasted no longer than three seconds or four, and then he said, "I've read *The Deer Park* and . . . the others," which startled me for it was the first time in a hundred similar situations, talking to someone whose knowledge of my work was casual, that the sentence did not come out, "I've read *The Naked and the Dead* . . . and the others." If one is to take the worst and assume that Kennedy was briefed for this interview (which is most doubtful), it still speaks well for the striking instincts of his advisers.

What was retained later is an impression of Kennedy's manners which were excellent, even artful, better than the formal good manners of Choate and Harvard, almost as if what was creative in the man had been given to the manners. In a room with one or two people, his voice improved, became low-pitched, even pleasant—it seemed obvious that in all these years he had never become a natural public speaker and so his voice was constricted in public, the symptom of all orators who are ambitious, throttled, and determined.

His personal quality had a subtle, not quite describable intensity, a suggestion of dry pent heat perhaps, his eyes large, the pupils grey, the whites prominent, almost shocking, his most forceful feature: he had the eyes of a mountaineer. His appearance changed with his mood, strikingly so, and this made him always more interesting than what he was saying. He would seem at one moment older than his age, forty-eight or fifty, a tall, slim, sunburned professor with a pleasant weathered face, not even particularly handsome; five minutes later, talking to a press conference on his lawn, three microphones before him, a television camera turning, his appearance would have gone through a metamorphosis, he would look again like a movie star, his coloring vivid, his manner rich, his gestures strong and quick, alive with that concentration of vitality a successful actor always seems to radiate. Kennedy had a dozen faces. Although they were not at all similar as people, the quality was reminiscent of someone like Brando whose expression rarely changes, but whose appearance seems to shift from one person into another as the minutes go by, and one bothers with this comparison because, like Brando, Kennedy's most characteristic quality is the remote and private air of a man who has traversed some lonely terrain of experience, of loss and gain, of nearness to death, which leaves him isolated from the mass of others.

> *The next day while they waited in vain for rescuers, the wrecked half of the boat turned over in the water and they saw that it would soon sink. The group decided to swim to a small island three miles away. There were other islands bigger and nearer, but the Navy officers knew that they were occupied by the Japanese. On one island, only one mile to the south, they could see a Japanese camp. McMahon, the engineer whose legs were disabled by burns, was unable to swim. Despite his own painfully crippled back, Kennedy swam the three miles with a breast stroke, towing behind him by a life-belt strap that he held between his teeth the helpless McMahon . . . it took Kennedy and the suffering engineer five hours to reach the island.*

The quotation is from a book which has for its dedicated unilateral title, *The Remarkable Kennedys,* but the prose is by one of the best of the war reporters, the former *Yank* editor, Joe McCarthy, and so presumably may be trusted in such details as this. Physical bravery does not of course guarantee a man's abilities in the White

House—all too often men with physical courage are disappointing in their moral imagination—but the heroism here is remarkable for its tenacity. The above is merely one episode in a continuing saga which went on for five days in and out of the water, and left Kennedy at one point "miraculously saved from drowning (in a storm) by a group of Solomon Island natives who suddenly came up beside him in a large dugout canoe." Afterward, his back still injured (that precise back injury which was to put him on crutches eleven years later, and have him search for "spinal-fusion surgery" despite a warning that his chances of living through the operation were "extremely limited") afterward, he asked to go back on duty and became so bold in the attacks he made with his PT boat "that the crew didn't like to go out with him because he took so many chances."

It is the wisdom of a man who senses death within him and gambles that he can cure it by risking his life. It is the therapy of the instinct, and who is so wise as to call it irrational? Before he went into the Navy, Kennedy had been ailing. Washed out of Freshman year at Princeton by a prolonged trough of yellow jaundice, sick for a year at Harvard, weak already in the back from an injury at football, his trials suggest the self-hatred of a man whose resentment and ambition are too large for his body. Not everyone can discharge their furies on an analyst's couch, for some angers can be relaxed only by winning power, some rages are sufficiently monumental to demand that one try to become a hero or else fall back into that death which is already within the cells. But if one succeeds, the energy aroused can be exceptional. Talking to a man who had been with Kennedy in Hyannis Port the week before the convention, I heard that he was in a state of deep fatigue.

"Well, he didn't look tired at the convention," one commented.

"Oh, he had three days of rest. Three days of rest for him is like six months for us."

One thinks of that three-mile swim with the belt in his mouth and McMahon holding it behind him. There are pestilences which sit in the mouth and rot the teeth—in those five hours how much of the psyche must have been remade, for to give vent to the bite in one's jaws and yet use that rage to save a life: it is not so very many men who have the apocalyptic sense that heroism is the First Doctor.

If one had a profound criticism of Kennedy it was that his public mind was too conventional, but that seemed to matter less than the fact of such a man in office because the law of political life had become so dreary that only a conventional mind could win an election. Indeed there could be no politics which gave warmth to one's body until the country had recovered its imagination, its pioneer lust for the unexpected and incalculable. It was the changes that might come afterward on which one could put one's hope. With such a man in office the myth of the nation would again be engaged, and the fact that he was Catholic would shiver a first existential vibration of consciousness into the mind of the White Protestant. For the first time in our history, the Protestant would have the pain and creative luxury of feeling himself in some tiny degree part of a minority, and that was an experience which might be incommensurable in its value to the best of them.

a vignette of Adlai Stevenson; the speeches: what happened when the teleprompter jammed: how U.S. Senator Eugene McCarthy played the matador. An observation on the name Fitzgerald

As yet we have said hardly a word about Stevenson. And his actions must remain a puzzle unless one dares a speculation about his motive, or was it his need?

So far as the people at the convention had affection for anyone, it was Stevenson, so far as they were able to generate any spontaneous enthusiasm, their cheers were again for Stevenson. Yet it was obvious he never had much chance because so soon as a chance would present itself he seemed quick to dissipate the opportunity. The day before the nominations, he entered the Sports Arena to take his seat as a delegate—the demonstration was spontaneous, noisy and prolonged; it was quieted only by Governor Collins' invitation for Stevenson to speak to the delegates. In obedience perhaps to the scruple that a candidate must not appear before the convention until nominations are done, Stevenson said no more than: "I am grateful for this tumultuous and moving welcome. After getting in and out of the Biltmore Hotel and this hall, I have decided I know whom you are going to nominate. It will be the last survivor." This dry reminder of the ruthlessness of politics broke the roar of excitement for his presence. The applause as he left the platform was like the dying fall-and-moan of a baseball crowd when a home run curves foul. The next day, a New York columnist talking about it said bitterly, "If he'd only gone through the motions, if he had just said that now he wanted to run, that he would work hard, and he hoped the delegates would vote for him. Instead he made that lame joke." One wonders. It seems almost as if he did not wish to win unless victory came despite himself, and then was overwhelming. There are men who are not heroes because they are too good for their time, and it is natural that defeats leave them bitter, tired, and doubtful of their right to make new history. If Stevenson had campaigned for a year before the convention, it is possible that he could have stopped Kennedy. At the least, the convention would have been enormously more exciting, and the nominations might have gone through half-a-dozen ballots before a winner was hammered into shape. But then Stevenson might also have shortened his life. One had the impression of a tired man who (for a politician) was sickened unduly by compromise. A year of maneuvering, broken promises, and destestable partners might have gutted him for the election campaign. If elected, it might have ruined him as a President. There is the possibility that he sensed his situation exactly this way, and knew that if he were to run for president, win and make a good one, he would first have to be restored, as one can indeed be restored, by an exceptional demonstration of love—love, in this case, meaning that the Party had a profund desire to keep him as their leader. The emotional truth of a last-minute victory for Stevenson over the Kennedy machine might have given him new energy; it would certainly have given him new faith in a country and a party whose good motives he was possibly beginning to doubt. Perhaps the fault he saw with his candidacy was that he attracted only the nicest people to himself and there were not enough of them. (One of the private amusements of the convention was to divine some of the qualities of the candidates by the style of the young women who put on hats and clothing and politicked in the colors of one presidential gent or another. Of course, half of them must have been hired models, but someone did the hiring and so it was fair to look for a common denominator. The Johnson girls tended to be plump, pie-faced, dumb sexy Southern; the Symingteeners seemed a touch mulish, stubborn, good-looking pluggers; the Kennedy ladies were the handsomest; healthy, attractive, tough, a little spoiled—they looked like the kind of girls who had gotten all the dances in high school and/or worked for a year as an airline hostess before marrying well. But the Stevenson girls looked to be doing it for no money; they were good sorts, slightly horsy-faced, one had the impression they played field hockey in college.) It was indeed the pure, the saintly, the clean-living, the pacifistic, the vegetarian who seemed most for Stevenson, and the less humorous in the Kennedy camp were heard to remark bitterly that Stevenson had nothing going for him but a bunch of Goddamn Beatniks. This might even have had its sour truth. The demonstrations outside the Sports Arena for Stevenson seemed to have more than a fair proportion of tall, emaciated young men with thin, wry beards and three-string guitars accompanied (again in undue proportion) by a contingent of ascetic, face-washed young Beat ladies in sweaters and dungarees. Not to mention all the Holden Caulfields one could see from here to the horizon. But of course it is unfair to limit it so, for the Democratic gentry were also committed half en masse for Stevenson, as well as a considerable number of movie stars, Shelley Winters for one: after the convention she remarked sweetly, "Tell me something nice about Kennedy so I can get excited about him."

What was properly astonishing was the way this horde of political half-breeds and amateurs came within distance of turning the convention from its preconceived purpose, and managed at the least to bring the only hour of thorough-going excitement the convention could offer.

But then nominating day was the best day of the week and enough happened to suggest that a convention out of control would be a spectacle as extraordinary in the American scale of spectator values as a close seventh game in the World Series or a tied fourth quarter in a professional-football championship. A political convention is after all not a meeting of a corporation's board of directors; it is a fiesta, a carnival, a pig-rooting, horse-snorting, band-playing, voice-screaming medieval get-together of greed, practical lust, compromised idealism, career-advancement, meeting, feud, vendetta, conciliation, of rabble-rousers, fist fights (as it used to be), embraces, drunks (again as it used to be) and collective rivers of animal sweat. It is a reminder that no matter how the country might pretend it has grown up and become tidy in its manners, bodiless in its legislative language, hygienic in its separation of high politics from private life, that the roots still come grubby from the soil, and that politics in America is still different from politics anywhere else because the politics has arisen out of the immediate needs, ambitions, and cupidities of the people, that our politics still smell of the bedroom and the kitchen, rather than having descended to us from the chill punctilio of aristocratic negotiation.

So. The Sports Arena was new, too pretty of course, tasteless in its design—it was somehow pleasing that the acoustics were so bad for one did not wish the architects well; there had been so little imagination in their design, and this arena would have none of the harsh grandeur of Madison Square Garden when it was aged by spectators' phlegm and feet over the next twenty years. Still it had some atmosphere; seen from the streets, with the spectators moving to the ticket gates, the bands playing, the green hot-shot special editions of the Los Angeles newspapers being hawked by the newsboys, there was a touch of the air of promise that precedes a bullfight, not something so good as the approach to the Plaza Mexico, but good, let us say, like the entrance into El Toreo of Mexico City, another architectural monstrosity, also with seats painted, as I remember, in rose-pink, and dark, milky sky-blue.

Inside, it was also different this nominating day. On Monday and Tuesday the air had been desultory, no one listened to the speakers, and everybody milled from one easy chatting conversation to another—it had been like a tepid Kaffeeklatsch for fifteen thousand people. But today there was a whip of anticipation in the air, the seats on the floor were filled, the press section was working, and in the gallery people were sitting in the aisles.

Sam Rayburn had just finished nominating Johnson as one came in, and the rebel yells went up, delegates started filing out of their seats and climbing over seats, and a pullulating dance of bodies and bands began to snake through the aisles, the posters jogging and whirling in time to the music. The dun color of the floor (faces, suits, seats and floor boards), so monotonous the first two days, now lit up with life as if an iridescent caterpillar had emerged from a fold of wet leaves. It was more vivid than one had expected, it was right, it felt finally like a convention, and from up close when one got down to the floor (where your presence was illegal and so consummated by sneaking in one time as demonstrators were going out, and again by slipping a five-dollar bill to a guard) the nearness to the demonstrators took on high color, that electric vividness one feels on the side lines of a football game when it is necessary to duck back as the ballcarrier goes by, his face tortured in the concentration of the moment, the thwomp of his tackle as acute as if one had been hit oneself.

That was the way the demonstrators looked on the floor. Nearly all had the rapt, private look of a passion or a tension which would finally be worked off by one's limbs, three hundred football players, everything from seedy delegates with jowl-sweating shivers to livid models, paid for their work that day, but stomping out their beat on the floor with the hypnotic adulatory grimaces of ladies who had lived for Lyndon these last ten years.

Then from the funereal rostrum, whose color was not so rich as mahogany nor so dead as a cigar, came the last of the requests for the delegates to take their seats. The seconding speeches began, one minute each; they ran for three and four, the minor-league speakers running on the longest as if the electric antenna of television was the lure of the Sirens, leading them out. Bored cheers applauded their concluding Götterdämmerungen and the nominations were open again. A favorite son, a modest demonstration, five seconding speeches, tedium.

Next was Kennedy's occasion. Governor Freeman of Minnesota made the speech. On the second or third sentence his television prompter jammed, an accident. Few could be aware of it at the moment; the speech seemed merely flat and surprisingly void of bravura. He was obviously no giant of extempore. Then the demonstration. Well-run, bigger than Johnson's, jazzier, the caliber of the costumes and decorations better chosen: the placards were broad enough, "Let's Back Jack," the floats were garish, particularly a papier-mâché or plastic balloon of Kennedy's head, six feet in diameter, which had nonetheless the slightly shrunken, over-red, rubbery look of a toy for practical jokers in one of those sleazy off-Times Square magic-and-gimmick stores; the band was suitably corny; and yet one had the impression this demonstration had been designed by some hands-to-hip interior decorator who said, "Oh, joy, let's have fun, let's make this *true* beer hall."

Besides, the personnel had something of the Kennedy *élan*, those paper hats designed to look like straw boaters with Kennedy's face on the crown, and small photographs of him on the ribbon, those hats which had come to symbolize the crack speed of the Kennedy team, that Madison Avenue cachet which one finds in bars like P. J. Clarke's, the elegance always giving its subtle echo of the Twenties so that the raccoon coats seem more numerous than their real count, and the colored waistcoats are measured by the charm they would have drawn from Scott Fitzgerald's eye. But there, it occurred to one for the first time that Kennedy's middle name was just that, Fitzgerald, and the tone of his crack lieutenants, the unstated style, was true to Scott. The legend of Fitzgerald had an army at last, formed around the self-image in the mind of every superior Madison Avenue opportunist that he was hard, he was young, he was In, his conversation was lean as wit, and if the work was not always scrupulous, well the style could aspire. If there came a good day . . . he could meet the occasion.

The Kennedy snake dance ran its thirty lively minutes, cheered its seconding speeches, and sat back. They were so sure of winning, there had been so many victories before this one, and this one had been scouted and managed so well, that hysteria could hardly be the mood. Besides, everyone was waiting for the Stevenson barrage which should be at least diverting. But now came a long tedium. Favorite sons were nominated, fat mayors shook their hips, seconders told the word to constituents back in Ponderwaygot County, treacly demonstrations tried to hold the floor, and the afternoon went by; Symington's hour came and went, a good demonstration, good as Johnson's (for good cause—they had pooled their demonstrators). More favorite sons, Governor Docking of Kansas declared "a genius" by one of his lady speakers in a tense go-back-to-religion voice. The hours went by, two, three, four hours, it seemed forever before they would get to Stevenson. It was evening when Senator Eugene McCarthy of Minnesota got up to nominate him.

The gallery was ready, the floor was responsive, the demonstrators were milling like bulls in their pen waiting for the *toril* to fly open—it would have been hard not to wake the crowd up, not to make a good speech. McCarthy made a great one. Great it was by the measure of convention oratory, and he held the crowd like a matador, timing their *oles!*, building them up, easing them back, correcting any sag in attention, gathering their emotion, discharging it, creating new emotion on the wave of the last, driving his passes tighter and tighter as he readied for the kill. "Do not reject this man who made us all proud to be called Democrats, do not leave this prophet without honor in his own party." One had not heard a speech like this since 1948 when Vito Marcantonio's voice, his harsh, shrill, bitter, street urchin's voice screeched through the loud-speakers at Yankee Stadium and lashed seventy thousand people into an uproar.

"There was only one man who said let's talk sense to the American people," McCarthy went on, his muleta furled for the *naturales*. "There was only one man who said let's talk sense to the American people," he repeated. "He said the promise of America is the promise of greatness. This was his call to greatness. . . . Do not forget this man. . . . Ladies and Gentlemen, I present to you not the favorite son of one state, but the favorite son of the fifty states, the favorite son of every country he has visited, the favorite son of every country which has not seen him but is secretly thrilled by his name." Bedlam. The kill. "Ladies and Gentlemen, I present to you Adlai Stevenson of Illinois." Ears and tail. Hooves and bull. A roar went up like the roar one heard the day Bobby Thomson hit his home run at the Polo Grounds and the Giants won the pennant from the Dodgers in the third playoff game of the 1951 season. The demonstration cascaded onto the floor, the gallery came to its feet, the Sports Arena sounded like the inside of a marching drum. A tidal pulse of hysteria, exaltation, defiance, exhilaration, anger and roaring desire flooded over the floor. The cry which had gone up on McCarthy's last sentence had not paused for breath in five minutes, and troop after troop of demonstrators jammed the floor (the Stevenson people to be scolded the next day for having collected floor passes and sent them out to bring in new demonstrators) and still the sound mounted. One felt the convention coming apart. There was a Kennedy girl in the seat in front of me, the Kennedy hat on her head, a dimpled healthy brunette; she had sat silently through McCarthy's speech, but now, like a woman paying her respects to the power of natural thrust, she took off her hat and began to clap herself. I saw a writer I knew in the next aisle; he had spent a year studying the Kennedy machine in order to write a book on how a nomination is won. If Stevenson stampeded the convention, his work was lost. Like a reporter at a mine cave-in I inquired the present view of the widow. "Who can think," was the answer, half frantic, half elated, "just watch it, that's all." I found a cool one, a New York reporter, who smiled in rueful respect. "It's the biggest demonstration I've seen since Wendell Willkie's in 1940," he said, and added, "God, if Stevenson takes it, I can wire my wife and move the family on to Hawaii."

"I don't get it."

"Well, every story I wrote said it was locked up for Kennedy."

Still it went on, twenty minutes, thirty minutes, the chairman could hardly be heard, the demonstrators refused to leave. The lights were turned out, giving a sudden theatrical shift to the sense of a crowded church at midnight, and a new roar went up, louder, more passionate than anything heard before. It was the voice, it was the passion, if one insisted to call it that, of everything in America which was defeated, idealistic, innocent, alienated, outside and Beat, it was the potential voice of a new third of the nation whose psyche was ill from cultural malnutrition, it was powerful, it was extraordinary, it was larger than the decent, humorous, finicky, half-noble man who had called it forth, it was a cry from the Thirties when Time was simple, it was a resentment of the slick technique, the oiled gears, and the superior generals of Fitzgerald's Army; but it was also—and for this reason one could not admire it altogether, except with one's excitement—it was also the plea of the bewildered who hunger for simplicity again, it was the adolescent counterpart of the boss's depression before the unpredictable dynamic of Kennedy as President, it was the return to the sentimental dream of Roosevelt rather than the approaching nightmare of history's oncoming night, and it was inspired by a terror of the future as much as a revulsion of the present.

Fitz's Army held; after the demonstration was finally down, the convention languished for ninety minutes while Meyner and others were nominated, a fatal lapse of time because Stevenson had perhaps a chance to stop Kennedy if the voting had begun on the echo of the last cry for him, but in an hour and a half depression crept in again and emotions spent, the delegates who had wavered were rounded into line. When the vote was taken, Stevenson had made no gains. The brunette who had taken off her hat was wearing it again, and she clapped and squealed when Wyoming delivered the duke and Kennedy was in. The air was sheepish, like the mood of a suburban couple who forgive each other for cutting in and out of somebody else's automobile while the country club dance is on. Again, tonight, no miracle would occur. In the morning the papers would be moderate in their description of Stevenson's last charge.

a sketch of the republicans gathered in convention: the choice between the venturesome and the safe; what may happen at three o'clock in the morning on a long dark night

One did not go to the other convention. It was seen on television, and so too much cannot be said of that. It did however confirm one's earlier bias that the Republican Party was still a party of church ushers, undertakers, choirboys, prison wardens, bank presidents, small-town police chiefs, state troopers, psychiatrists, beauty-parlor operators, corporation executives, Boy-Scout leaders, fraternity presidents, tax-board assessors, community leaders, surgeons, Pullman porters, head nurses and the fat sons of rich fathers. Its candidate would be given the manufactured image of an ordinary man, and his campaign, so far as it was a psychological campaign (and this would be far indeed), would present him as a simple, honest, dependable, hard-working, ready-to-learn, modest, humble, decent, sober young man whose greatest qualification for president was his profound abasement before the glories of the Republic, the stability of the mediocre, and his own unworthiness. The apocalyptic hour of Uriah Heep.

It would then be a campaign unlike the ones which had preceded it. Counting by the full spectrum of complete Right to absolute Left, the political differences would be minor, but what would be not at all minor was the power of each man to radiate his appeal into some fundamental depths of the American character. One would have an inkling at last if the desire of America was for drama or stability, for adventure or monotony. And this, this appeal to the psychic direction America would now choose for itself was the element most promising about this election, for it gave the possibility that the country might be able finally to rise above the deadening verbiage of its issues, its politics, its jargon, and live again by an image of itself. For in some part of themselves the people might know (since these candidates were not old enough to be revered) that they had chosen one young man for his mystery, for his promise that the country would grow or disintegrate by the unwilling charge he gave to the intensity of the myth, or had chosen another young man for his unstated oath that he would do all in his power to keep the myth buried and so convert the remains of Renaissance man as rapidly as possible into mass man. One might expect them to choose the enigma in preference to the deadening certainty. Yet one must doubt America's bravery. This lurching, unhappy, pompous and most corrupt nation—could it have the courage finally to take on a new image for itself, was it brave enough to put into office not only one of its ablest men, its most efficient, its most conquistadorial (for Kennedy's capture of the Democratic Party deserves the word), but also one of its more mysterious men (the national psyche must shiver in its sleep at the image of Mickey Mantle-cum-Lindbergh in office, and a First Lady with an eighteenth-century face). Yes, America was at last engaging the fate of its myth, its consciousness about to be accelerated or cruelly depressed in its choice between two young men in their forties who, no matter how close, dull, or indifferent their stated politics might be, were radical poles apart, for one was sober, the apotheosis of opportunistic lead, all radium spent, the other handsome as a prince in the unstated aristocracy of the American dream. So, finally, would come a choice which history had never presented to a nation before—one could vote for glamour or for ugliness, a staggering and most stunning choice—would the nation be brave enough to enlist the romantic dream of itself, would it vote for the image in the mirror of its unconscious, were the people indeed brave enough to hope for an acceleration of Time, for that new life of drama which would come from choosing a son to lead them who was heir apparent to the psychic loins? One could pause: it might be more difficult to be a President than it ever had before. Nothing less than greatness would do.

Yet if the nation voted to improve its face, what an impetus might come to the arts, to the practices, to the lives and to the imagination of the American. If the nation so voted. But one knew the unadmitted specter in the minds of the Democratic delegates: that America would go to sleep on election eve with the polls promising Kennedy a victory on the day to come, yet in its sleep some millions of Democrats and Independents would suffer a nightmare before the mystery of uncharted possibilities their man would suggest, and in a terror of all the creativities (and some violences) that mass man might now have to dare again, the undetermined would go out in the morning to vote for the psychic security of Nixon the way a middle-aged man past adventure holds to the stale bread of his marriage. Yes, this election might be fearful enough to betray the polls and no one in America could plan the new direction until the last vote was counted by the last heeler in the last ambivalent ward, no one indeed could know until then what had happened the night before, what had happened at three o'clock in the morning on that long dark night of America's search for a security cheaper than her soul.

postscript to the third presidential paper

This piece had more effect than any other single work of mine, and I think this is due as much to its meretriciousness as to its merits. I was forcing a reality, I was bending reality like a field of space to curve the time I wished to create. I was not writing with the hope that perchance I could find reality by being sufficiently honest to perceive it, but on the contrary was distorting reality in the hope that thereby I could affect it. I was engaging in an act of propaganda.

During the period after Kennedy was nominated, there was great indifference to him among the Democrats I knew; disaffection was general; outright aversion was felt by most of the liberal Left—the white collar SANE sort of professional who had been for Stevenson. The Kennedy machine worked well to overcome apathy and inertia; so did the debates with Nixon. Through the early Fall, before the election, people who had been going along with the Democratic Party for years began somewhat resignedly to accept their fate: they would go out after all and vote for John F. Kennedy. But there was no real enthusiasm, no drive. My piece came at the right time for him—three weeks before the election. It added the one ingredient Kennedy had not been able to find for the stew—it made him seem exciting, it made the election appear important. Around New York there was a turn in sentiment; one could feel it; Kennedy now had glamour.

As will be seen in the essay on Jackie Kennedy, I took to myself some of the critical credit for his victory. Whether I was right or wrong in fact may not be so important as its psychological reality in my own mind. I had invaded No Man's Land, I had created an archetype of Jack Kennedy in the public mind which might or might not be true, but which would induce people to vote for him, and so would tend to move him into the direction I had created. Naturally there would be forces thrusting him back out of No Man's Land, back to conventional politics, but so far as I had an effect, it was a Faustian one, which as if I had made a pact with Mephisto to give me an amulet, an art-work, which might arouse a djinn in history.

The night Kennedy was elected, I felt a sense of woe, as if I had made a terrible error, as if somehow I had betrayed the Left and myself. It was a spooky emotion. In the wake of the election, one note was clear—the strength the Left had been gaining in the last years of Eisenhower's administration would now be diluted, preempted, adulterated, converted and dissolved by the compromises and hypocrisies of a new Democratic administration. And so I began to follow Kennedy's career with obsession, as if I were responsible and guilty for all which was bad, dangerous, or potentially totalitarian within it. And the papers which follow are written under the shadow of this private fact, this conviction that I was now among the guilty, another genteel traitor in the land.

AFTERWORD

an eight-hour daylight man

In an April, 1959, issue of *The Des Moines Register,* I read about a hermit who had lived for some five years in Griffith Park in Los Angeles. Police who had been searching for a prowler picked him up, questioned, and released him. A thirty-two-year-old, Purple Heart veteran of World War II, he told police that he had decided to withdraw from life because he "saw no future in anything." The accompanying photograph showed what looked like Robinson Crusoe in a duck-billed cap. Upon release, the hermit, who had lived off the leavings of picnickers, "faded back into the protective covering of the big mountainous park."

That April I was living in Iowa City, teaching at the university there while completing work on my degree. I was writing a book of poems in lieu of the usual dissertation. Most of my poems were elegant trifles, but the best ones, those with a subject matter that gripped me, were about losers, members of a society dedicated to cutting the mustard who couldn't or wouldn't. This hermit, then, was a ready-made hero for one of my poems—especially since Los Angeles was my hometown and I knew Griffith Park and. . . . I clipped the story and photo, and put them to one side.

A few nights later, after my wife and I had returned from a movie (*Warlock*, a western), and she had gone to bed, I sat up—insomnia my companion—and wrote the following poem.

evening in the park

The children have packed up the light
And gone home for the bedtime story
In which Jack wakes the Sleeping Fury.
I count tin cans and comic books;
I listen for the wheel of night,
That furry rim, those velvet spokes.

Some know it by the rush of stars;
I know it by the rush of thought;
Images, like the shrill onslaught
Of cyclists on a black-top road,
Come on and catch me unawares:
I am the victim of their mood.

It is a rehash of the day,
The rooms remembered for their anger,
The crowded stairways for their danger,
And what the light did to a mirror
You thought you knew. It is a way
Of being faithful to one's terror.

I will sit here a little while,
Recalling how I read about
A man who found a strange way out,
The hermit of this wooded park,
Gaunt Crusoe of a nowhere isle,
Who hides his bushel in the dark.

He may be watching even now,
His dark hands up his darker sleeves,
The last of the great make-believes.
He moves in an enormous grave,
The wilderness pressed to his brow,
A man of motion without drive.

I wonder, Does he name the trees?
And to what end? Or like a bird,
Does he know calls that know no word?
And does he conjure without number?
And when, against the moon, he sees
My silhouette, does he remember?

Batman is whispering in the wind;
The cans are jewelled with the stars,
Evening Venus and red-eyed Mars.
I am an eight-hour daylight man,
And I must go to keep my mind
Familiar and American.

I wrote "Evening in the Park" in an hour and a half, an amazingly short time for me, for I usually labored over a poem for days and sometimes weeks. I went to bed that night, feeling pleased with the speed of the thing, the fifth stanza, and the last word of the poem "American." The next day I showed it to two or three fellow poets. They assured me it was pretty good, and one of them, Don Justice, suggested the only change I was to make, the changing of "very" to "wooded" in the phrase "this wooded park." Their praise persuaded me that it was good enough to be included in my book, but I still distrusted the poem: it had come too easily; it had practically written itself.

That June I moved back to Los Angeles, my degree in my bag, to a new job. The now defunct *Los Angeles Mirror* greeted me with a front-page story about my hermit. He had come down from the hills to see his friends, Detectives Riding and Fox, the officers who had questioned him. He had an important secret that he could convey only to them. Well, he's in for it now, I thought, and I was right. He was detained for observation; his parents arrived from Nebraska; he went back in their care. It was only what one might have always expected, and it irritated me: it made my poem seem less than valid, and I was beginning to like my poem.

One night some months later, I was at a cocktail party, one of those academic-literary affairs where the young academic drunk weeps because he teaches in the well-paid Siberia of the West Coast, where the wives pretend they've read any author you mention, and where, worst of all, some New Yorker attacks Los Angeles for its lack of culture. It was one of the last sort who got to me that night, making me, a native Angelene, something of a chauvinist. I have lost, someplace between my last drink and the next morning's head, whatever argument I may have resorted to, or maybe I had no argument, maybe I simply stood there with a vague smile on my face. In any event, I do remember the drive my wife and I took after the party.

My teetotal wife did the driving, but I was the one who chose our destinations. I was bent on searching out the various places where I had lived, the schools I had attended. I didn't begin with the hospital where I was born, for I knew that had been torn down, but I did try to find the first house I had lived in. It was gone; a shopping center stood where it had been. I sought out my favorite house, the one I had lived in at the age of ten. It was there—in the center of a red-light district; I remembered a quiet neighborhood where nothing ever happened. I turned my attention to the schools. My grammar school was still there, but it was brick where it had been stucco. And my junior high school was a freeway. I gave up.

It was probably a year after that night before I got around to writing the second of my hermit poems. It was a year in which I had collected other bits of evidence that I was a man without even a personal sense of tradition. For instance, though I now taught at my old undergraduate school, it no longer had the same location, and there was talk that its name was to be changed (talk that is now fact). Change of this sort was common to Los Angeles, I knew, but since I had come to believe that what happens in Los Angeles now will happen elsewhere in America in a few short years, I felt more and more that my case was not a unique one. Of course, I had heard it said for years that Americans are without tradition. It is a commonplace among American and European intellectuals, but it had become an insight for me; I suppose a poet's insights are likely to be truisms—with this difference: the poet *feels* them personally.

All right, so I had some notions centering around the word "tradition," and I wanted to write about what finally had happened to my hermit (it had the acrid smell of truth)—so what? So one night when I had worn out the possible distractions, the detective story, the Late Late, and my wife had again left me to my insomnia, I wrote the second of my two poems about friend hermit.

hermit's return

I have loved you foolishly, my unaltered
ego, as children
love an invisible friend.
Your Purple Heart and honest parents
were the very things to leave, and if you had
a secret wound, it was

a harbor where the darkness rode at anchor
in imperial calm.
And you had gone; I could stand
on the back porch, the television
voices all around me in the dark, and think
you out there, or mistake

a low star for your campfire, and feel the heat.
Yet, for all I knew,
it was I who drew you down,
so friendly, dog-like, among the cops,
the bald psychiatrist, the weeping parents,
the man from Channel 2.

The power of love is spoken of elsewhere.
I note in passing
only how cold the nights are
of late, though they are not, I suppose,
as cold as the nights you have where they have you,
at home, in Nebraska.

Like the first poem, this one happened quickly. An hour? two hours? I don't really remember. But quickly. Perhaps too quickly, for I now know what I wanted to say, to at least imply between the lines—God knows, I have talked about it enough by way of preface at poetry readings—but I cannot honestly say that it's really in the two poems, so let me spell it out.

The eight-hour daylight man needs no introduction; he is the author, the reader, Mr. Average Citizen weary enough of his routine and its familiar terrors to seek a moment alone in which to contemplate some alternative to his own life. The alternative is the hermit's life, an extreme example of the desire to get away from it all. The hermit has not only gone off (pun intended) but gone back. The great mountainous, wooded park in the heart of the city is the last wilderness. As an alternative to the city, it is terrifying: a man can survive there—the hermit has—but how has he survived? Isn't the hermit really mad? And madness—isn't it a withdrawal from reality? Isn't it better to go back to the familiar terrors of what we call reality? The eight-hour daylight man goes, but he doesn't stop thinking about the alternative. The television voices won't let him.

The second poem is the author's recognition of the hermit as an extension of himself, "my unaltered ego." It is a lament for the wilderness. For if there is an American tradition, it is the tradition of the wilderness and the great kooks who blazed it, men whose madness the wilderness tolerated—or demanded. The eight-hour daylight man lives in a highly organized society in which the range of acceptable behavior is necessarily greatly diminished. His identity, like the identity of a chess piece, is defined by the rules of the game, but unlike the chess piece, the eight-hour daylight man can imagine other moves, other games, or no game at all. If he has a great park near him, he can flee to that. He can take Miltown. He can join the John Birch Society. He can write anonymous crank letters.

Recently, I gave a poetry reading at which I rehearsed these comments at some length. The next day, I received the following unsigned letter.

> *You are a very cruel person, an intensely cruel person.*
> *Why did you write those poems about that poor disabled veteran, a winner of the pirple heart?*
> *He lived there in the park of course because he had no home and no job.*

> *That is why he stayed in the park and ate the leavings of other people. Certainly you cannot be a veteran yourself or you would have never written such cruel poems about another one. Since you have been so cruel, I imagine God has some terrible handships in store for you. I imagine you will have to suffer an even harder life than that poor man did. I don imagine you will want to laugh and write poems about that.*

My anonymous correspondent may be right about the "handships" in store for me, but write about them I will, for my poems are the moves I make in a sad game he and I both play.

HENRI COULETTE

BIOGRAPHICAL NOTES

JAMES BALDWIN, the most eloquent voice in the civil rights movement, is a novelist (*Another Country*, 1961), essayist (*The Fire Next Time*, 1963), and playwright (*Blues for Mister Charlie*, 1964).

Former managing editor of *The New Leader*, DANIEL BELL is now a lecturer in sociology at Columbia University. He is the author of *The End of Ideology* (1960) and *Work and Its Discontents* (1946), as well as the editor of the collection *The New American Right* (1955).

Born in Quebec in 1915 of Russian-Jewish parents, SAUL BELLOW grew up in the slums of Montreal and Chicago. His best known works are the award-winning novels *The Adventures of Augie March* (1953) and *Herzog* (1964). He has been teaching at the University of Chicago.

WILLIAM BLAKE (1757–1827) was one of England's greatest artists, engravers, printers, teachers, and poets. A mystic and rebel, his work still stands as the most powerful attack in English on the rational, bourgeois life.

In such works as *The Stranger* (1942), *The Plague* (1947), and *The Rebel* (1951), ALBERT CAMUS sought meaning in the midst of the absurd. In 1957, at the age of 43, he won the Nobel Prize for Literature; three years later, he was killed in an automobile accident.

DEMETRIOS CAPETANAKIS emigrated to England from his native Greece in 1939. He died in 1944 at the age of thirty-two, leaving a small but valuable collection of poems and essays written in English.

HART CRANE was born in Ohio in 1899; he supported himself by writing advertising copy, riveting, candy-packing, and other diverse jobs. In 1926 his first spectacular book of poetry appeared, *White Buildings*, which was followed in 1930 by *The Bridge*. In 1932, unable to write, he committed suicide.

Born in 1907, LOREN EISELEY spent much of his youth exploring the salt flats and ponds near his native Lincoln, Nebraska. He completed his graduated work at the University of Pennsylvania where he is presently provost of the university. Since the publication of *The Immense Journey* in 1957 he has in a series of books established himself as a writer of rare imaginative and scientific resources.

S. S. GARDONS is the pseudonym of a well-known Pulitzer prize-winning American poet.

PIERRE GASCAR'S book of short stories *Beasts and Men* (1953) won two of France's highest literary honors, the Prix Goncourt and the Prix de Critiques. He served with the French army in 1939 and 1940; from 1940 to 1945 he was a prisoner of war.

ALLEN GINSBURG was born in 1926, the son of Louis Ginsburg, lyric poet and school teacher of Paterson, New Jersey. His book *Howl* was published in 1955 in San Francisco and established him as the chief voice of the Beat Generation.

PAUL GOODMAN has described himself as "a man of letters in the old sense, one who thinks that the literary process itself, the criticism of life, adds a new and indispensable element." He is a poet, novelist, professional psychologist, and social and literary critic as well as one of America's foremost writers and thinkers in the area of education.

THOM GUNN was born in England in 1929 and educated at Cambridge, where he wrote many of the poems in his first book, *Fighting Terms* (1954). Since 1955 he has lived mainly in the U.S. and is presently a Lecturer in English at the University of California, Berkeley.

Born in 1914 in Beatrice, Nebraska, WELDON KEES will probably be remembered as a poet although he wrote music and played jazz piano, painted, made movies, and achieved a reputation as a photographer. In 1955 his car was found abandoned on the approach to the Golden Gate Bridge; he has not been heard from since.

Presently librarian at the University of Hull, PHILIP LARKIN is the author of two novels and three books of poetry, the most recent of which, *The Whit-Sun Weddings,* was published in the United States in 1964.

D. H. LAWRENCE used much of his own early life as the son of a Nottingham coal miner as the material for his novel *Sons and Lovers* (1913). Although today he is most widely known as the author of the long banned novel *Lady Chatterly's Lover* (1928), he first gained attention as a poet. He spent much of his adult life wandering through Europe and America, and he brilliantly recorded those years in a succession of travel books. In 1931 he died of tuberculosis at the age of 45.

Born in Boston, ROBERT LOWELL served five months in a federal prison as a conscientious objector during World War II; twenty-one years later because of his objections to President Johnson's foreign policy he declined an invitation to the White House Arts Festival. In between he authored six books of poetry.

MARY MCCARTHY has brilliantly chronicled her own coming of age in *Memories of a Catholic Girlhood* (1957), and that of the Vassar girls of her generation in *The Group* (1963). Her bright style and bitter wit have many imitators among the women of the New York literary world.

DWIGHT MACDONALD is the author of *Memoirs of a Revolutionist* (1957) and *Against the American Grain* (1962). During World War II he founded and edited single-handedly *Politics,* an important magazine of dissent. He is presently a staff writer for the *New Yorker* and movie reviewer for *Esquire.*

NORMAN MAILER wrote the most successful American novel of the Second World War, *The Naked and the Dead* (1948). His decline as a novelist and his ascendency as a celebrity are chronicled in two more recent books, *Advertisements for Myself* (1959) and *The Presidential Papers* (1964).

Born in London in 1927 and educated at Oxford, JAMES MICHIE is now an editor for an English publishing company. He has published one book of poetry, *Possible Laughter* (1959).

Born in New York City in 1891, HENRY MILLER lived in Paris in the 1930s where he wrote his first outrageous masterpieces, *Tropic of Cancer* (1934) and *Tropic of Capricorn* (1939), which were not legally obtainable in the U.S. until the 1960s. He has settled in Big Sur, California, and an artist colony has sprung up around him.

In his young manhood, GEORGE ORWELL served with the British constabulary in India. In America, his reputation rests on two political novels, *Animal Farm* (1946) and *1984* (1949), but in England, Orwell's memory is honored for that social and political conscience so evident in *Homage to Catalonia* (1938).

Translator, poet, and social critic, KENNETH REXROTH gained national prominence as the "Big Daddy of the Beat Generation." Born in 1905 in South Bend, Indiana, he settled in San Francisco. In 1964 *Natural Numbers*, a selected edition of his poetry appeared.

JEAN-PAUL SARTRE, philosopher, novelist, playwright, social critic, is the step-father of Existentialism. His autobiography, *Words*, was published in 1964—the same year he rejected the Nobel Prize for Literature.

ALAN SILLITOE quit school at the age of fourteen to work in a bicycle factory in Nottingham, England. After his discharge from the RAF he retired to the island of Majorca to stretch his discharge allowance and write stories, novels, and poems. Two of his works, *Saturday Night and Sunday Morning* (1959) and *The Loneliness of the Long-distance Runner* (1959), have been turned into highly successful films.

LOUIS SIMPSON was born in 1923 in Jamaica, British West Indies. His service with an American Airborne Division in the Battle of Bastogne provided the background for his long poem "The Runner." His fourth book of poetry, *At the End of the Open Road* (1963), won the Pulitzer Prize for poetry in 1965.

During his long career as a physician in Rutherford, New Jersey, WILLIAM CARLOS WILLIAMS delivered 2,000 babies, and wrote novels, short stories, plays, essays, and great poems. Today, his is the one influence common to all schools of American poetry.

Since his graduation from Princeton in 1916 EDMUND WILSON has been America's most articulate observer of the cultural and political scene. He has also authored fiction, poetry, and plays and served on the staffs of such magazines as *Vanity Fair, The New Republic,* and *New Yorker.*

INDEX OF AUTHORS AND TITLES